The Origin and Evolution of Life,

On the theory of action, reaction and interaction of energy

Henry Fairfield Osborn

Alpha Editions

This edition published in 2020

ISBN : 9789354022418

Design and Setting By
Alpha Editions
email - alphaedis@gmail.com

THE ORIGIN AND EVOLUTION OF LIFE

ON THE THEORY OF ACTION REACTION AND INTERACTION OF ENERGY

BY

HENRY FAIRFIELD OSBORN

SC.D. PRINCETON, HON. LL.D. TRINITY, PRINCETON, COLUMBIA, HON. D.SC. CAMBRIDGE
HON. PH.D. CHRISTIANIA

RESEARCH PROFESSOR OF ZOOLOGY, COLUMBIA UNIVERSITY
VERTEBRATE PALÆONTOLOGIST U. S. GEOLOGICAL SURVEY, CURATOR EMERITUS OF VERTEBRATE PALÆONTOLOGY IN THE AMERICAN MUSEUM OF NATURAL HISTORY

AUTHOR OF "FROM THE GREEKS TO DARWIN"
"THE AGE OF MAMMALS," "MEN OF THE OLD STONE AGE"

WITH 136 ILLUSTRATIONS

NEW YORK
CHARLES SCRIBNER'S SONS
1917

PREFACE

In these lectures we may take some of the initial steps toward an energy conception of Evolution and an energy conception of Heredity and away from the matter and form conceptions which have prevailed for over a century.

The first half of this volume is therefore devoted to what we know of the capture, storage, release, and reproduction of energy in its simplest and most elementary living phases; the second half is devoted to the evolution of matter and form in plants and animals, also interpreted largely in terms of energy and mechanics. Lest the reader imagine that through the energy conception I am at present even pretending to offer an explanation of the miracles of adaptation and of heredity, some of these miracles are recited in the second part of this volume to show that the germ evolution is the most incomprehensible phenomenon which has yet been discovered in the universe, for the greater part of what we see in animal and plant forms is only the visible expression of the invisible evolution of the heredity-germ.

We are not ready for a clearly developed energy conception of the origin of life, still less of evolution and of heredity; yet we believe our theory of the actions, reactions, and interactions of living energy will prove[1] to be a step in the right direction.

It is true that in the organism itself, apart from the heredity-germ, we have made great advances[2] in the energy

[1] Some of the reasons for this assertion are presented in the successive chapters of this volume and summarized in the Conclusion.

[2] One of the most influential works in this direction is Jacques Loeb's *Dynamics of Living Matter*, a synthesis of many years of physicochemical research on the actions and reactions of living organisms. See also Loeb's more recent work, *The Organism as a Whole*, published since these lectures were written.

conception. We observe many of the means by which energy is stored, and some of the complicated methods by which it is captured, protected, and released. We shall see that highly evolved organisms, such as the large reptiles and mammals and man, present to the eye of the anatomist and physiologist an inconceivable complexity of energy and form; but this we may in part resolve by reading the pages of this volume backward, Chinese fashion, from the mammal[1] to the monad, in which we reach a stage of relative simplicity. Thus the organism as an arena for energy and matter, as a *complex* of intricate actions, becomes in a measure conceivable. The heredity-germ, on the contrary, remains inconceivable in each of its three powers, namely, in the Organism which it produces, in the succession of germs to which it gives rise, and in its own evolution in course of time.

Having now stated the main object of these lectures, I invite the reader to study the following pages with care, because they review some of the past history and introduce some of the new spirit and purpose of the search for causes in the domain of energy. I begin with matters which are well known to all biologists and proceed to matters which are somewhat more difficult to understand and more novel in purpose.

In this review we need not devote any time or space to fresh arguments for the truth of evolution. The demonstration of evolution as a universal law of living nature is the great intellectual achievement of the nineteenth century. Evolution has outgrown the rank of a theory, for it has won a place in natural law beside Newton's law of gravitation, and in one sense holds a still higher rank, because evolution is the universal master, while gravitation is one among its many

[1] Man is not treated at all in this volume, the subject being reserved for the final lectures in the Hale Series.

agents. Nor is the law of evolution any longer to be associated with any single name, not even with that of Darwin, who was its greatest exponent.[1] It is natural that evolution and Darwinism should be closely connected in many minds, but we must keep clear the distinction that evolution is a law, while Darwinism is merely one of the several ways of interpreting the workings of this law.

In contrast to the unity of opinion on the *law* of evolution is the wide diversity of opinion on the *causes* of evolution. In fact, the causes of the evolution of life are as mysterious as the law of evolution is certain. Some contend that we already know the chief causes of evolution, others contend that we know little or nothing of them. In this open court of conjecture, of hypothesis, of more or less heated controversy, the great names of Lamarck, of Darwin, of Weismann figure prominently as leaders of different schools of opinion; while there are others, like myself,[2] who for various reasons belong to no school, and are as agnostic about Lamarckism as they are about Darwinism or Weismannism, or the more recent form of Darwinism, termed Mutation by de Vries.

In truth, from the period of the earliest stages of Greek thought man has been eager to discover some natural cause of evolution, and to abandon the idea of supernatural intervention in the order of nature. Between the appearance of *The Origin of Species*, in 1859, and the present time there have been great waves of faith in one explanation and then in another: each of these waves of confidence has ended in disappointment, until finally we have reached a stage of very general

[1] See *From the Greeks to Darwin* (Macmillan & Co., 1894), by the present author, in which the whole history of the evolution idea is traced from its first conception down to the time of Darwin.

[2] Osborn, H. F., "The Hereditary Mechanism and the Search for the Unknown Factors of Evolution," *The Amer. Naturalist*, May, 1895, pp. 418–439.

scepticism. Thus the long period of observation, experiment, and reasoning which began with the French natural philosopher Buffon, one hundred and fifty years ago, ends in 1916 with the general feeling that our search for causes, far from being near completion, has only just begun.

Our present state of opinion is this: we know to some extent *how* plants and animals and man evolve; we do not know *why* they evolve. We know, for example, that there has existed a more or less complete chain of beings from monad to man, that the one-toed horse had a four-toed ancestor, that man has descended from an unknown ape-like form somewhere in the Tertiary. We know not only those larger chains of descent, but many of the minute details of these transformations. We do not know their internal causes, for none of the explanations which have in turn been offered during the last hundred years satisfies the demands of observation, of experiment, of reason. It is best frankly to acknowledge that the chief causes of the orderly evolution of the germ are still entirely unknown, and that our search must take an entirely fresh start.

As regards the continuous adaptability and fitness of living things, we have a reasonable interpretation of the causes of some of the phenomena of adaptation, but they are the smaller part of the whole. Especially mysterious are the chief phenomena of adaptation in the germ; the marvellous and continuous fitness and beauty of form and function remain largely unaccounted for. We have no scientific explanation for those processes of development from within, which Bergson[1] has termed "l'évolution créatrice," and for which Driesch[2] has abandoned a natural explanation and assumed

[1] Bergson, Henri, 1907, *L'Evolution Créatrice*.
[2] Driesch, Hans, 1908, *The Science and Philosophy of the Organism.*

the existence of an *entelechy*, that is, an internal perfecting influence.

This confession of failure is part of the essential honesty of scientific thought. We recall the fact that our baffled state of mind is by no means new, for in Kant's work of 1790, his *Methodical System of the Teleological Faculty of Judgment*, he divides all things in nature into the "inorganic," in which natural causes prevail, and the "organic," in which the active teleological (*i. e.*, purposive) principle of adaptation is supposed to prevail. There was in Kant's mind a cleft between the domain of primeval matter and the domain of life, for in the latter he assumes the presence of a supernatural principle, of final causes acting toward definite ends. This view is expressed in his *Teleological Faculty of Judgment* as follows:

"But he" (the archæologist of Nature) "must for this end ascribe to the common mother an organization ordained purposely with a view to the needs of all her offspring, otherwise the possibility of suitability of form in the products of the animal and vegetable kingdoms cannot be conceived at all."[1]

"It is quite certain that we cannot become sufficiently acquainted with organized creatures and their hidden potentialities by aid of purely mechanical natural principles; much less can we explain them; and this is so certain, that we may boldly assert that it is absurd for man even to conceive such an idea, or to hope that a Newton may one day arise able to make the production of a blade of grass comprehensible, according to natural laws ordained by no intention; such an insight we must absolutely deny to man."[2]

For a long period after *The Origin of Species* appeared, Haeckel and many others believed that Darwin had arisen as the Newton for whom Kant did not dare to hope; but no

[1] Kant, Emmanuel, 1790, § 79.

[2] *Ibid.*, § 74.

one now claims for Darwin's law of natural selection a rank equal to that of Newton's law of gravitation.

If we admit the possibility that Kant was right, and that we can never become sufficiently acquainted with organized creatures and their hidden potentialities by aid of purely natural principles, we may be compelled to regard the origin and evolution of life as an ultimate law like the law of gravitation, which may be mathematically and physically defined, but cannot be resolved into any causes. We are not willing, however, to make such an admission at the present time and to abandon the search for causes.

The question then arises, why has our long and arduous search after the causes of evolution so far been unsuccessful? One reason why our search may have failed appears to be that the chief explorers have been trained in one school of thought, namely, the *school of the naturalist.* They all began their studies with observations on the external form and color of animals and plants; they have all observed the end results of long processes of evolution. Buffon derived his ideas of the causes of evolution from the comparison of the wild and domestic animals of the Old and New Worlds; Goethe observed the comparative anatomy of man and of the higher animals; Lamarck observed the higher phases of the vertebrate and invertebrate animals; Darwin observed the form of most of the domestic animals and cultivated plants and, finally, of man, and noted the adaptive significance of the colors of flowers and birds, and the relations of flowers with birds and insects; de Vries compared the wild and cultivated species of plants. Thus all the great naturalists in turn—Buffon, Goethe, Lamarck, Darwin, and de Vries—have attempted to reason backward, as it were, from the highly organized appearances of form and color to their causes. The same is true of the palæontologists:

Cope turned from the form of the teeth and skeleton backward to considerations of cause and energy, Osborn[1] reached a conception of evolution as of the relations of fourfold form, and hence proposed the word tetraplasy.

The Heredity theories of Darwin, of de Vries, of Weismann have also been largely in the material conceptions of fine particles of matter such as "pangens" and "determinants." There has been some consideration of function and of the internal phenomena of organisms, but there has been little or no serious attempt to reverse the mental processes of the naturalist and substitute those of the physicist in considering the *causes* of evolution.[2]

Moreover, all the explanations of evolution which have been offered by three generations of naturalists align themselves under two main ideas only. The first is the idea that the causes of evolution are chiefly from without inward, namely, beginning in the environment of the body and extending into the germ: this idea is *centripetal*. The second idea is just the reverse: it is *centrifugal*, namely, that the causes begin in the germ and extend outward into the body and into the environment.

The pioneer of the first order of ideas is Buffon, who early reached the opinion that favorable or unfavorable changes of environment directly alter the hereditary form of succeeding generations. Lamarck,[3] the founder of a broader and more modern conception of evolution, concluded that the changes of form and function in the body and nervous system induced by habit and environment accumulate in the germ,

[1] Osborn, H. F., "Tetraplasy, the Law of the Four Inseparable Factors of Evolution," *Jour. Acad. Nat. Sci. Phila.*, special anniversary volume issued September 14, 1912, pp. 275–300.

[2] See fuller exposition on pp. 10–23 of this volume.

[3] For a fuller exposition of the theory of Lamarck, see pp. 143, 144.

and are handed on by heredity to succeeding generations. This essential idea of LAMARCKISM was refined and extended by Herbert Spencer, by Darwin himself, by Cope and many others; but it has thus far failed of the crucial test of observation and experiment, and has far fewer adherents to-day than it had forty years ago.

We now perceive that Darwin's original thought turned to the opposite idea, namely, to sudden changes in the heredity-germ itself[1] as giving rise spontaneously to more or less adaptive changes of body form and function which, if favorable to survival, might be preserved and accumulated through natural selection. This pure DARWINISM has been refined and extended by Wallace, Weismann, and especially of late by de Vries, whose "mutation theory" is pure Darwinism in a new guise.

Weismann's great contribution to thought has been to point out the very sharp distinction which undoubtedly exists between the hereditary forces and predispositions in the heredity-germ and the visible expression of these forces in the organism. It is in the "germ-plasm," as Weismann terms it—in this volume termed the "heredity-chromatin"—that the real evolution of all predispositions to form and function is taking place, and the problem of causes of evolution has become an infinitely more difficult one since Weismann has compelled us to realize that the essential question is the *causes of germinal evolution* rather than the causes of bodily evolution or of environmental evolution.

Again, despite the powerful advocacy of pure Darwinism by Weismann and de Vries in the new turn that has been given to our search for causes by the rediscovery of the law of Mendel and the heredity doctrines which group under MEN-

[1] Osborn, H. F., "Darwin's Theory of Evolution by the Selection of Minor Saltations," *The Amer. Naturalist*, February, 1912, pp. 76–82.

DELISM,[1] it may be said that Darwin's law of selection as a natural explanation of the origin of *all* fitness in form and function has also lost its prestige at the present time, and all of Darwinism which now meets with universal acceptance is the *law of the survival of the fittest*, a limited application of Darwin's great idea as expressed by Herbert Spencer. Few biologists to-day question the simple principle that the fittest tend to survive, that the unfit tend to be eliminated, and that the present aspect of the entire living world is due to this great pruning-knife which is constantly sparing those which are best fitted or adapted to any conditions of environment and cutting out those which are less adaptive. But as Cope pointed out, the *survival* of fitness and the *origin* of fitness are two very different phenomena.

If the naturalists have failed to make progress in the search for causes, I believe it is chiefly because they have attempted to reason backward from highly complex plant and animal forms to causes. The cart has always been placed before the horse; or, to express it in another way, thought has turned from the *forms of living matter* toward a problem which involves the *phenomena of living energy;* or, still more briefly, we have been thinking from matter backward into energy rather than from energy forward into matter and form.

All speculation on the origin of life, fruitless as it may at first appear, has the advantage that it compels a sudden reversal of the naturalist's point of view, for we are forced to work from energy upward into form, because, at the beginning, form is nothing, energy is everything. Energy appears to be the chief end of life—the first efforts of life work toward the capture of energy, the storage of energy, the release of

[1] Mendelism chiefly refers to the distinction and laws of distribution of separable or unit characters in the germ and in the individual in course of its development.

energy. The earliest adaptations we know of are designed for the capture and storage of energy.

Matter in the state of relative rest known as plant and animal form is present, but, in the simplest and lowliest types of life, form does not conceal and mask the processes of energy as it does in the higher types. Similarly, the earliest fitness we discover in the bacteria or monads is the fitness of grouping and organizing different kinds of energy—the energy of molecules, of atoms, of electrons as displayed in the twenty-six or more chemical elements which enter into life.

In searching among these early episodes of life in its origin we discover that four complexes of energy are successively added and combined. The Inorganic Environment of the sun, of the earth, of the water, of the atmosphere is exploited thoroughly in search of energy by the Organism: the organism itself becomes an organism only by utilizing the energy of the environment and by coordinating its own internal energies. Whether the Germ as the special centre of heredity and reproduction of energy is as ancient as the organism we do not know; but we do know that it becomes a distinct and highly complex centre of potential energy which directs the way to the entire energy complex of the newly developing organism. Finally, as organisms multiply and acquire various kinds of energy, the Life Environment arises as a new factor in the energy complex. Thus in the process of the origin and early evolution of life, complexes of four greater and lesser energy groups arise, namely: INORGANIC ENVIRONMENT: the energy content in the sun, the earth, the water, and the air; ORGANISM: the energy of the individual, developing and changing the cells and tissues of the body, including that part of the germ which enters every cell; HEREDITY-GERM: the energies of the heredity substance (heredity-chromatin) concentrated in the reproductive cells of continuous and successive generations, as well as in all the cells and tissues of the organism; and LIFE ENVIRONMENT: beginning with the monads and algæ and ascending in a developing scale of plants and animals.

There are here *four evolutions* of energy rather than one, and the problem of causes is how the four evolutions are adjusted to each other; and especially how the evolution of the germ adjusts itself to that of the inorganic environment and of the life environment, and to the temporary evolution of the organism itself.

I do not propose to evade the difficulties of the problem of the origin and evolution of life by minimizing any of them.

Whether our approach through energy will lead to the discovery of some at least of the unknown causes of evolution remains to be determined by many years of observation and experiment. Whereas our increasing knowledge of energy in matter reveals an infinity of energized particles even in the infinitely minute aggregations known as molecules—an infinity which we observe but do not comprehend—we find in our search for causes of the origin and evolution of life that we have reached an entirely new point of departure, namely, that of the physicist and chemist rather than the old point of departure of the naturalist. We have obtained a starting-point for new and untried paths of exploration which may be followed during the present century—paths which have long been trodden with a different purpose by physicists and chemists, and by physiologists and biochemists in the study of the organism itself.

The reader may thus follow, step by step, my own experience and development of thought in preparing these lectures. The reason why I happened to begin this volume with the problem of energy and end with that of the evolution of form is that these lectures were prepared and delivered midway in a cosmic-evolution series which opened with Sir Ernest Rutherford's[1] discourse on "The Constitution of Matter and the Evolution of the Elements," and continued with "The Evolution of the Stars and the Formation of the Earth," by Doctor William Wallace Campbell,[2] and "The Evolution of the Earth," by Professor Thomas Chrowder Chamberlin.[3] My friend George Ellery Hale placed upon me the responsibility of weaving the partly known and still more largely unknown narrative which connects the forms of energy and matter observed in the sun and stars with the forms of energy and matter which we observe in the bodies of our own mammalian ancestors. Certainly we appear to inherit some, if not all, of our physicochemical characters from the sun; and to this degree we may claim kinship with the stellar universe. Some of our distinctive characters and functions are actually properties of our ancestral star. Physically and chemically we are the offspring of our great luminary, which certainly contributes to us all our chemical elements and all the physical properties which bind them together.

Some day a constellation of genius will unite in one laboratory on the life problem. This not being possible at present, I have endeavored during the past two years[4] for the purposes

[1] Rutherford, Sir Ernest, "The Constitution of Matter and the Evolution of the Elements," first series of lectures on the William Ellery Hale foundation, delivered in April, 1914; *Pop. Sci. Mon.*, August, 1915, pp. 105–142.

[2] Campbell, William Wallace, "The Evolution of the Stars and the Formation of the Earth," second series of lectures on the William Ellery Hale foundation, delivered December 7 and 8, 1914; *Pop. Sci. Mon.*, September, 1915, pp. 200–235; *Scientific Monthly*, October, 1915, pp. 1–17; November, 1915, pp. 177–194; December, 1915, pp. 238–255.

[3] Chamberlin, Thomas Chrowder, "The Evolution of the Earth," third series of lectures on the William Ellery Hale foundation, delivered April 19–21, 1915; *Scientific Monthly*, May, 1916, pp. 417–437; June, 1916, pp. 536–556.

[4] I first opened a note-book on this subject in the month of April, 1915, when I was invited by Doctor George Ellery Hale to undertake the preparation of these lectures.

of my own task to draw a large number of specialists together in correspondence and in a series of personal conferences and discussions; and whatever merits this volume may possess are partly due to their generous response in time and thought to my invitation. Their suggestions are duly acknowledged in footnotes throughout the text. I have myself approached the problem through a synthesis of astronomy, geology, physics, chemistry, and biology.

In consulting authorities on this subject I have made one exception, namely, the problem of the origin of life itself with its vast literature going back to the ancients—I have read none of it and quoted none of it. In order to consider the problem from a fresh and unbiassed point of view, I have also purposely refrained from reading any of the recent and authoritative treatises of Schäfer,[1] Moore,[2] and others on the origin of life. It will be interesting for the reader to compare the conclusions previously reached by these distinguished chemists with those presented in the following pages.

For invaluable guidance in the phenomena of physics I am deeply indebted to my colleague Professor Michael I. Pupin, of Columbia University, who has given me his views as to the fundamental relation of Newton's laws of motion to the modern laws of heat and energy (thermodynamics), and has clarified the laws of action, reaction, and interaction from the physical standpoint. Without this aid I could never have developed what I believe to be the new biological principle set forth in this work. I owe to him the confirmation of the use of the word *interaction* as a physical term, which had occurred to me first as a biological term.

[1] Schäfer, Sir Edward A., *Life, Its Nature, Origin, and Maintenance*. Longmans, Green & Co., New York, 1912.

[2] Moore, Benjamin, *The Origin and Nature of Life*, Henry Holt & Co., New York; Williams & Norgate, London, 1913.

As to the physicochemical actions and reactions of the living organism I have drawn especially from Loeb's *Dynamics of Living Matter.* In the physicochemical section I am also greatly indebted to the very suggestive work of Henderson entitled *The Fitness of the Environment,* from which I have especially derived the notion that fitness long antedates the origin of life. Professor Hans Zinsser, of Columbia University, has aided in a review of Ehrlich's theory of antibodies and the results of later research concerning them. Professor Ulric Dahlgren, of Princeton University, has aided the preparation of this work with valuable notes and suggestions on the light, heat, and chemical rays of the sun, and on phosphorescence and electric phenomena in the higher organisms.

In the geochemical and geophysical section I am indebted to my colleagues in the National Academy, F. W. Clarke and George F. Becker, not only for the revision of parts of the text, but for many valuable suggestions and criticisms.

For suggestions as to the chemical conditions which may have prevailed in the earth during the earliest period in the origin of life, as well as for criticisms and careful revision of the chemical text I am especially indebted to my colleague in Columbia University, Professor William J. Gies.

In the astronomic section I desire to express my indebtedness to George Ellery Hale, of the Mount Wilson Observatory, for the use of photographs, and to Henry Norris Russell, of Princeton University, for notes upon the heat of the primordial earth's surface. In the early narrative of the earth's history and in the subsequent geographic and physiographic charts and maps Professor Charles Schuchert and Professor Joseph Barrell, of Yale University, kindly cooperated with the loan of illustrations and otherwise. In the section on the evolution of bacteria, which is a part pertaining to the idea of the early evolution of energy in living matter, I enjoyed the cooperation of Doctor I. J. Kligler, formerly of the American Museum of Natural History, and now at the Rockefeller Institute for Medical Research.

In the botanical section I am especially indebted to Professor T. H. Goodspeed, of the University of California, and to Doctor Marshall Avery Howe, of the Botanical Gardens, for many valuable notes and suggestions, as well as for certain illustrations. In the early zoological section I am indebted to my colleagues at Columbia University, Professor Edmund B. Wilson and Professor Gary N. Calkins. Especial thanks are due to Mr. Roy W. Miner, of the American Museum, for his careful comparisons of recent forms of marine life with the Cambrian forms discovered by Doctor Charles Walcott, who supplied me with the beautiful photographs shown in Chapter IV.

In preparing the chapters on the evolution of the vertebrates, I have turned to my colleague Professor W. K. Gregory, of the American Museum and Columbia University, who has aided both with notes and suggestions, and in the supervision of various illustrations relating to the evolution of vertebrate form. The illustrations are chiefly from the collections of the American Museum of Natural History, as portrayed in original drawings by Charles R. Knight, Erwin S. Christman, and Richard Deckert. The entire work has been faithfully collated and put through the press by my research assistant, Miss Christina D. Matthew.

It affords me great pleasure to dedicate this work to the astronomer friend whose enthusiasm for my own field of work in biology and palæontology has always been a source of encouragement and inspiration.

Henry Fairfield Osborn.

American Museum of Natural History,
February 26, 1917.

CONTENTS

INTRODUCTION

PART I. THE ADAPTATION OF ENERGY

CHAPTER I

Preparation of the Earth for Life

CHAPTER II

The Sun and the Physicochemical Origins of Life

CHAPTER III

Energy Evolution of Bacteria, Algæ, and Plants

PART II. THE EVOLUTION OF ANIMAL FORM

CHAPTER IV

The Origins of Animal Life and Evolution of the Invertebrates

CHAPTER V

Visible and Invisible Evolution of the Vertebrates

CHAPTER VI

Evolution of Body Form in the Fishes and Amphibians

CHAPTER VII

Form Evolution of the Reptiles and Birds

CHAPTER VIII

Evolution of the Mammals

APPENDIX

ILLUSTRATIONS

TABLES

THE ORIGIN AND EVOLUTION OF LIFE

INTRODUCTION

Four questions as to the origin of life. Vitalism or mechanism? Creation or evolution? Law or chance? The energy concept of life. Newton's laws of motion. Action and reaction. Interaction. The four complexes of energy. Darwin's law of Natural Selection.

We may introduce this great subject by putting to ourselves four leading questions: First, Is life upon the earth something new? Second, Does life evolution externally resemble stellar evolution? Third, Is there evidence that similar internal physicochemical laws prevail in life evolution and in lifeless evolution? Fourth, Are life forms the result of law or of chance?

Four Questions as to the Origin of Life

Our first question is one which has not yet been answered by science,[1] although there are two opinions regarding it. Does the origin of life represent the beginning of something new in the cosmos, or does it represent the continuation and evolution of forms of matter and energy already found in the earth, in the sun, and in the other stars?

The traditional opinion is that something new entered this and possibly other planets with the appearance of life; this view is also involved in all the older and newer hypotheses

[1] Science consists of the body of well-ascertained and verified facts and laws of nature. It is clearly to be distinguished from the mass of theories, hypotheses, and opinions which are of value in the progress of science.

which group around the idea of *vitalism* or the existence of specific, distinctive, and adaptive energies in living matter—energies which do not occur in lifeless matter.

The more modern scientific opinion is that life arose from a recombination of forces pre-existing in the cosmos. To hold to this opinion, that life does not represent the entrance either of a new form of energy or of a new series of laws, but is simply another step in the general evolutionary process, is certainly consistent with the development of mechanics, physics, and chemistry since the time of Newton and of evolutionary thought since Buffon, Lamarck, and Darwin. Descartes (1644) led all the modern natural philosophers in perceiving that the explanation of life should be sought in the physical terms of motion and matter. Kant at first (1755-1775) adopted and later (1790) receded from this opinion.

These contrasting opinions, which are certainly as old as Greek philosophy and probably much older, are respectively known as the *vitalistic* and the *mechanistic.*

We may express as our own opinion, based upon the application of uniformitarian evolutionary principles, that when life appeared on the earth some energies pre-existing in the cosmos were brought into relation with the chemical elements already existing. In other words, since every advance thus far in the quest as to the nature of life has been in the direction of a physicochemical rather than of a vitalistic explanation, from the time when Lavoisier (1743-1794) put the life of plants on a solar-chemical basis, if we logically follow the same direction we arrive at the belief that the last step into the unknown—one which possibly may never be taken by man—will also be physicochemical in all its measurable and observable properties, and that the origin of life, as well as its development, will ultimately prove to be a true evolution within the pre-existing cosmos. Without being either a *mechanist* or a *materialist*, one may hold the opinion that life is a continuation of the evolutionary process rather than an exception to the rest of the cosmos, because both mechanism and materialism are words borrowed from other sources which do not in the least convey the impression which the activities of the cosmos make upon us. This impression is that of limitless and ordered energy.

Our second great question relates to the exact significance of the term *evolution* when applied to lifeless and to living matter. Is the development of life evolutionary in the same sense or is it essentially different from that of the inorganic world? Let us critically examine this question by comparing the evolution of life with what is known of the evolution of the stars, of the formation of the earth; in brief, of the comparative anatomy and physiology of the universe as developed by the physicist Rutherford,[1] by the astronomer Campbell,[2] and by the geologist Chamberlin.[3] Or we may compare the evolution of life to the possible evolution of the chemical elements themselves from simpler forms, in passing from primitive nebulæ through the hotter stars to the planets, as first pointed out by Clarke[4] in 1873, and by Lockyer in 1874.

In such comparisons do we find a correspondence between the orderly development of the stars and the orderly development of life? Do we observe in life a continuation of processes which in general present a picture of the universe slowly cooling off and running down? Or, after hundreds of millions of years of more or less monotonous repetition of purely physicochemical and mechanical reaction, do we find that electrons,

[1] Rutherford, Sir Ernest, 1915.
[2] Campbell, William Wallace, 1915.
[3] Chamberlin, Thomas Chrowder, 1916.
[4] Clarke, F. W., 1873, p. 323.

atoms, and molecules break forth into new forms and manifestations of energy which appear to be "creative," conveying to our eyes at least the impression of incessant genesis of new combinations of energy, of matter, of form, of function, of character?

To our senses it appears as if the latter view were the correct one, as if something new is breathed into the aging dust, as if the first appearance of life on this planet marks an actual reversal of the previous order of things. Certainly the cosmic processes cease to run down and begin to build up, abandoning old forms and constructing new ones. Through these activities within matter in the living state the dying earth, itself a mere cinder from the sun, develops new chemical compounds; the chemical elements of the ocean are enriched from new sources of supply, as additional amounts of chemical compounds, produced by organisms from the soil or by elements in the earth that were not previously dissolved, are liberated by life processes and ultimately carried out to sea; the very composition of the rocks is changed; a new life crust begins to cover the earth and to spread over the bottom of the sea. Our old inorganic planet is reorganized, and we see in living matter a reversal of the melancholy conclusion reached by Campbell[1] that "Everything in nature is growing older and changing in condition; slowly or rapidly, depending upon circumstances; the meteorological elements and gravitation are tearing down the high places of the earth; the eroded materials are transported to the bottoms of valleys, lakes, and seas; and these results beget further consequences."

Thus it certainly *appears*, in answer to our second question, that *living matter does not follow the old evolutionary order,* but represents a new assemblage of energies and new types

[1] Campbell, William Wallace, 1915, p. 209.

of action, reaction, and interaction—to use the terms of thermodynamics—between those chemical elements which may be as old as the cosmos itself, unless they prove to represent an evolution from still simpler elements.

Such evolution, we repeat with emphasis, is not like that of the chemical elements or of the stars; the evolutionary process now takes an entirely new and different direction. Although it may arise through combinations of pre-existing energies, it is essentially constructive and apparently though not actually creative[1] it is continually giving birth to an infinite variety of new forms and functions which never appeared in the universe before. It is a continuous creation or creative evolution. Although this creative power is something new derived from the old, it presents the first of the numerous contrasts between the living and the lifeless world.

Our third great question, however, relates to the continuation of the same physicochemical laws in living as in lifeless matter, and puts the second question in another aspect. Is there a *creation* in the strict sense of the term, namely, that some *new form of energy* arises? No, so far as we observe, the process is still *evolutionary rather than creative*, because all the new characters and forms of life appear to arise out of new combinations of pre-existing matter. In other words, the *old* forms of energy transformations appear to be taking a *new* direction.

I shall attempt to show that since in their *simple* forms living processes are known to be physicochemical and are

[1] Creation (L. *creatio*, *creare*, pp. *creatus*; akin to Gr. *κραίνειν*, complete; Sanskrit, √*kar*, make), in contradistinction to evolution, is the production of something new out of nothing, the act of producing both the material and the form of that which is made. Evolution is the production of something new out of the building-up and recombination of something which already exists.

more or less clearly interpretable in terms of action, reaction, and interaction, we are compelled to believe that *complex* forms will also prove to be interpretable in the same terms. None the less, if we affirm that the entire trend of our observation is in the direction of physicochemical explanations rather than of vitalism and vitalistic hypotheses, this is very far from affirming that the explanation of life is purely materialistic, or purely mechanistic, or that any of the present physicochemical explanations are final or satisfying to our reason.

Chemists and biological chemists have very much more to discover. May there not be in the assemblage of cosmic chemical elements necessary to life, which we shall distinguish as the "*life elements*," some *known* element which thus far has not betrayed itself in chemical analysis? This is not impossible, because a known element like radium, for example, might well be wrapped up in living matter but remain as yet undetected, owing to its suffusion or presence in excessively small quantities or to its possession of properties that have escaped notice. Or, again, some *unknown* chemical element, to which the hypothetical term *bion* might be given, may lie awaiting discovery within this complex of known elements. Or an unknown source of energy may be active here.

It is, however, far more probable from our present state of knowledge that unknown principles of action, reaction, and interaction between living forms await discovery; such principles are indeed adumbrated in the as yet partially explored activities of various chemical messengers in the bodies of plants and animals.

We are now prepared for the fourth of our leading questions. If it be determined that the evolution of non-living matter follows certain physical laws, and that the living world conforms to many if not to all of these laws, the final question which arises is: Does the living world also conform to law in its most important aspect, namely, that of fitness or adaptation, or does law emerge from chance? In other words, in the origin and evolution of living things, does nature make a departure from its previous orderly procedure and substitute chance for law? This is perhaps the very oldest biologic question that has entered the human mind, and it is one on which the widest difference of opinion exists even to-day.

Let us first make clear what we mean by the distinction between law and chance.

Astronomers have described the orderly development of the stars, and geologists the orderly development of the earth: is there also an orderly development of life? Are life forms, like celestial forms, the result of law or are they the result of chance?

That life forms have reached their present stage through the operations of *chance* has been the opinion held by a great line of natural philosophers from Democritus and Empedocles to Darwin, and including Poulton, de Vries, Bateson, Morgan, Loeb, and many others of our own day.

Chance is the very essence of the original Darwinian selection hypothesis of evolution. William James[1] and many other eminent philosophers have adopted the "chance" view as if it had been actually demonstrated. Thus James observes: "Absolutely impersonal reasons would be in duty bound to show more general convincingness. Causation is indeed too obscure a principle to bear the weight of the whole structure of theology. As for the argument from design, see how Darwinian ideas have revolutionized it. Conceived as we now conceive them, as so many fortunate escapes from almost lim-

[1] James, William, 1902, pp. 437–439.

itless processes of destruction, the benevolent adaptations which we find in nature suggest a deity very different from the one who figured in the earlier versions of the argument. The fact is that these arguments do but follow the combined suggestions of the facts and of our feeling. They prove nothing rigorously. They only corroborate our pre-existent partialities." Again, to quote the opinion of a recent biological writer: "And why not? Nature has always preferred to work by the hit-or-miss methods of chance. In biological evolution millions of variations have been produced that one useful one might occur."[1]

I have long maintained that this opinion is a biological dogma;[2] it is one of the string of hypotheses upon which Darwin hung his theory of the origin of adaptations and of species, a hypothesis which has gained credence through constant reiteration, for I do not know that it has ever been demonstrated through the actual observation of any evolutionary series.

That life forms have arisen through *law* has been the opinion of another school of natural philosophers, headed by Aristotle, the opponent of Democritus and Empedocles. This opinion has fewer scientific and philosophical adherents; yet Eucken,[3] following Schopenhauer, has recently expressed it as follows: "From the very beginning the predominant philosophical tendency has been against the idea that all the forms we see around us have come into existence solely through an accumulation of accidental individual variations, by the mere blind concurrence of these variations and their actual survival, without the op-

[1] Davies, G. R., 1916, p. 583.

[2] Biology, like theology, has its dogmas. Leaders have their disciples and blind followers. All great truths, like Darwin's law of selection, acquire a momentum which sustains half-truths and pure dogmas.

[3] Eucken, Rudolf, 1912, p. 257.

eration of any inner law. Natural science, too, has more and more demonstrated its inadequacy."

A modern chemist also questions the probability of the environmental fitness of the earth for life being a mere chance process, for Henderson remarks: "There is, in truth, not one chance in countless millions of millions that the many unique properties of carbon, hydrogen, and oxygen, and especially of their stable compounds, water and carbonic acid, which chiefly make up the atmosphere of a new planet, should simultaneously occur in the three elements otherwise than through the operation of a natural law which somehow connects them together. There is no greater probability that these unique properties should be without due cause uniquely favorable to the organic mechanism. These are no mere accidents; an explanation is to seek. It must be admitted, however, that no explanation is at hand."[1]

Unlike our first question as to whether the principle of life introduced something new in the cosmos, a question which is still in the stage of pure speculation, this fourth question of law versus chance in the evolution of life is no longer a matter of opinion, but of direct observation. So far as law is concerned, we observe that the evolution of life forms is like that of the stars: their origin and evolution as revealed through palæontology go to prove that Aristotle was essentially right when he said that "Nature produces those things which, being continually moved by a certain principle contained in themselves, arrive at a certain end."[2] What this internal moving principle is remains to be discovered. We may first exclude the possibility that it acts either through supernatural or teleologic interposition through an externally creative power. Although its visible results are in a high degree purposeful, we

[1] Henderson, Lawrence J., 1913, p. 276.

[2] Osborn, H. F., 1894, p. 56.

may also exclude as unscientific the vitalistic theory of an *entelechy* or any other form of internal perfecting agency distinct from known or unknown physicochemical energies.

Since certain forms of adaptation which were formerly mysterious can now be explained without the assumption of an entelechy we are encouraged to hope that all forms may be thus explained. The fact that the causes underlying the origin of many forms of adaptation are still unknown, unconceived, and perhaps inconceivable, does not inhibit our opinion that adaptation will prove to be a continuation of the previous cosmic order rather than the introduction of a new order of things. If, however, we reject the vitalistic hypotheses of the ancient Greeks, and the modern vitalism of Driesch, of Bergson, and of others, we are driven back to the necessity of further experiment, observation, and research, guided by the imagination and checked by verification. As indicated in our Preface, the old paths of research have led nowhere, and the question arises: What lines shall new researches and experiments follow?

The Energy Concept of Life

While we owe to matter and form the revelation of the existence of the great *law* of evolution, we must reverse our thought in the search for *causes* and take steps toward an energy conception of the origin of life and an energy conception of the nature of heredity.

So far as the *creative* power of energy is concerned, we are on sure ground: in physics energy controls matter and form; in physiology function controls the organ; in animal mechanics motion controls and, in a sense, creates the form of muscles and bones. In every instance some kind of energy or, work precedes some kind of form, rendering it probable that energy also precedes and controls the evolution of life.

The total disparity between invisible energy and visible form is the second point which strikes us as in favor of such a conception, because the most phenomenal thing about the heredity-germ is its microscopic size as contrasted with the titanic beings which may rise out of it. The electric energy transmitted through a small copper wire is yet capable of moving a long and heavy train of cars. The discovery by Becquerel and Curie of radiant energy and of the properties of radium helps us in the same way to understand an energy conception of the heredity-germ, for in radium the energy per unit of mass is enormously greater than the energy quanta which we were accustomed to associate with units of mass; whereas, in most man-made machines with metallic wheels and levers, and in certain parts of the animal machine constructed of muscle and bone, the work done is proportionate to the size and form. The slow dissipation or degradation of energy in radium has been shown by Curie to be concomitant with the giving off of an enormous amount of heat, while Rutherford and Strutt declare that in a very minute amount of active radium the energy of degradation would entirely dominate and mask all other cosmic modes of transformation of energy; for example, it far outweighs that arising from the gravitational energy which is an ample supply for our cosmic system, the explanation being that the minutest energy elements of which radium is composed are moving at incredible velocities, approaching often the velocity of light, *i. e.*, 180,000 miles per second. The energy of radium differs from the supposed energy of life in being constantly dissipated and degraded; its apparently unlimited power is being lost and scattered.

We may imagine that the energy which lies in the life-germ of heredity is very great per unit of mass of the matter which contains it, but that the life-germ energy, unlike that of radium, is in process of accumulation, construction, conservation, rather than of dissipation and destruction.

Following the time (1620) when Francis Bacon divined that heat consists of a kind of motion or brisk agitation of the particles of matter, it has step by step been demonstrated that the energy of heat, of light, of electricity, the electric energy of chemical configurations, the energy of gravitation, are all utilized in living as well as in lifeless substances. Moreover, as remarked above (p. 5), no form of energy has thus far been discovered in living substances which is peculiar to them and not derived from the inorganic world. In a broad sense all these manifestations of energy are subject to Newton's dynamical laws[1] which were formulated in connection with the motions of the heavenly bodies, but are found to apply equally to all motions great or little.

These three fundamental laws are as follows:[2]

I	I
Corpus omne perseverare in statu suo quiescendi vel movendi uniformiter in directum, nisi quatenus illud a viribus impressis cogitur statum suum mutare.	Every body perseveres in its state of rest, or of uniform motion in a right line, unless it is compelled to change that state by forces impressed thereon.

[1] I am indebted to my colleague M. I. Pupin for valuable suggestions in formulating the physical aspect of the principles of action and reaction. He interprets Newton's third law of motion as the foundation not only of modern dynamics in the Newtonian sense but in the most general sense, including biological phenomena. With regard to the *first law of thermodynamics*, it is a particular form of the principle of conservation of energy as applied to heat energy; Helmholtz, who first stated the principle of conservation of energy, derived it from Newtonian dynamics. The *second law of thermodynamics* started from a new principle, that of Carnot, which apparently had no direct connection with Newton's third law of motion; this second law, however, in its most general form cannot be fully interpreted except by statistical dynamics, which are a modern offshoot of Newtonian dynamics.

[2] Newton's three laws of motion, first published in Newton's *Principia* in 1687.

II

Mutationem motus proportionalem esse vi motrici impressæ, et fieri secundum lineam rectam qua vis illa imprimitur.

II

The alteration of motion is ever proportional to the motive force impressed; and is made in the direction of the right line in which that force is impressed.

III

Actioni contrariam semper et æqualem esse reactionem: sive corporum duorum actiones in se mutuo semper esse æquales et in partes contrarias dirigi.

III

To every action there is always opposed an equal reaction: or the mutual actions of two bodies upon each other are always equal, and directed to contrary parts.

Newton's third law of the equality of *action* and *reaction* is the foundation of the modern doctrine of energy,[1] not only in the Newtonian sense but in the most general sense.[2] Newton divined the principle of the conservation of energy in mechanics; Rumford (1798) maintained the universality of the laws of energy; Joule (1843) established the particular principle of the conservation of energy, namely of the exact equivalence between the amount of heat produced and the amount of mechanical energy destroyed; and Helmholtz in his great memoir *Über die Erhaltung der Kraft* extended this system of conservation of energy throughout the whole range of natural phenomena. A familiar instance of the so-called *transformation of energy* is where the sudden arrest of a cool but rapidly moving body produces heat. This was developed as the *first law of thermodynamics*.

At the same time there arose the distinction between *potential energy*, which is stored away in some latent form or manner so that it can be drawn upon for work—such energy

[1] The term *Energy* (Gr. ἐνέργεια; ἐν in; ἔργον, work) in physical science denotes an accumulated capacity for doing mechanical work, and may be either *kinetic* (energy of heat or motion) or *potential* (latent or stored energy).

[2] M. I. Pupin, see note above.

being exemplified mechanically by the bent spring, chemically by gunpowder, and electrically by a Leyden jar—and *kinetic energy*, the active energy of motion and of heat.

While all active mechanical energy or work may be converted into an equivalent amount of heat, the opposite process of turning heat into work involves more or less loss, dissipation, or degradation of energy. This is known as the *second law of thermodynamics* and is the outgrowth of a principle discovered by Sadi Carnot (1824), and developed by Kelvin (1852, 1853). The far-reaching conception of cyclic processes in energy enunciated in Kelvin's principle of the dissipation of available energy puts a diminishing limit upon the amount of heat energy available for mechanical purposes. The available kinetic energy of motion and of heat which we can turn into work or mechanical effect is possessed by any system of two or more bodies in virtue of the relative rates of motion of their parts, velocity being essentially relative.

These two great dynamical principles that the energy of motion can be converted into an equivalent amount of heat, and that a certain amount of heat can be converted into a more limited amount of power were discovered through observations on the motions of larger masses of matter, but they are believed to apply equally to such motions as are involved in the smallest electrically charged atoms (ions) of the chemical elements and the particles flying off in radiant energy as phosphorescence. Such movements of infinitesimal particles underlie all the physicochemical laws of action and reaction which have been observed to occur within living things. In all physicochemical processes within and without the organism by which energy is captured, stored, transformed, or released the actions and reactions are equal, as expressed in Newton's third law.

Actions and reactions refer chiefly to what is going on between the parts of the organism in chemical or physical contact, and are subject to the two dynamical principles referred to above. *Interactions*, on the other hand, refer to what is going on between material parts which are connected with each other by other parts, and cannot be analyzed at all by the two great dynamical principles alone without a knowledge of the structure which connects the interacting parts. For example, in interaction between distant bodies the cause may be very feeble, yet the potential or stored energy which may be liberated at a distant point may be tremendous. Action and reaction are chiefly simultaneous, whereas interaction connects actions and reactions which are not simultaneous; to use a simple illustration: when one pulls at the reins the horse feels it a little later than the moment at which the reins are pulled—there is interaction between the hand and the horse's mouth, the reins being the interacting part. An interacting nerve-impulse starting from a microscopic cell in the brain may give rise to a powerful muscular action and reaction at some distant point. An interacting enzyme, hormone, or other chemical messenger circulating in the blood may profoundly modify the growth of a great organism.

Out of these physicochemical principles has arisen the conception of a living organism as composed of an incessant series of actions and reactions operating under the dynamical laws which govern the transfer and transformation of energy.

The central theory which is developed in our speculation on the Origin of Life is that every physicochemical action and reaction concerned in the transformation, conservation, and dissipation of energy, *produces also, either as a direct result or as a by-product, a physicochemical agent of interaction which permeates and affects the organism as a whole or affects only some special part.* Through such interaction the organism is made a unit and acts as one, because the activities of all its parts are correlated. This idea may be expressed in the following simplified scheme of the functions or *physiology* of the organism:

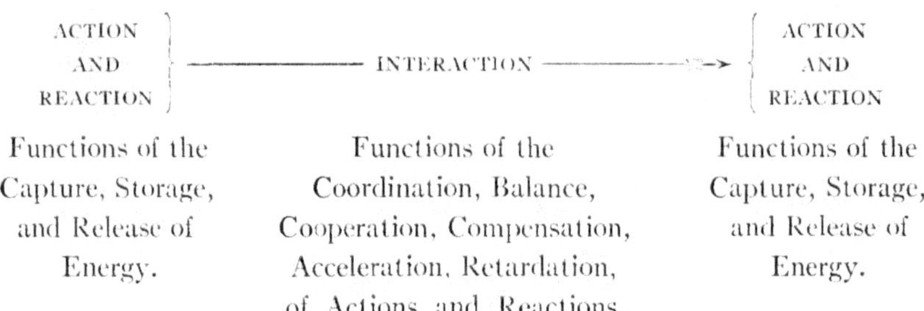

Since it is known that *many* actions and reactions of the organism—such as those of general and localized growth, of nutrition, of respiration—are coordinated with other actions and reactions through interaction, it is but a step to extend the principle and suppose that *all actions and reactions* are similarly coordinated; and that while there was an evolution of action and reaction there was also a corresponding evolution of interaction, for without this the organism would not evolve harmoniously.

Evidence for such universality of the interaction principle has been accumulating rapidly of late, especially in experimental medicine[1] and in experimental biology.[2] It is a further step in our theory to suppose that the *directing power of heredity* which regulates the initial and all the subsequent steps of development in action and reaction, gives the orders, hastens development at one point, retards it at another, is an elaboration of the principle of interaction. In lowly organisms

[1] See the works of Cushing and Crile cited below.

[2] See the recent experiments of Morgan and Goodale.

like the monads these interactions are very simple; in higher organisms like man these interactions are elaborated through physicochemical and other agents, some of which have already been discovered although doubtless many more await discovery. Thus we conceive of the origin and development of the organism as a concomitant evolution of the action, reaction, and interaction of energy. Actions and reactions are borrowed from the inorganic world, and elaborated through the production of the new organic chemical compounds; it is the peculiar evolution and elaboration of the physical principle of interaction which distinguishes the living organism.

Thus the evolution of life may be rewritten in terms of invisible energy, as it has long since been written in terms of visible form. All visible tissues, organs, and structures are seen to be the more or less simple or elaborate agents of the different modes of energy. One after another special groups of tissues and organs are created and coordinated—organs for the *capture* of energy from the inorganic environment and from the life environment, organs for the *storage* of energy, organs for the *transformation* of energy from the potential state into the states of motion and heat. Other agents of control are evolved to bring about a harmonious *balance* between the various organs and tissues in which energy is *released*, hastened or *accelerated*, slowed down or *retarded*, or actually arrested or *inhibited*.

In the simplest organisms energy may be captured while the organism as a whole is in a state of rest; but at an early stage of life special organs of locomotion are evolved by which energy is sought out, and organs of prehension by which it may be seized. Along with these motor organs are developed organs of *offense* and *defense* of many kinds, by means of which stored energy is protected from capture or invasion by other organisms. Finally, there is the most mysterious and comprehensive process of all, by which all these manifold modes of energy are *reproduced* in another organism. The evolution of these complex modes of action, reaction, and interaction is traced through all the early chapters of this volume and is summed up in Chapter V (p. 152) as a physicochemical introduction to the evolution of vertebrate form.

The Four Complexes of Energy

The theoretic evolution of the four complexes is somewhat as follows:

(1) In the order of time the *Inorganic Environment* comes first; energy and matter are first seen in the sun, in the earth, in the air, and in the water—each a very wonderful complex of energies in itself. They form, nevertheless, an entirely orderly system, held together by gravitation, moving under Newton's laws of motion, subject to the more newly discovered laws of thermodynamics. In this complex we observe actions and reactions, the sum of the taking in and the giving out of energy, the conservation of energy. We also observe interactions wherein the energy released at certain points may be greater than the energy received, which is merely a stimulus for the beginning of the local energy transformations. This energy is distributed among the eighty or more chemical elements of the sun and other stars. These elements are combined in plants into complex substances, generally with a storage of energy. Such substances are disintegrated into simple substances in animals, generally with a release of energy. All these processes are termed by us physicochemical.

(2) With life something new appears in the universe, namely, a union of the internal and external adjustment of energy which we appropriately call an *Organism*. In the course of the evolution of life every law and property in the physico-chemical world is turned to advantage; every chemical element is assembled in which inorganic properties may serve organic functions. There is an immediate or gradual separation of the organism into two complexes of energy, namely, first, the energy complex of the organism, which is perishable with the term of the life of the individual, and second, the germ or heredity substance, which is perpetual.

(3) The idea that the germ is an energy complex is an as yet unproved hypothesis; it has not been demonstrated. The *Heredity-germ* in some respects bears a likeness to latent or potential interacting energy, while in other respects it is entirely unique. The supposed germ energy is not only cumulative but is in a sense imperishable, self-perpetuating, and continuous during the whole period of the evolution of life upon the earth, a conception which we owe chiefly to the law of the continuity of the germ-plasm formulated by Weismann. Some of the observed phenomena of the germ in Heredity are chiefly analogous to those of *interaction* in the Organism, namely, directive of a series of actions and reactions, but in general we know no complete physical or inorganic analogy to the phenomena of heredity; they are unique in nature.

(4) With the multiplication and diversification of individual organisms there enters a new factor in the environment, namely, the energy complex of the *Life Environment*.

Thus there are combined certainly three, and possibly four, complexes of energy, of which each has its own actions, reactions, and interactions. The evolution of life proceeds by sustaining these actions, reactions, and interactions and constantly building up new ones: at the same time the potentiality of reproducing these actions, reactions, and interactions in the course of the development of each new organism is gradually being accumulated and perpetuated in the germ.

From the very beginning every individual organism is competing with other organisms of its own kind and of other kinds, and the law of the survival of the fittest is operating between the forms and functions of organisms as a whole and between their separate actions, reactions, and interactions. This, as Weismann pointed out, while apparently a selection of the individual organism itself, is actually a selection of the heredity-germ complex, of its potentialities, powers, and predispositions. Thus *Selection* is not a form of energy nor a part of the energy complex; it is an arbiter between different complexes and forms of energy; it antedates the origin of life just as adaptation or fitness antedates the origin of life, as remarked by Henderson.

Thus we arrive at a conception of the relations of organisms to each other and to their environment as of an enormous and always increasing complexity, sustained through the interchange of energy. Darwin's principle of the survival or elimination of various forms of living energy is, in fact, adumbrated in the survival or elimination of various forms of lifeless energy as witnessed among the stars and planets. In other words, Darwin's principle operates as one of the *causes of evolution* in making the lifeless and living worlds what they now appear to be, but not as one of the energies of evolution. Selection merely determines which one of a combination of energies shall survive and which shall perish.

The complex of four interrelated sets of physicochemical energies which I have previously set forth (p. xvi) as the most fundamental biologic scheme or principle of development may now be restated as follows:

In each organism the phenomena of life represent the action, reaction, and interaction of four complexes of physicochemical energy, namely, those of (1) the Inorganic Environment, (2) the developing Organism (protoplasm and body-chromatin), (3) the germ or Heredity-chromatin, (4) the Life Environment. Upon the resultant actions, reactions, and interactions of potential and kinetic energy in each organism Selection is constantly operating wherever there is competition with the corresponding actions, reactions, and interactions of other organisms.[1]

This principle I shall put forth in different aspects as the central thought of these lectures, stating at the outset and often recurring to the admission that it involves several unknown principles and especially the largely hypothetical question whether there is a relation between the action, reaction, and interaction of the internal energies of the germ or heredity-chromatin with the external energies of the inorganic environment, of the developing organism, and of its life environment. In other words, while this is a principle which largely governs the Organism, it remains to be discovered whether it also governs the causes of the Evolution of the Germ.

As observed in the Preface (p. xvii) we are studying not one but four simultaneous evolutions. Each of these evolutions appears to be almost infinite in itself as soon as we examine it in detail, but of the four that of the germ or heredity-chromatin so far surpasses all the others in complexity that it appears to us infinite.

The physicochemical relations between these four evolutions, including the activities of the single and of the multiplying organisms of the Life Environment, may be expressed in

[1] Compare Osborn, H. F., 1917, p. 8.

diagrammatic form, and somewhat more technically than in the Preface, as follows:

<table>
<tr><td>ORGANISM A

Under

Newton's Laws of Motion
and
Modern Thermodynamics

Actions, Reactions, and Interactions
of the</td><td></td><td>ORGANISMS B–Z

Under

Newton's Laws of Motion
and
Modern Thermodynamics

Actions, Reactions, and Interactions
of the</td></tr>
<tr><td>1. Inorganic Environment:
physicochemical energies of space, of the sun, earth, air, and water.</td><td></td><td>1. Inorganic Environment:
physicochemical energies of space, of the sun, earth, air, and water.</td></tr>
<tr><td>2. Organism:
physicochemical energies of the developing individual in the tissues, cells, protoplasm, and cell-chromatin.

3. Heredity-Germ:
physicochemical energies of the heredity-chromatin, included in the reproductive cells and tissues.</td><td>Under

Darwin's Law
of
Natural Selection

Survival of the fittest: competition, selection, and elimination of the energies and forms.</td><td>2. Organism:
physicochemical energies of the developing individual in the tissues, cells, protoplasm, and cell-chromatin.

3. Heredity-Germ:
physicochemical energies of the heredity-chromatin included in the reproductive cells and tissues.</td></tr>
<tr><td>4. Life Environment:
physicochemical energies of other organisms.</td><td></td><td>4. Life Environment:
physicochemical energies of other organisms.</td></tr>
</table>

If a single name is demanded for this conception of evolution it might be termed the *tetrakinetic* theory in reference to the four sets of internal and external energies which play upon and within every individual and every race. In respect to form it is a *tetraplastic*[1] theory in the sense that every living plant and animal form is plastically moulded by four sets of energies. The derivation of this conception of life and of the possible causes of evolution from the laws which have been developed out of the Newtonian system, and from those of the other great Cambridge philosopher, Charles Darwin, are clearly shown in the above diagram.

In these lectures we shall consider in order, first, the evolution of the inorganic environment necessary to life; second, theories of the origin of life in regard to the time when it occurred and the accumulation of various kinds of energy through which it probably originated; and, third, the orderly development of the differentiation and adaptation of the most primitive forms. Throughout we shall point out some of the more notable examples of the apparent operation of our fundamental biologic principle of the action, reaction, and interaction between the inorganic environment, the organism, the germ, and the life environment.

The apparently insuperable difficulties of the problem of the causes of evolution in the germ or heredity-chromatin—causes which are at present almost entirely beyond the realm of observation and experiment—will be made more evident through the development of the second part of our subject, namely, the evolution of the higher living forms of energy upon the earth so far as they have been followed from the stage of monads or bacteria up to that of the higher mammals.

[1] Osborn, H. F., 1912.2.

PART I. THE ADAPTATION OF ENERGY

CHAPTER I

PREPARATION OF THE EARTH FOR LIFE

Primordial environment—the lifeless earth. Age of the earth and beginning of the life period. Primordial environment—the lifeless water. Salt as a measure of the age of the ocean. Primordial chemical environment. Primordial environment—the atmosphere.

In the spirit of the preparatory work of the great pioneers of geology, such as Hutton, Scrope, and Lyell, and of the history of the evolution of the working mechanism of organic evolution, as developed by Darwin and Wallace,[1] our inferences as to past processes are founded upon the observation of present processes. In general, our narrative will therefore follow the "uniformitarian" method of interpretation first presented in 1788 by Hutton,[2] who may be termed the Newton of geology, and elaborated in 1830 by Lyell,[3] the master of Charles Darwin. The uniformitarian doctrine is this: present continuity implies the improbability of past catastrophism and violence of change, either in the lifeless or in the living world; moreover, we seek to interpret the changes and laws of past time through those which we observe at the present time. This was Darwin's secret, learned from Lyell.

Cosmic Primordial Environment—The Lifeless Earth

Let us first look at the cosmic environment, the inorganic world before the entrance of life. Since 1825, when Cuvier[4]

[1] Judd, John W., 1910.
[2] Hutton, James, 1795.
[3] Lyell, Charles, 1830.
[4] Cuvier, Baron Georges L. C. F. D., 1825.

published his famous *Discours sur les Révolutions de la Surface du Globe*, the past history of the earth, of its waters, of the atmosphere, and of the sun—the four great complexes of inorganic environment—has been written with some approach to precision. Astronomy, physics, chemistry, geology, and palæontology have each pursued their respective lines of observation, resulting in some concordance and much discordance of opinion and theory. In general we shall find that opinion founded upon life data has not agreed with opinion founded upon physical or chemical data, arousing discord, especially in connection with the problems of the age of the earth and the stability of the earth's surface.

In our review of these matters we may glance at opinions, whatever their source, but our narrative of the chemical origin and history of life on the earth will be followed by observations on living matter mainly as it is revealed in palæontology and as it exists to-day, rather than on hypotheses and speculations upon pre-existing states.

The formation of the earth's surface is a prelude to our considering the first stage of the environment of life. According to the planetesimal theory, as set forth by Chamberlin,[1] the earth, instead of consisting of a primitive molten globe as postulated by the old nebular hypothesis of Laplace, originated in a nebulous knot of solid matter as a nucleus of growth which was fed by the infall or accretion of scattered nebulous matter (planetesimals) coming within the sphere of control of this knot. The temperature of these accretions to the early earth could scarcely have been high, and the mode of addition of these planetesimals one by one explains the very heterogeneous matter and differentiated specific gravity of the continents and oceanic basins. The present form of the earth's surface is the

[1] Chamberlin, Thomas Chrowder, 1916.

result of the combined action of the lithosphere (the rocks), hydrosphere (the water), and atmosphere (the air). Liquefaction of the rocks occurred locally and occasionally as the result of heat generated by increased pressure and by radioactivity; but the planetesimal hypothesis assumes that the present elastic rigid condition of the earth prevailed—at least in its outer half—throughout the history of its growth from the small original nebular knot to its present proportions and caused the permanence of its continents and of its oceanic basins. We are thus brought to conditions that are fundamental to the evolution of life on the earth. According to the opinion of Chamberlin, cited by Pirsson and Schuchert,[1] life on the earth may have been possible when it attained the present size of Mars.

According to Becker,[2] who follows the traditional theory of a primitive molten globe, the earth first presented a nearly smooth, equipotential surface, determined not by its mineral composition, but by its density. As the surface cooled down a temperature was reached at which the waters of the gaseous envelope united with the superficial rocks and led to an aqueo-igneous state. After further cooling the second and final consolidation followed, dating the origin of the granites and granitary rocks. The areas which cooled most rapidly and best conducted heat formed shallow oceanic basins, whereas the areas of poor conductivity which cooled more slowly stood out as low continents. The internal heat of the cooling globe still continues to do its work, and the cyclic history of its surface is completed by the erosion of rocks, by the accumulation of sediments, and by the following subsidence of the areas loaded

[1] Pirsson, Louis V., and Schuchert, Charles, 1915, p. 535.
[2] George F. Becker, letter of October 15, 1915.

down by these sediments. It appears that the internal heat engine is far more active in the slowly cooling continental areas than in the rapidly cooling areas underlying the oceans, as manifested in the continuous outflows of igneous rocks, which, especially in the early history of the earth—at or before the time when life appeared—covered the greater part of the earth's surface. The ocean beds, being less subject to the work of the internal heat engine, have always been relatively plane; except near the shores, no erosion has taken place.

The Age of the Earth and Beginning of the Life Period

The age of the earth as a solid body affords our first instance of the very wide discordance between physical and biological opinion. Among the chief physical computations are those of Lord Kelvin, Sir George Darwin, Clarence King, and Carl Barus.[1] In 1879 Sir George Darwin allowed 56,000,000 years as a probable lapse of time since the earth parted company with the moon, and this birthtime of the moon was naturally long prior to that stage when the earth, as a cool, crusted body, became the environment of living matter. Far more elastic than this estimate was that of Kelvin, who, in 1862, placed the age of the earth as a cooling body between 20,000,000 and 400,000,000 years, with a probability of 98,000,000 years. Later, in 1897, accepting the conclusions of King and Barus calculated from data for the period of tidal stability, Kelvin placed the age limit between 20,000,000 and 40,000,000 years, a conclusion very unwelcome to evolutionists.

As early as 1859 Charles Darwin led the biologists in demanding an enormous period of time for the processes of evo-

[1] Becker, George F., 1910, p. 5.

lution, being the first to point out that the high degree of evolution and specialization seen in the invertebrate fossils at the very base of the Palæozoic was in itself a proof that pre-Palæozoic evolution occupied a period as long as or even longer than the post-Palæozoic. In 1869 Huxley renewed this demand for an enormous stretch of pre-Palæozoic or pre-Cambrian time; and as recently as 1896 Poulton[1] found that 400,000,000 years, the greater limit of Kelvin's original estimate, was none too much.

Later physical computations greatly exceeded this biological demand, for in 1908 Rutherford[2] estimated the time required for the accumulation of the radium content of a uranium mineral found in the Glastonbury granitic gneiss of the Early Cambrian as no less than 500,000,000 years. This physical estimate of the age of the Early Cambrian is eighteen times as great as that attained by Walcott[3] in 1893 from his purely geologic computation of the time rates of deposition and maximum thickness of strata from the base of the Cambrian upward; but recent advances in our knowledge of the radioactive elements preclude the possibility of any trustworthy determination of the age of the elements through the methods suggested by Joly and Rutherford.

We thus return to the estimates based upon the time required for the deposition of sediments as by far the most reliable, especially for our quest of the beginning of the life period, because erosion and sedimentation imply conditions of the earth, of the water, and of the atmosphere more or less comparable to those under which life is known to exist. These geologic estimates, which begin with that of John Phillips in 1860, may be tabulated as follows:

[1] Poulton, Edward B., 1896, p. 808.
[2] Rutherford, Sir Ernest, 1906, p. 189.
[3] Walcott, Charles D., 1893, p. 675.

Estimates of Time Required for the Processes of Past Deposition and Sedimentation at Rates Similar to Those Observed at the Present Day [1]

Year	Authority	Estimate
1860.	John Phillips	38– 96 million years.
1890.	De Lapparent	67– 90 million years.
1893.	Walcott (27,640,000 years since the base of the Cambrian Palæozoic; 17,500,000 years or upward for the pre-Palæozoic.)	55– 70 million years.
1899.	Geikie (Minimum 100 million years; maximum—slowest known rates of deposition—400 million years.)	100–400 million years.
1909.	Sollas (The larger estimate of 80 million years on the theory that pre-Palæozoic sediments took as much time as those from the base of the Cambrian upward, allowing for gaps in the stratigraphic column.)	34– 80 million years.

These estimates give a maximum of sixty-four miles as the total accumulation of sedimentary rocks, which is equivalent to a layer 2,300 feet thick over the entire face of the earth.[2] From these purely geologic data the time ratio of the entire life period is now calculated in terms of millions of years, assuming the approximate reliability of the geologic time scale. The actual amount of rock weathered and deposited was probably far greater than that which has been preserved.

In general, these estimates are broadly concordant with those reached by an entirely different method, namely, the amount of sodium chloride (common salt) contained in the ocean,[3] to understand which we must first take another glance at the geography and chemistry of the primordial earth.

The lifeless primordial earth can best be imagined by looking at the lifeless surface of the moon, featured by volcanic

[1] Becker, George F., 1910, pp. 2, 3, 5.

[2] Clarke, F. W., 1916, p. 30.

[3] See *Salt as a Measure of the Age of the Ocean*, p. 35.

action with little erosion or sedimentation because of the lack of water.

The surface of the earth, then, was chiefly spread with granitic masses known as batholiths and with the more superficial volcanic outpourings. There were volcanic ashes; there

Fig. 1. The Moon's Surface.

"The lifeless primordial earth can best be imagined by looking at the lifeless surface of the moon." A portion of the moon's surface, many miles in diameter, illuminated by the rising or setting sun and showing the craters and areas of lava outflow. The Meteor Crater of Arizona, formerly known as Coon Butte—a huge hole, 4,500 feet in diameter and 600 feet in depth, made by a falling meteorite—is strikingly similar to these lunar craters and suggests the possibility that, instead of being the result of volcanic action, the craters of the moon may have been formed by terrific impacts of meteoric masses. Photograph from the Mt. Wilson Observatory.

were gravels, sands, and micas derived from the granites; there were clays from the dissolution of granitic feldspars; there were loam mixtures of clay and sand; there was gypsum from mineral springs.

Bare rocks and soils were inhospitable ingredients for any but the most rudimentary forms of life such as were adapted to feed directly upon the chemical elements and their simplest compounds, or to transform their energy without the friendly aid of sunshine. The only forms of life to-day which can exist in such an inhospitable environment as that of the lifeless earth are certain of the simplest bacteria, which, as we shall see, feed directly upon the chemical elements.

It is interesting to note that, in the period when the sun's light was partly shut off by watery and gaseous vapors, the *early volcanic condition of the earth's surface* may have supplied life with fundamentally important chemical elements, as well as with the heat-energy of the waters or of the soils. Volcanic emanations contain[1] free hydrogen, both oxides of carbon, and frequently hydrocarbons such as methane (CH_4) and ammonium chloride: the last compound is often very abundant. Volcanic waters sometimes contain ammonium (NH_4) salts, from which life may have derived its first nitrogen supply. For example, in the Devil's Inkpot, Yellowstone Park, ammonium sulphate forms 83 per cent of the dissolved saline matter: it is also the principal constituent of the mother liquor of the boric fumaroles of Tuscany, after the boric acid has crystallized out. A hot spring on the margin of Clear Lake, California, contains 107.76 grains per gallon of ammonium bicarbonate.

There were absent from the primordial earth the greater part of the fine sediments and detrital material which now cover three-fourths of its surface, and from which a large part of the sodium content has been leached. The original surface of the earth was thus composed of granitic and other igneous rocks to the exclusion of all others,[2] the essential constituents of these rocks being the lime-soda feldspars from which the sodium of the ocean has since been leached. Waters issuing from such rocks are, as a rule, *relatively* richer in silica than

[1] Clarke, F. W., 1916, chap. VIII., also pp. 107, 199, 243, 244.
[2] Becker, George F., 1910, p. 12.

waters issuing from modern sedimentary areas. They thus furnish a favorable environment for the development of such low organisms (or their ancestors) as the existing diatoms, radiolarians, and sponges, which have skeletons composed of hydrated silica, mineralogically of opal.

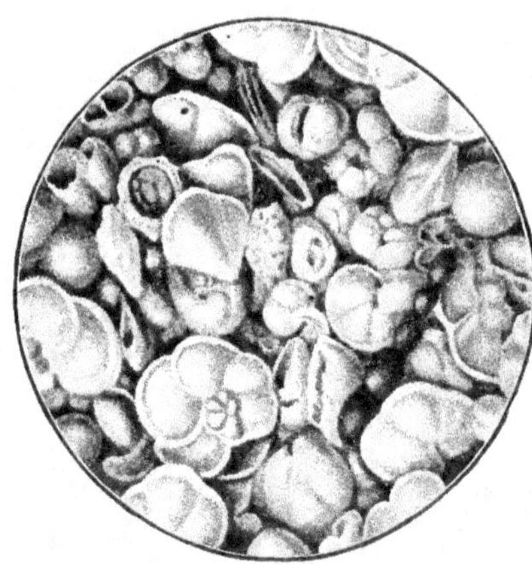

FIG. 2. DEEP-SEA OOZE, THE FORAMINIFERA.

Photograph of a small portion of a calcareous deposit on the sea bottom formed by the dropping down from the sea surface of the dead shells of foraminifera, chiefly *Globigerina*, greatly magnified. Such calcareous deposits extend over large areas of the sea bottom. Reproduced from *The Depths of the Ocean*, by Sir John Murray and Doctor Johan Hjort by permission of the Macmillan Company.

The decomposition and therefore the erosion of the massive rocks was slower then than at present, for none of the life agencies of bacteria, of algæ, of lichens, and of the higher plants, which are now at work on granites and volcanic rocks in all the humid portions of the earth, had yet appeared. On the other hand, much larger areas of these rocks were exposed than at present.

In brief, to imagine the primal lifeless earth we must *subtract* all those portions of mineral deposits which as they exist to-day are mainly of organic origin, such as the organic carbonates and phosphates of lime,[1] the carbonaceous shales as well as the carbonaceous limestones, the graphites derived from carbon, the silicates derived from diatoms, the iron deposits made

[1] It seems improbable that organisms originally began to use carbon or phosphorus in *elementary* form: carbonates and phosphates were probably available at the very beginning and resulted from oxidations or decompositions.—W. J. Gies.

Phosphate of lime, apatite, is an almost ubiquitous component of igneous rocks, but in very small amount. In more than a thousand analyses of such rocks, the average percentage of P_2O_5 is 0.25 per cent.—F. W. Clarke.

by bacteria, the humus of the soil containing organic acids, the soil derived from rocks which are broken up by bacteria, and even the ooze from the ocean floor, both calcareous and

TABLE I

AVERAGE DISTRIBUTION OF THE CHEMICAL ELEMENTS IN EARTH, AIR, AND WATER AT THE PRESENT TIME[1]

(*Life Elements in Italics*)

	The Rocks, Lithosphere, 93 per cent	The Waters, Hydrosphere, 7 per cent	The Atmosphere	Average, Including Atmosphere
Oxygen	47.33	85.79	20.8 (variable to some extent)	50.02
Silicon	27.74	......	....	25.80
Aluminum	7.85	......	....	7.30
Iron	4.50	......	....	4.18
Calcium	3.47	.05	....	3.22
Magnesium	2.24	.14	....	2.08
Sodium	2.46	1.14	....	2.36
Potassium	2.46	.04	....	2.28
Hydrogen	.22	10.67	variable	.95
Titanium	.46	......	....	.43
Carbon	.19	.002	variable	.18
Chlorine	.06	2.07	....	.20
Bromine	......	.008	....	..
Phosphorus	.12	......	....	.11
Sulphur	.12	.09	....	.11
Barium	.08	......	....	.08
Manganese	.08	......	....	.08
Strontium	.02	......	....	.02
Nitrogen	......	......	78.0 (variable to some extent)	.03
Fluorine	.10	......	....	.10
All other elements	.50	......	....	.47

silicious, formed from the shells of foraminifera and the skeletons of diatoms. Thus, before the appearance of bacteria, of algæ, of foraminifera, and of the lower plants and lowly invertebrates, the surface of the earth was totally different from

[1] Clarke, F. W., 1916, p. 34.

what it is at present; and thus the present chemical composition of terrestrial matter, of the sea, and of the air, as indicated by Table I, is by no means the same as its primordial composition 80.000,000 years ago.

In Table I all the chemical "life elements" which enter more or less freely into organic compounds are indicated by italics, *showing that life has taken up and made use of practically all the chemical elements of frequent occurrence* in the rocks, waters, and air, with the exception of aluminum, barium, and strontium, which are extremely rare in life compounds, and of titanium, which thus far has not been found in any. But even these elements appear in artificial organic compounds, showing combining capacity without biological "inclination" thereto. In the life compounds, as in the lithosphere and hydrosphere, it is noteworthy that the elements of least atomic weight (Table II) predominate over the heavier elements.

Primordial Environment—The Lifeless Water

According to the nebular theory of Laplace the waters originated in the primordial atmosphere; according to the planetesimal theory of Chamberlin[1] and Moulton,[2] the greater volume of water has been gradually added from the interior of the earth through the vaporous discharges of hot springs. As Suess observes: "The body of the earth has given forth its ocean."

From the beginning of Archæozoic time, namely, back to a period of 80,000,000 years, we have little biologic or geologic evidence as to the stability of the earth. From the beginning of the Palæozoic, namely, for the period of the last 30,000,000 years, the earth has been in a condition of such stability that

[1] Chamberlin, Thomas Chrowder, 1916. [2] Moulton, F. R., 1912, p. 244.

the oceanic tides and tidal currents were similar to those of the present day; for the early strata are full of such evidences as ripple marks, beach footprints, and other proofs of regularly recurrent tides.[1]

As in the case of the earth, the chemistry of the lifeless primordial seas is a matter of inference, *i. e.*, of subtraction of those chemical elements which have been added as the infant earth has grown older. The relatively simple chemical content of the primordial seas must be inferred by deducting the mineral and organic products which have been sweeping into the ocean from the earth during the last 80,000,000 to 90,000,000 years; and also by deducting those that have been precipitated as a result of chemical reactions, calcium chloride reacting with sodium phosphate, for example, to yield precipitated calcium phosphate and dissolved sodium chloride.[2] The present waters of the ocean are rich in salts which have been derived by solution from the rocks of the continents.

Thus we reach our first conclusion as to the origin of life, namely: it is probable that life originated on the continents, either in the moist crevices of rocks or soils, in the fresh waters of continental pools, or in the slightly saline waters of the bordering primordial seas.

Salt as a Measure of the Age of the Ocean

As long ago as 1715 Edmund Halley suggested that the amount of salt in the ocean might afford a means of computing its age. Assuming a primitive fresh-water ocean, Becker[3] in 1910 estimated its age as between 50,000,000 and 70,000,000 years, probably closer to the upper limit. The accumulation of sodium was probably more rapid in the early geologic periods

[1] Becker, George F., 1910, p. 18.
[2] W. J. Gies.
[3] Becker, George F., 1910, pp. 16, 17.

than at the present time, because the greater part of the earth's surface was covered with the granitic and igneous rocks which have since been largely covered or replaced by sedimentary rocks, a diminution causing the sodium content from the earth to be constantly decreasing.[1] This is on the assumption that the primitive ocean had no continents in its basins and that the continental areas were not much greater than at the present time, namely, 20.6 per cent to 25 per cent of the surface of the globe.

Age of the Ocean Calculated from its Sodium Content[2]

1876.	T. Mellard Reade.	
1899.	J. Joly	80– 90 million years.
1900.	J. Joly	90–100 million years.
1909.	Sollas	80–150 million years.
1910.	Becker	50– 70 million years.
1911.	F. W. Clarke and Becker	94,712,000 years.
1915.	Becker	60–100 million years.
1916.	Clarke	somewhat less than 100 million years.

From the mean of the foregoing computations it is inferred that the age of the ocean since the earth assumed its present form is somewhat less than 100,000,000 years. The 63,000,000 tons of sodium which the sea has received yearly by solution from the rocks has been continually uniting with its equivalent of chlorine to form the salt ($NaCl$) of the existing seas.[3] So with the entire present content of the sea, its sulphates as well as its chlorides of sodium and of magnesium, its potassium, its calcium as well as those rare chemical elements which occasionally enter into the life compounds, such as copper, fluorine, boron, barium—all these earth-derived elements were much

[1] Becker, George F., 1915, p. 201; 1910, p. 12.
[2] After Becker, George F., 1910, pp. 3–5; and Clarke, F. W., 1916, pp. 150, 152.
[3] Becker, George F., 1910, pp. 7, 8, 10, 12.

rarer in the primordial seas than at the present time. Yet from the first the air in sea-water was much richer in oxygen than the atmosphere.[1]

As compared with primordial sea-water, which was relatively fresh and free from salts and from nitrogen, existing sea-water is an ideal chemical medium for life. As a proof of the special adaptability of existing sea-water to present biochemical conditions, a very interesting comparison is that between the chemical composition of the chief body fluid of the highest animals, namely, the blood serum, and the chemical composition of sea-water, as given by Henderson.[2]

CHEMICAL COMPOSITION OF PRESENT SEA-WATER AND OF BLOOD SERUM

"*Life Elements*"	In Sea-Water	In Blood Serum
Sodium	30.59	39.0
Magnesium	3.79	0.4
Calcium	1.20	1.0
Potassium	1.11	2.7
Chlorine	55.27	45.0
SO_4 (sulphur tetroxide)	7.66	....
CO_3 (carbon trioxide)	0.21	12.0
Bromine	0.19	....
P_2O_5 (phosphorous pentoxide)	....	0.4

Primordial Chemical Environment

Since the primal sea was devoid of those earth-borne nitrogen compounds which are indirectly derived first from the atmosphere and then from the earth through the agency of the nitrifying bacteria, those who hold to the hypothesis of the *marine origin* of protoplasm fail to account for the necessary proportion of nitrogenous matter there to begin with.

[1] Pirsson, Louis V., and Schuchert, Charles, 1915, p. 84.
[2] Henderson, Lawrence J., 1913, p. 187.

When we consider that those chemical "life elements" which are most essential to living matter were for a great period of time either absent or present in a highly dilute condition in the ocean, it appears that we must abandon the ancient Greek conception of the origin of life in the sea, and reaffirm our conclusion that the lowliest organisms originated either in moist earths or in those terrestrial waters which contained nitrogen. Nitrate and nitrite occasionally arise from the union of nitrogen and oxygen in electrical discharges during thunder-storms, and were presumably thus produced before life began. These and related nitrogen compounds, so essential for the development of protoplasm, may have been specially *concentrated* in *pools of water* to degrees particularly *favorable* for the *origin of protoplasm.*[1]

It appears, too, that every great subsequent higher life phase—the bacterial phase, the chlorophyllic algal phase, the protozoan phase—was also primarily of fresh-water and secondarily of marine habitat. From terrestrial waters or soils life may have gradually extended into the sea. It is probable that the succession of marine forms was itself determined to some extent by adaptation to the increasing concentration of saline constituents in sea-water. That the invasion of the sea upon the continental areas occurred at a very early period is demonstrated by the extreme richness and profusion of marine life at the base of the Cambrian.

That life originated in water (H_2O) there can be little doubt, hydrogen and oxygen ranking as primary elements with nitrogen. The fitness of water to life is maximal[2] both as a solvent in all the bodily fluids, and as a vehicle for most of the other chemical compounds. Further, since water itself is a solvent

[1] Suggested by Professor W. J. Gies.

[2] These notes upon water are chiefly from the very suggestive treatise, "The Fitness of the Environment," by Henderson, Lawrence J., 1913.

that fails to react with many substances (with nearly all biological substances) it serves also as a factor of biochemical stability.

In relation to the application of our theory of action, reaction, and interaction to the processes of life, the most important property of water is its electric property, known as the dielectric constant. Although itself only to a slight degree dissociated into ions, it is the bearer of dissolved electrolytic substances and thus possesses a high power of electric conductivity, properties of great importance in the development of the electric energy of the molecules and atoms in ionization. Thus water is the very best medium of electric ionization in solution, and was probably essential to the mechanism of life from its very origin.[1]

Through all the electric changes of its contained solvents water itself remains very stable, because the molecules of hydrogen and oxygen are not easily dissociated; their union in water contributes to the living organism a series of properties which are the prime conditions of all physiological and functional activity. The great surface tension of water as manifested in capillary action is of the highest importance to plant growth; it is also an important force acting within the formed colloids, the protoplasmic substance of life.

Primordial Environment—The Atmosphere

It is significant that the simplest known living forms derive their chemical "life elements" partly from the earth, partly from the water, and partly from the atmosphere. This was not improbably true also of the earliest living forms.

One of the mooted questions concerning the primordial

[1] Henderson, Lawrence J., 1913, p. 256.

atmosphere[1] is whether or no it contained free oxygen. The earliest forms of life were probably dependent on atmospheric oxygen, although certain existing bacterial organisms, known as "anaërobic," are now capable of existing without it.

The primordial atmosphere was heavily charged with water vapor (H_2O) which has since been largely condensed by cooling. In the early period of the earth's history volcanoes[2] were also pouring into the atmosphere much greater amounts of carbon dioxide (CO_2) than at the present time. At present the amount of carbon dioxide in the atmosphere averages about three parts in 10,000, but there is little doubt that the primordial atmosphere was richer in this compound, which next to water and nitrogen is by far the most important both in the origin and in the development of living matter. The atmospheric carbon dioxide is at present continually being withdrawn by the absorption of carbon in living plants and the release of free oxygen; it is also washed out of the air by rains. On the other hand, the respiration of animals, the combustion of carbonaceous matter, and the discharges from volcanoes are continually returning it to the air in large quantities.

As to carbon, from our present knowledge we cannot conceive of organisms that did not consist, from the instant of initial development, of protoplasm containing hydrogen, oxygen, nitrogen, and *carbon*. Probably carbon dioxide, the most likely source of carbon from the beginning, was reduced in the primordial environment by other than chlorophyllic agencies, by simple chemical influences.

Since carbon is a less dominant element[3] than nitrogen in the life processes of the simplest bacteria, we cannot agree with the theory that carbon dioxide was coequal with water

[1] Becker, George F., letter of October 15, 1915.
[2] Henderson, Lawrence J., 1913, p. 134.
[3] Jordan, Edwin O., 1908, p. 66.

as a primary compound in the origin of life; it probably was more widely utilized after the chlorophyllic stage of plant evolution, for not until chlorophyll appeared was life equipped with the best means of extracting large quantities of carbon dioxide from the atmosphere.

The stable elements of the present atmosphere, for which alone estimates can be given, are essentially as follows:[1]

	By Weight	By Volume
Oxygen	23.024	20.941
Nitrogen	75.539	78.122
Argon	1.437	.937
	100.000	100.000

Atmospheric carbon dioxide (CO_2), which averages about three parts in every 10,000, and water (H_2O) are always present in varying amounts; besides argon, the rare gases helium, xenon, neon, and krypton are present in traces. None of the rare gases which have been discovered in the atmosphere, such as helium, argon, xenon, neon, krypton, and niton—the latter a radium emanation—are at present known to have any relation to the life processes. Carbon dioxide[2] exists in the atmosphere as an inexhaustible reservoir of carbon, only slightly depleted by the drafts made upon it by the action of chlorophyllic plants or by its solution in the waters of the continents and oceans. Soluble in water and thus equally mobile, of high absorption coefficient, and of universal occurrence, it constitutes a reservoir of carbon for the development of plants and animals, radiant energy being required to make this carbon available for biological use. Carbon dioxide in water

[1] Clarke, F. W., letter of March 7, 1916.
[2] Henderson, Lawrence J., 1913, pp. 136–139.

forms carbonic acid, one of the few instances of biological decomposition of water. This compound is so unstable that it has never been obtained. Carbon dioxide is derived not only through chlorophyllic agencies by means of free oxygen, but also by the action of certain anaërobic bacteria and moulds without the presence of free oxygen, as, for example, through the catalytic action of zymase, the enzyme of yeast, which is soluble in water. Loeb[1] dwells upon the importance of the bicarbonates as regulators in the development of the marine organisms by keeping neutral the water and the solutions in which marine animals live. Similarly the life of fresh-water animals is also prolonged by the addition of bicarbonates.

[1] Loeb, Jacques, 1906, pp. 96, 97.

CHAPTER II

THE SUN AND THE PHYSICOCHEMICAL ORIGINS OF LIFE

Heat and light. Chemical "life elements" as they exist in the sun. Primordial environment—electric energy and the sun's heat. Capture of the energy of sunlight. Action and reaction as adaptive properties of the life elements. Interaction or coordination of the properties of the life elements. Adaptation in the colloidal state. Cosmic properties and life functions of the chief chemical life elements. Pure speculation as to the primary physicochemical stages of life. Evolution of actions and reactions. Evolution of interactions. New organic compounds.

We will now consider the sun as the source of heat, light, and other forms of energy which conditioned the origin of life.

Heat and Light

It is possible that in the earlier stages of the earth's history the sun's light and heat may have been different in amount from what they are at present; so far as can be judged from the available data it seems probable that, if perceptibly different, they were greater then than now. But if they were greater, the atmosphere must have been more full of clouds—as that of Venus apparently is to-day—and have reflected away into space much more than the 45 per cent of the incident radiation which it reflects at present. On the earth's surface, beneath the cloud layer, the temperature need not have been much higher than the present mean temperature, but was doubtless much more equable, with more moisture, while the amount of sunlight reaching the earth's surface may have been less intense and continuous than at present.

The following are among the reasons why the primordial solar influences upon the earth may have differed from the present solar influences. It appears probable that the lifeless surface of the primordial earth was like that of the moon—covered not only with igneous rocks but with piles of heat-stor-

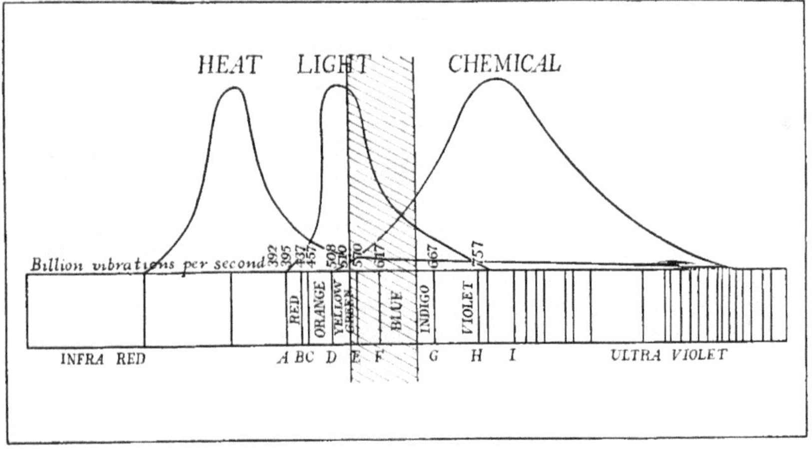

FIG. 3. LIGHT, HEAT, AND CHEMICAL INFLUENCE OF THE SUN.

Diagram showing how the increase, maximum, and decrease of heat, light, and chemical energy derived from the sun correspond to the velocity of the vibrations. After Ulric Dahlgren.

ing débris, as recently described by Russell[1]—and if, like the moon, the earth had had no atmosphere, then the reflecting power of its surface would have represented a loss of only 40 per cent of the sun's heat. But a large amount of aqueous vapor and of carbon dioxide in the primordial atmosphere probably served to form an atmospheric blanket which inhibited the radiation from the earth's surface of such solar heat as penetrated to it, and also prevented excessive changes of temperature. Thus there was on the primal earth a greater regularity of the sun's heat-supply, with more moisture.

[1] Russell, H. N., 1916, p. 75.

To sum up, if the primordial atmosphere contained more aqueous vapor and carbon dioxide than at present, the greater cloudiness of the atmosphere would have very considerably increased the albedo, that is, the reflection of solar heat, as well as light, away into space. If the earth's surface was covered with loose débris, it would have retained more of the solar heat which reached it *directly;* but, with such an atmosphere as is postulated, very little of the solar radiation would have reached the surface directly. What is true of the indirect access of the supply of light from the sun would also be true of the supply of heat. On the other hand, the greater blanketing power of the atmosphere would tend to keep the surface as warm as it is now, in spite of the smaller direct supply of heat.

It is also possible that, through the agency of thermal springs and the heat of volcanic regions, primordial life forms may have derived their energy from the heat of the earth as well as from that of the sun. This is in general accord with the fact that the most primitive organisms surviving upon the earth to-day, the bacteria, are dependent upon heat rather than upon light for their energy.

We have thus far observed that the primal earth, air, and water contained all the chemical elements and three of the most simple but important chemical compounds, namely, water, nitrates, and carbon dioxide, which are known to be essential to the bacterial or prechlorophyllic, and algal and higher chlorophyllic stages of the life process.

Chemical "Life Elements" as They Exist in the Sun

An initial step in the origin of life was the coordination or bringing together of these elements which, so far as we know, had never been chemically coordinated before and which are widely distributed in the solar spectrum. Therefore, before examining the properties of these elements, it is interesting to trace them back from the earth into the sun and thus into the cosmos. It is through these "properties" which in life

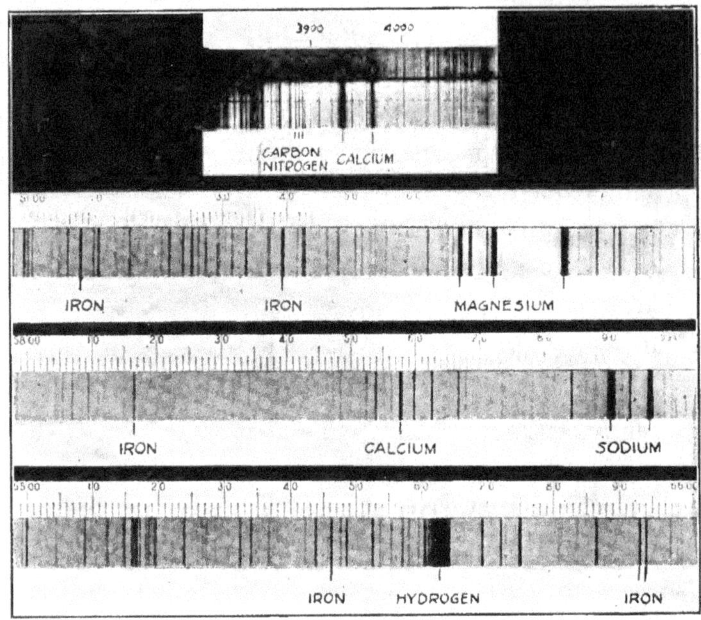

FIG. 4. CHEMICAL LIFE ELEMENTS IN THE SUN.

Three regions of the solar spectrum with lines showing the presence of such essential life elements as carbon, nitrogen, calcium, iron, magnesium, sodium, and hydrogen. From the Mount Wilson Observatory.

subserve "functions" and "adaptations" that all forms of life, from monad to man, are linked with the universe.

Excepting hydrogen and oxygen, the principal elements which enter into the formation of living protoplasm are minor constituents of the mass of matter sown throughout space in comparison with the rock-forming elements.[1] Again excepting hydrogen, their lines in the solar spectrum are for the most

[1] Russell, Henry Norris, letter of March 6, 1916.

part weak, and only shown on high dispersion plates, while hydrogen is represented by very strong lines, as shown by spectroheliograms of solar prominences. The lines of oxygen are relatively faint; it appears principally as a compound, titanium oxide (TiO_2) in sun-spots, although a triple line in the extreme red seems also to be due to it. In the chromosphere, or higher atmosphere of the sun, hydrogen is not in a state of combustion, and the fine hydrogen prominences show radiations comparable to those in a vacuum tube.[1]

Nitrogen, the next most important life element, is displayed in the so-called cyanogen bands of the ultra-violet, made visible by high-dispersion photographs.

Carbon is shown in many lines in green, which are relatively bright near the sun's edge; it is also present in comets, and carbonaceous meteorites (Orgueil, Kold Bokkeveld, etc.) are well known. Graphite occurs in meteoric irons.

In the solar spectrum so far as studied no lines of the "life elements," phosphorus, sulphur, and chlorine, have been detected. On the other hand, the metallic elements which enter into the life compounds, iron, sodium, and calcium, are all represented by strong lines in the solar spectrum, the exception being potassium in which the lines are faint. Of the eight metallic elements which are most abundant in the earth's crust, as well as the non-metallic elements carbon and silicon, six are also among the eight strongest in the solar spectrum. In general, however, the important life elements are very widely distributed in the stellar universe, showing most prominently in the hotter stars, and in the case of hydrogen being universal.

We have now considered the source of four "life elements," namely, HYDROGEN, OXYGEN, NITROGEN, and CARBON, also the

[1] Hale, George Ellery, letter of March 10, 1916.

presence in the sun and stars of the metallic elements. Before passing to the properties of these and other life elements let us consider how lifeless energy is transformed into living energy.

PRIMORDIAL ENVIRONMENT—ELECTRIC ENERGY AND THE SUN'S HEAT

As remarked above, in the change from the lifeless to the life world, the *properties of the chemical life elements* become known as the *functions of living matter.* Stored energy becomes known as nutriment or food.

The earliest function of living matter appears to have been to capture and transform the *electric energy* of those chemical elements which throughout we designate as the "life elements." This function appears to have developed only in the presence of *heat energy*, derived either from the earth or from the sun or from both; this is the first example in the life process of the capture and utilization of energy wherever it may be found. At a later stage of evolution life captured the *light energy* of the sun through the agency of chlorophyll, the green coloring matter of plants. In the final stage of evolution the intellect of man is capturing and controlling physicochemical energy in many of its forms.

The primal dependence of the electric energy of life on the original heat energy of the earth or on solar heat is demonstrated by the universal behavior of the most primitive organisms, because when the temperature of protoplasm is lowered to 0° C: the velocity of the chemical reactions becomes so small that in most cases all manifestations of life are suspended, that is, life becomes latent. Some bacteria grow at or very near the freezing-point of water (0° C.) and possibly primordial bacteria-like organisms grew below that point. Even now the common "hay bacillus" grows at 6° C.[1] Rising temperatures increase the velocity of the biochemical reactions of protoplasm up to an optimum temperature, beyond which they are increasingly injurious and finally fatal to all organisms. In hot springs some of the Cyanophyceæ (blue-green algæ), primitive plants intermediate in evolution between bacteria and algæ, sustain temperatures as high as 63° C. and, as a rule, are killed by a temperature of 73° C., which is probably the coagulation point of their proteins. Setchell found bacteria living in water of hot springs at 89° C.[2] In the next higher order of the Chlorophyceæ (green algæ) the temperature fatal to life is lower, being 43° C.[3] Very much higher temperatures are endured by the spores of certain bacilli which survive until temperatures of from 105° C. to 120° C. are reached. There appears to be no known limit to the amount of dry cold which they can withstand.[4]

It is this power of the relatively water-free spores to resist heat and cold which has suggested to Richter (1865), to Kelvin, and to Arrhenius (1908) that living germs may have pervaded space and may have reached our planet either in company with meteorites (Kelvin)[5] or driven by the pressure of light (Arrhenius).[6] The fact that so far as we know life on the earth has only originated once or during one period, and not repeatedly, does not appear to favor these hypotheses; nor is it courageous to put off the problem of life origin into cosmic

[1] Jordan, Edwin O., 1908, pp. 67, 68.

[2] *Op. cit.*, p. 68.

[3] Loeb, Jacques, 1906, p. 106.

[4] Cultures of bacteria have even been exposed to the temperature of liquid hydrogen (about —250° C.) without destroying their vitality or sensibly impairing their biologic qualities. This temperature is far below that at which any chemical reaction is known to take place, and is only about 23 degrees above the absolute zero point at which, it is believed, molecular movement ceases. On the other hand, when bacteria are frozen in water during the formation of natural ice the death rate is high. See Jordan, Edwin O., 1908, p. 69.

[5] Poulton, Edward B., 1896, p. 818.

[6] Pirsson, Louis V., and Schuchert, Charles, 1915, pp. 535, 536.

space instead of resolutely seeking it within the forces and elements of our own humble planet.

The thermal conditions of living matter point to the probability that life originated at a time when portions at least

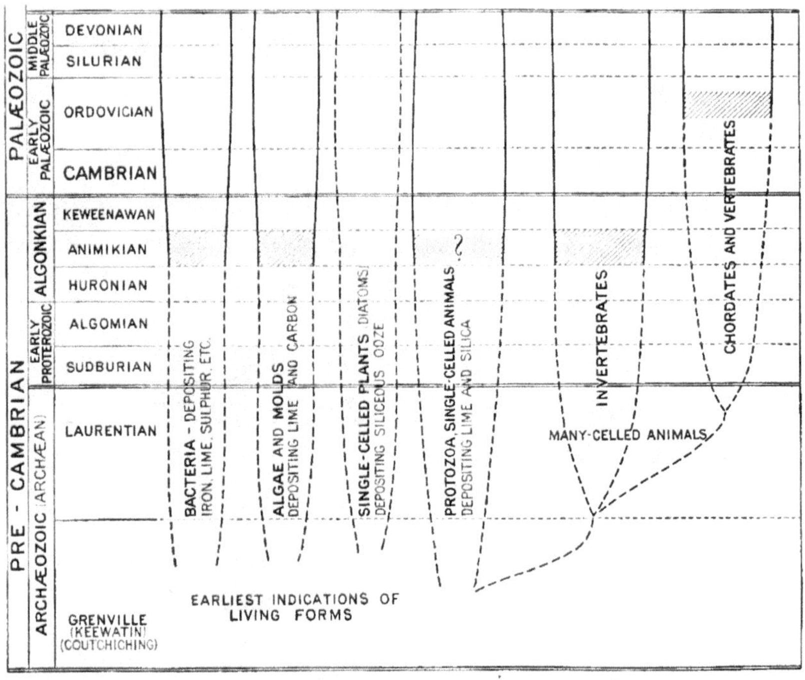

Fig. 5. The Earliest Phyla of Plant and Animal Life.

Chart showing the theoretic derivation of chordates and vertebrates from some invertebrate stock, and of the invertebrates from some of the protozoa. The diagonal lines indicate the geologic date of the *earliest known fossil* forms in the middle Algonkian. The earliest well-known invertebrate fauna is in the Middle Cambrian (see pp. 118–134, and Figs. 20–27). Although diatoms are among the simplest known living forms and probably represent a very early stage in the evolution of life, no fossil forms are known earlier than two species from the Lias, while all the rest date from the Cretaceous.

of the earth's surface and waters had temperatures of between 89° C. and 6° C.; and also to the possibility of the origin of life before the atmospheric vapors admitted a regular supply of sunlight.

Capture of the Energy of Sunlight

After the sun's heat living matter appears to have captured the sun's light, which is essential, directly or indirectly, to all living energy higher than that of the most primitive bacteria. The discovery by Lavoisier (1743–1794) and the development (1804) by de Saussure[1] of the theory of photosynthesis, namely, that sunshine combining solar heat and light is a perpetual source of living energy, laid the foundations of biochemistry and opened the way for the establishment of the law of the conservation of energy within the living organism.

Thus arose the first conception of the cycle of the elements continually passing through plants and animals which was so grandly formulated by Cuvier in 1817:[2] "La vie est donc un tourbillon plus ou moins rapide, plus ou moins compliqué, dont la direction est constante, et qui entraîne toujours des molécules de mêmes sortes, mais où les molécules individuelles entrent et d'où elles sortent continuellement, de manière que la *forme* du corps vivant lui est plus essentielle que sa *matière*."

Chemical Composition of Chlorophyll[3]

Element	Per cent
Carbon	73.34
Hydrogen	9.72
Nitrogen	5.68
Oxygen	9.54
Phosphorus	1.38
Magnesium	0.34
	100.00

The green coloring matter of plants is known as chlorophyll; its chemical composition according to Hoppe-Seyler's

[1] De Saussure, N. T., 1804.
[2] Cuvier, Baron Georges L. C. F. D., 1817, p. 13.
[3] Sachs, Julius, 1882, p. 758.

analysis is given here. Potassium is essential for its assimilating activity. Iron (often accompanied by manganese), although essential to the production of chlorophyll, is not contained in it. The chlorophyll-bearing leaves of the plant in the presence of sunlight separate oxygen atoms from the carbon and hydrogen atoms in the molecules of carbon dioxide (CO_2) and of water (H_2O), storing up the energy of the hydrogen and carbon products in the carbohydrate substances of the plant, an energy which is stored by deoxidation (separation of oxygen), and which can be released only through reoxidation (addition of oxygen). Thus the celluloses, sugars, starches, and other similar substances deposit their kinetic or stored energy in the tissues of the plant and release that energy through the addition of oxygen, the amount of oxygen required being the same as that needed to burn these substances in the air to the same degree; in brief, through a combustion which generates heat.[1] Thus living matter utilizes the energy of the sun to draw a continuous stream of electric energy from the chemical elements in the earth, the water, and the atmosphere.

This was the first step in the interpretation of life processes in the terms of physics and chemistry, rather than in terms of a peculiar vitalism. What had previously been regarded as a special vital force in the life of plants thus proved to be an adaptation of physicochemical forces. The chemical action of chlorophyll is even now not fully understood, but it is known to absorb most vigorously the solar rays between *B* and *C* of the spectrum,[2] and these rays are most effective in the assimilation of energy or food by the plant. While the effect of the solar rays between *D* and *E* is minimal, those beyond *F* are again effective. In heliotropic movements both of plants and

[1] W. J. Gies. [2] Loeb, Jacques, 1906, p. 115.

animals the blue rays are more effective than the red.[1] Spores given off as ciliated cells from the algæ seek first the blue rays. Since the food supply of animals is primarily derived from chlorophyll-bearing plants, animals are less directly dependent on the solar light and solar heat, while the chemical life of plants fluctuates throughout the day with the variations of light and temperature. Thus Richards[2] finds in the cacti that the breaking down of the acids through the splitting of the acid compounds is a respiratory process caused by the alternate oxidation and deoxidation of the tissues through the action of the sun.

The solar energy transformed into the chemical potential energy of the compounds of carbon, hydrogen, and oxygen in the plants is transmuted by the animal into motion and heat and then dissipated. Thus in the life cycle we observe both the conservation and the degradation of energy, corresponding with the first and second laws of thermodynamics developed in physics by the researches of Newton, Helmholtz, Phillips, Kelvin, and others.[3] The remaining life processes correspond in many ways to Newton's third law of motion.

Action and Reaction as Adaptive Properties of the Life Elements

The adaptation of the chemical elements to life processes is due to their incessant action and reaction, each element having its peculiar and distinctive forms of action and reaction, which in the organism are transmuted into functions. Such activity of the life elements is largely connected with forms of electric energy which the physicists call *ionization*, while the correlated or coordinated *interaction* of various groups

[1] *Op. cit.*, p. 127. [2] Richards, Herbert M., 1915, pp. 34, 73–75.
[3] Henderson, Lawrence J., 1913, pp. 15–18.

of life elements is largely connected with processes which the chemists term *catalysis.*

Ionization, the actions and reactions of all the elements and electrolytic compounds—according to the hypothesis of Arrhenius, first put forth in 1887—is primarily due to electrolytic dissociation whereby the molecules of all acids (*e. g.*, carbonic acid, H_2CO_3), bases (*e. g.*, sodium hydroxide, NaOH), and salts (*e. g.*, sodium chloride, NaCl) give off streams of the electrically charged particles known as ions. Ionization is dependent on the law of Nernst that the greater the dielectric capacity of the solvent (*e. g.*, water) the more rapid will be the dissociation of the substances dissolved in it, other conditions remaining the same.

IONIZATION OF THE ELEMENTS THUS FAR DISCOVERED IN LIVING ORGANISMS

Mainly or Wholly with or in Negative Ions[1]		Mainly or Wholly with or in Positive Ions[1]		
Non-metallic		Metallic		
Carbon[2] (*e. g.*,[4] carbonates)	**Silicon**	**Hydrogen**[6]	**Iron**[7]	**Lithium**
Oxygen[2] (*e. g.*,[4] sulphates)	**Iodine**	**Potassium**	**Copper**	**Nickel**
Nitrogen[2,3] (*e. g.*,[4] nitrates)	**Bromine**	**Sodium**	**Aluminum**	**Radium**
Phosphorus[2] (*e. g.*,[4] phosphates)	**Fluorine**	**Calcium**	**Barium**	**Strontium**
Sulphur[2] (*e. g.*,[4] sulphates)	**Boron**	**Magnesium**	**Cobalt**	**Zinc**
Chlorine (*e. g.*,[4] chlorides)	**Arsenic**[5]	**Manganese**	**Lead**	

[1] An ion is an atom or group of atoms carrying an electric charge. The positive ions (cations) of the metallic elements move toward the cathode; the negative ions (anions) given off by the non-metallic elements move toward the anode.

[2] Together with hydrogen conspicuous in living colloids and non-electrolytes—very little in the indicated ionized forms.

[3] Occurs also, as NH_4, in *positive* ions. Here the hydrogen overbalances the nitrogen.

[4] Substances occurring in living matter.

[5] Arsenic itself is a metal, but in living compounds it is an analogue of phosphorus and occurs in *negative* ions when ionized.

[6] Pictet has obtained results indicating that liquid and solid hydrogen are metallic. Hydrogen is metallic in *behavior*, though non-metallic in *appearance*.

[7] Iron in living compounds is chiefly non-ionized, colloidal. Apparently this is also true of copper, aluminum, barium, cobalt, lead, nickel, strontium, and zinc. As to radium, however, there is no information on this point.

Thus, ions are atoms or groups of atoms carrying electric charges which are positive when given off from metallic elements, and negative when given off from non-metallic elements. Electrolytic molecules, according to this theory, are constantly dissociating to form ions, and the ions are as constantly recombining to form molecules. Since the salts of the various mineral elements are constantly being decomposed through electrolytic ionization, they play an important part in all the life phenomena; and since similar decomposition is induced by currents of electricity, indications are that all the development of living energy is in a sense electric.

The ionizing electric properties of the life elements are a matter of prime importance. We observe at once in the table above that all the great structural elements which make up the bulk of plant and animal tissues are of the non-metallic group with negative ions, with the single exception of hydrogen which has positive ions. All these elements are of low atomic weight, and several of them develop a great amount of heat in combustion, hydrogen and carbon leading in this function of the release of energy, which invariably takes place in the presence of oxygen. On the other hand, the lesser components of living compounds are the metallic elements with positive ions, such as potassium, sodium, calcium, and magnesium, calcium combining with carbon or with phosphorus as the great structural or skeletal builder in animals. There is also so much carbonaceous protein in the animal skeleton that calcium in animals takes the place of carbon in plants only in the sense that it reduces the *proportion* of carbon in the skeleton: it shares the honors with carbon.

In general the electric action and reaction of the non-metallic and the metallic elements dissolved or suspended in water are now believed to be the chief phenomena of the internal functions of life, for these functions are developed always in the presence of oxygen and with the energy either of the heat of the earth or of the sun, or of both the heat and light of the sun.

Finally, we observe that ionization is connected with the radioactive elements, of which thus far only radium has been detected in the organic compounds, although the others may be present.

Phosphorescence in plants and animals is treated by Loeb[1] and others as a form of radiant energy. While developed in a number of living animals—including the typical glowworms in which the phenomenon was first investigated by Faraday—the living condition is not essential to it because phosphorescence continues after death and may be produced in animals by non-living material. Many organisms show phosphorescence at comparatively low temperatures, yet the presence of free oxygen appears to be necessary.

In Rutherford's experiments on radioactive matter[2] he tells us that in the phosphorescence caused by the approach of an emanation of radium to zinc sulphate the atoms throw off the alpha particles to the number of five billion each second, with velocities of 10,000 miles a second; that the alpha particles in their passage through air or other medium produce from the neutral molecules a large number of negatively charged ions, and that this ionization is readily measurable.

Interaction or Coordination of the Properties of the Life Elements

The actions and reactions of the life elements, which are mainly contemporaneous, direct, and immediate, do not suffice to form an organism. As soon as the grouping of chemical elements reaches the stage of an organism *interaction* also becomes essential, for the chemical activities of one region of the

[1] Loeb, Jacques, 1906, pp. 66–68. [2] Rutherford, Sir Ernest, 1915, p. 115.

organism must be harmonized with those of all other regions; the principle of interaction may apply at a distance and the results may not be contemporaneous. This is actually inferred to be the case in single-celled organisms, such as the *Amœba.*[1]

The interacting and coordinating form of lifeless energy which has proved to be of the utmost importance in the life processes is that recognized in the early part of the nineteenth century and denoted by the term *catalysis,* first applied by Berzelius in 1835. A catalyzer is a substance which modifies the velocity of any chemical reaction without itself being used up by the reaction. Thus chemical reactions may be accelerated or retarded, and yet the catalyzer lose none of its energy. In a few cases it has been definitely ascertained that the catalytic agent does itself experience a series of changes. The theory is that catalytic phenomena depend upon the alternate decomposition and recomposition, or the alternate attachment and detachment of the catalytic agent.

Discovered as a property in the inorganic world, catalysis has proved to underlie the great series of functions in the organic world which may be comprised in the physical term *interaction.* The researches of Ehrlich and others fully justify Huxley's prediction of 1881 that through therapeutics it would become possible "to introduce into the economy a molecular mechanism which, like a cunningly contrived torpedo, shall find its way to some particular group of living elements and cause an explosion among them, leaving the rest untouched." In fact, the interacting agents known as "enzymes" are such living catalyzers,[2] and accelerate or retard reactions in the body by forming intermediary unstable compounds which are rapidly decomposed, leaving the catalyzer (*i. e.*, enzyme) free to repeat the action. Thus a small quantity of an enzyme

[1] Calkins, Gary N., 1916, pp. 259, 260.

[2] Loeb, Jacques, 1906, pp. 26, 28.

can decompose indefinite quantities of a compound. The activity of enzymes is rather in the nature of the "interaction" of our theory than of direct action and reaction, because the results are produced at a distance and the energy liberated may be entirely out of proportion to the internal energy of the catalyzer. The enzymes, being themselves complex organic compounds, act specifically because they do not affect alike the different organic compounds which they encounter in the fluid circulation.

Adaptation in the Colloidal State

In the lifeless world matter occurred both in the crystalloidal and colloidal states. It is in the latter state that life originated. It is a state peculiarly favorable to action, reaction, and interaction, or the free interchange of physicochemical energies. Each organism is in a sense a container full of a watery solution in which various kinds of colloids are suspended.[1] Such a suspension involves a play of the energies of the free particles of matter in the most delicate equilibrium, and the suspended particles exhibit the vibrating movement attributed to the impact of the molecules.[2] These free particles are of greater magnitude than the individual molecules; in fact, they represent molecules and multimolecules, and all the known properties of the compounds known as "colloids" can be traced to feeble molecular affinities between the molecules themselves, causing them to unite and to separate in multimolecules. Among the existing living colloids are certain carbohydrates, like starch or glycogen, proteins (compounds of carbon, hydrogen, oxygen, and nitrogen with sulphur or phosphorus), and the higher fats. The colloids of protoplasm are dependent for their stability on the constancy of acidity and

[1] Bechhold, Heinrich, 1912.

[2] Smith, Alexander, 1914, p. 305.

alkalinity, which is more or less regulated by the presence of bicarbonates.[1]

Electrical charges in the colloids[2] are demonstrated by currents of electricity sent through a colloidal solution, and are interpreted by Freundlich as due to electrolytic dissociation of the colloidal particles, alkaline colloids being positively charged, while acid colloids are negatively charged. The concentration of hydrogen and hydroxyl ions in the ocean and in the organism is automatically regulated by carbonic acid.[3]

Among the colloidal substances in living organisms the so-called enzymes are very important, since they are responsible for many of the processes in the organism. Possibly enzymes are not typical colloids and perhaps, in pure form, they may not be classified as such; but if they are not colloids they certainly behave like colloids.[4]

COSMIC PROPERTIES AND LIFE FUNCTIONS OF THE CHIEF CHEMICAL LIFE ELEMENTS

Of the total of eighty-two or more chemical elements thus far discovered at least twenty-nine are known to occur in living organisms either invariably, frequently, or rarely, as shown in Table II of the Life Elements. Whether essential, frequent, or of rare occurrence, each one of these elements—as described below—has its single or multiple services to render to the organism.

Hydrogen, the life element of least atomic weight, is always near the surface of the typical hot stars. Rutherford[5] tells us that, while the hydrogen atom is the lightest known, its negatively charged electrons are only about 1/1800 of the mass of

[1] Henderson, Lawrence J., 1913, pp. 157–160.
[2] Loeb, Jacques, 1906, pp. 34, 35.
[3] Henderson, Lawrence J., 1913, p. 257.
[4] Hedin, Sven G., 1915, pp. 164, 173.
[5] Rutherford, Sir Ernest, 1915, p. 113.

the hydrogen atom: they are liberated from metals on which ultra-violet light falls, and can be released from atoms of mat-

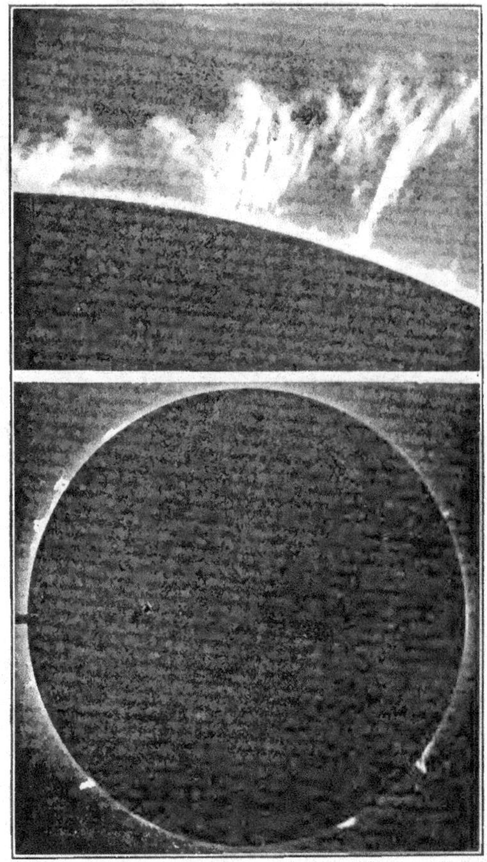

FIG. 6. HYDROGEN VAPOR IN THE SOLAR ATMOSPHERE

Hydrogen, which far exceeds any other element in the amount of heat it yields upon oxidation (see Table II, p. 67) and ranks among the four most important of the chemical life elements, is also invariably present at the surface of all typical hot stars, including the sun. The large masses of hydrogen vapor known as "solar prominences" which burst forth from every part of the sun, are here shown as photographed during a total eclipse. The upper figure presents a detail from the lower, greatly enlarged From the Mount Wilson Observatory.

ter by a variety of agencies. Hydrogen is present in all acids and in most organic compounds. It also has the highest power of combustion.[1] Its ions are very important factors in animal respiration and in gastric digestion.[2] It is very active in dissociating or separating oxygen from various compounds, and through its affinity for oxygen forms water (H_2O), the principal constituent of protoplasm.

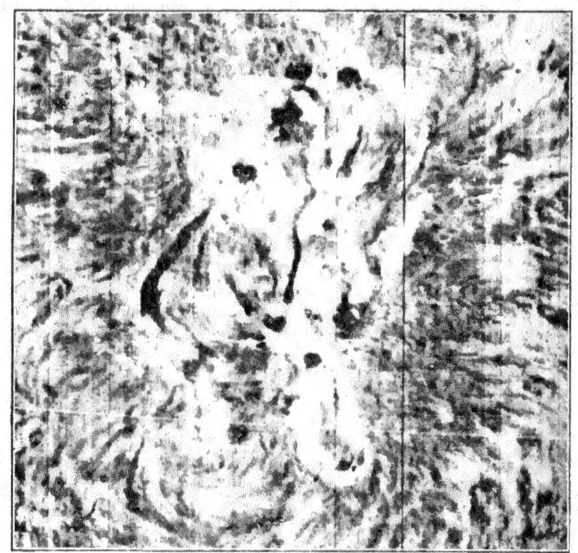

FIG. 7. HYDROGEN FLOCCULI SURROUNDING A GROUP OF SUN-SPOTS. The vortex structure is clearly shown. After Hale. From the Mount Wilson Observatory.

Oxygen, like hydrogen, has an attractive power which brings into the organism other elements useful in its various functions. It makes up two-thirds of all animal tissue, as it makes up one-half of the earth's crust. Besides these attractive and synthetic functions, its great service is as an oxidizer in the release of energy; it is thus always circulating in the tissues. Through this it is involved in all heat production and in all mechanical work, and affects cell division and growth.[3]

[1] Henderson, Lawrence J., 1913, pp. 218, 230, 245.
[2] W. J. Gies.
[3] Loeb, Jacques, 1906, p. 16.

Nitrogen comes next in importance to hydrogen and oxygen as structural material[1] and when combined with carbon and sulphur gives the plant and animal world one of the chief organic food constituents, protein. It was present on the primordial earth, not only in the atmosphere but also in the gases and waters emitted by volcanoes. Combined with hydrogen it forms various radicles of a basic character (*e. g.*, NH_2 in amino-acids, NH_4 in ammonium compounds); combined with oxygen it yields acidic radicles, such as NO_3 in nitrates. It combines with carbon in $- C \equiv N$ radicles and in $\equiv C - NH_2$ and $= C = NH$ forms, the latter being particularly important in protoplasmic chemistry.[2] This life element forms the basis of all explosives, it also confers the necessary instability upon the molecules of protoplasm because it is loath to combine with and easy to dissociate from most other elements. Thus we find nitrogen playing an important part in the physiology of the most primitive organisms known, the nitrifying bacteria.

Carbon also exists at or near the surface of cooling stars which are becoming red.[3] It unites vigorously with oxygen, tearing it away from neighboring elements, while its tendency to unite with hydrogen is less marked. At lower heats the carbon compounds are remarkably stable, but they are by no means able to resist great heats; thus Barrell[4] observes that a chemist would immediately put his finger on the element carbon as that which is needed to endow organic substance with complexity of form and function, and its selection in the origin of plant life was by no means fortuitous. Including the artificial products, the known carbon compounds exceed 100,000, while there are thousands of compounds of C, H, and O, and hundreds of C and H.[5] Carbon is so dominant in living mat-

[1] Henderson, Lawrence J., 1913, p. 241.
[2] W. J. Gies.
[3] Henderson, Lawrence J., 1913, p. 55.
[4] Joseph Barrell, letter of March 20, 1916.
[5] Henderson, Lawrence J., 1913, pp. 193, 194.

ter that biochemistry is very largely the chemistry of carbon compounds; and it is interesting to observe that in the evolution of life each of these biological compounds must have arisen suddenly as a saltation or mutation, there being no continuity between one chemical compound and another.

Phosphorus is essential in the nucleus of the cell,[1] being a large constituent of the intranuclear germ-plasm known as chromatin, which is the seat of heredity. It enters largely into the structure of nerves and brain and also, in the form of phosphates of calcium and magnesium, serves an entirely diverse function as building material for the skeletons of animals. Phosphates are important factors in the maintenance of normal uniformity of reaction in the blood.

Sulphur, uniting with nitrogen, oxygen, hydrogen, and carbon, is an essential constituent of the proteins of plants and animals.[2] It is especially conspicuous in the epidermal protein known as keratin, which by its insolubility mechanically protects the underlying tissues.[3] Sulphur is also contained in one of the physiologically important substances of bile.[4] Sulphates are important factors in the protective destruction, in the liver, of poisons of bacterial origin normally produced in and absorbed from the large intestine.

Potassium is able to separate hydrogen from its union with oxygen in water, and is the most active of the metals, biologically considered, in its positive ionization.[5] Through stimulation and inhibition potassium salts play an important part in the regulation of life phenomena, and they are essential to the living tissues of plants and animals, fresh-water and marine plants in particular storing up large quantities in their tissues.[6]

[1] *Op. cit.*, p. 241.

[2] *Op. cit.*, p. 242.

[3] Pirsson, Louis V., and Schuchert, Charles, 1915, p. 434.

[4] W. J. Gies.

[5] Cæsium is more electropositive.—F. W. Clarke.

[6] Loeb, Jacques, 1906, p. 94.

Potassium is of service to life in building up complex compounds from which the potassium cannot be dissociated as a free ion; it is thus one of the building stones of living matter.[1]

Magnesium is fourth in order of activity among the metallic elements. It is essential to chlorophyll, the green coloring matter of plants, which in the presence of sunshine is able

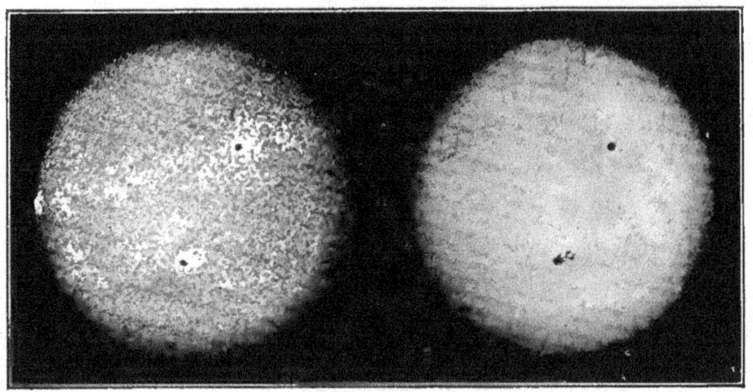

FIG. 8. THE SUN, SHOWING SUN-SPOTS AND CALCIUM VAPOR.

Calcium, a life element essential to all plants and animals, and especially abundant in the bones and teeth of vertebrates, is also a constituent of the solar atmosphere, as shown by these two photographs of the sun, both displaying the same view and the same group of sun-spots. The one at the left, made by calcium rays alone with the spectro-heliograph,[1] shows in addition the clouds of calcium vapor which are not evident in the photograph at the right. From the Mount Wilson Observatory.

[1] An instrument devised by Professor George E. Hale for taking photographs of the sun by the light of a single ray of the spectrum (calcium, hydrogen, etc.).

to dissociate oxygen from the carbon of carbon dioxide and from the hydrogen of water. It is also found in the skeletons of many invertebrates and in the coralline algæ, and is an important factor in inhibiting or restraining many biochemical processes.

Calcium is third in order of activity among the metallic elements. According to Loeb[2] it plays an important part in

[1] *Op. cit.*, p. 72.

[2] *Op. cit.*, 1906, p. 94.

the life phenomena through stimulation (irritability) and inhibition. It unites with carbon as carbonate of lime and is contained in many of those animal skeletons which, through deposition, make up an important part of the earth's crust.

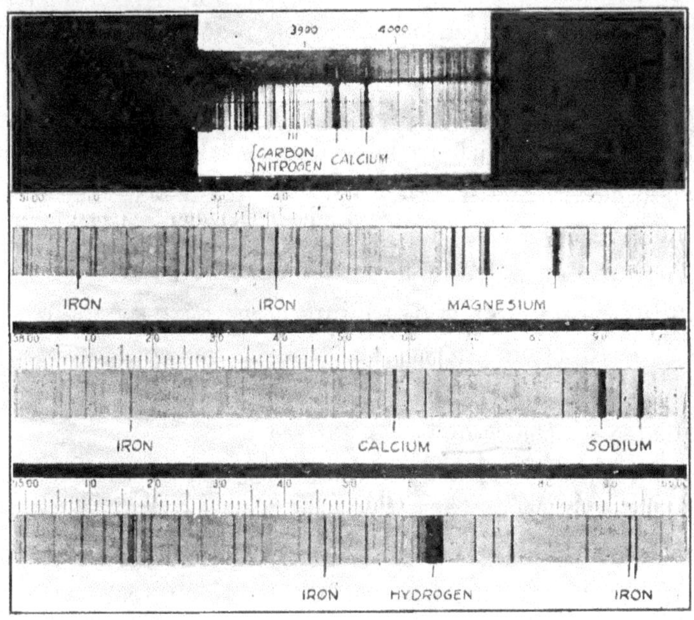

FIG. 9. CHEMICAL LIFE ELEMENTS IN THE SUN.

Three regions of the solar spectrum with lines showing the presence of such essential life elements as carbon, nitrogen, calcium, iron, magnesium, sodium, and hydrogen. From the Mount Wilson Observatory.

In invertebrates the carbonates, except in certain brachiopods, are far more important as skeletal material than the phosphates: the limestones form only about five per cent of the sedimentaries. Shales and sandstones are far more abundant.

Iron is essential for the production of chlorophyll,[1] though, unlike magnesium, it is not contained in it. It is present as well in all protoplasm, while in the higher animals it serves, in

[1] Sachs, Julius, 1882, p. 699.

the form of oxyhemoglobin, as a carrier of oxygen from the lungs to the tissues.[1]

Sodium is less important in the nutrition of plant tissues, but serves an essential function in all animal life in relation to movement through muscular contraction.[2] Its salts, like those of calcium, play an important part in the regulation of life phenomena through stimulation and inhibition.[3]

Iodine, with its negative ionization, becomes useful through its capacity to unite with hydrogen in the functioning of the brown algæ and in many other marine organisms. It is also an organic constituent in the thyroid gland of the vertebrates.[4] The iodine content of crinoids—stalked echinoderms—varies widely in organisms gathered from different parts of the ocean according to the temperature and the iodine content of the sea-water. Iodine and *bromine* are important constituents of the organic axes of gorgonias.

Chlorine, like iodine, a non-metallic element with negative ions, is abundant in marine algæ and present in many other plants, while in animals it is present in both blood and lymph. In union with hydrogen as hydrochloric acid it serves a very important function in the gastric digestion of proteins.[5]

Barium, rarely present in plants, has been used in animal experimentation by Loeb, who has shown that its salts induce muscular peristalsis and accelerate the secretory action of the kidneys.[6]

Copper ranks first in electric conductivity. In the invertebrates, in the form of hemocyanine, it acts as an oxygen carrier in the fluid circulation to the tissues.[7] It is always present in certain molluscs, such as the oyster, and also in the plumage

[1] Henderson, Lawrence J., 1913, p. 241.
[2] Loeb, Jacques, 1906, p. 79.
[3] *Op. cit.*, pp. 94, 95.
[4] Henderson, Lawrence J., 1913, p. 242.
[5] *Op. cit.*, p. 242.
[6] Loeb, Jacques, 1906, p. 93.
[7] Henderson, Lawrence J., 1913, p. 241.

TABLE II. ADAPTIVE FUNCTIONS OF THE LIFE ELEMENTS IN PLANTS AND ANIMALS

Atomic Weight	*Heat Combustion Per Gram*	*Element*	*Symbol*	*Plants*	*Animals*
				ELEMENTS INVARIABLY PRESENT IN LIVING ORGANISMS	
1.008	34.702 cal. (H_2)	**Hydrogen**	H	**Hydrogen, carbon, oxygen,** and **nitrogen**—"H, C, O, N"—are *essential and of chief rank* in all life processes; forming, with **sulphur,** practically all plant and animal proteins and, with **phosphorus,** forming the nucleoproteins.	
12.005	8.08 "	**Carbon**	C		
16.00		**Oxygen**	O		
14.01	0.143 "	**Nitrogen**	N		
31.04	5.747 "	**Phosphorus**	P	In nucleoproteins and phospholipins.	In nucleoproteins and phospholipins: in some brachiopods; in blood; and in vertebrate bone and teeth.
32.06	2.22 "	**Sulphur**	S	In most proteins, 0.1–5.0 per cent.	In most proteins, 0.1–5.0 per cent.
39.10	1.745 "	**Potassium**	K	Abundant in marine plants, esp. "kelps" (larger *Phæophyceæ*); activity of chlorophyll depends on it.	In blood, muscle, etc.
24.32	6.077 "	**Magnesium**	Mg	Present in large quantities in *Corallinaceæ* (a family of calcified red algæ).	Present in echinoderms and alcyonarians; present in all parts of vertebrates, esp. in bones.
40.07	3.284 "	**Calcium**	Ca	Present in large quantities in certain algæ (chiefly marine).	In all parts of vertebrates; abundant in bones and teeth.
55.84	1.353 "	**Iron**	Fe	Essential in the formation of protoplasm; present in chlorophyll.	Essential in the formation of protoplasm, and in the higher animals; essential in hemoglobin as an oxygen-carrier.
23.00	3.293 "	**Sodium**	Na	Believed essential to all plants, but not demonstrated; found in marine plants, esp. *Phæophyceæ*.	Present in all animals; abundant in blood and lymph.
35.46	0.254 "	**Chlorine**	Cl	Present in many plants; believed by some to be essential; abundant in marine algæ, esp. in the *Phæophyceæ*.	Present in all animals; abundant in blood and lymph; present in the gastric juice.
28.3		**Silicon**	Si	Found in all plants; present in large quantities in the *Diatomaceæ*, both fresh-water and marine; in form of "silica" constitutes 0.5–7.0 per cent of the ash of ordinary marine algæ.	Present in radiolarians and siliceous sponges; also in all the higher animals.
				ELEMENTS FREQUENTLY PRESENT IN LIVING ORGANISMS	
126.92	0.1766 cal.	**Iodine**	I	In marine plants, esp. the "brown algæ," *Phæophyceæ*; in *Laminaria* and *Fucus*; also in some Gorgonias.	Essential in the higher animals (thyroid).
54.93		**Manganese**	Mn	In some plants.	In most animals in very slight proportions.
79.92		**Bromine**	Br	In marine plants, esp. the "brown algæ," *Phæophyceæ*; in some Gorgonias.	In some animals in very slight proportions.
19.0		**Fluorine**	F	In a few plants.	In some animals—constituent of bones and teeth; in shells of mollusks and in vertebrate bones.
				ELEMENTS RARELY PRESENT IN LIVING ORGANISMS	
27.1		**Aluminum** [1]	Al	In a few plants.	In a few animals.
74.96	1.403 cal.	**Arsenic** [1]	As		In some animals.
137.37	0.952 "	**Barium** [1]	Ba	In a few plants.	
11.0		**Boron**	B	In some plants.	
58.97		**Cobalt** [1]	Co	In a few plants.	
63.57	0.585 "	**Copper** [1]	Cu	In a few plants.	Traces in some corals; essential in some lower animals as oxygen-carrier.
207.20	0.245 "	**Lead** [1]	Pb		Traces in some corals.
6.94		**Lithium**	Li	In some plants.	
58.68		**Nickel** [1]	Ni	In a few plants.	
226.0		**Radium** [1]	Ra	In some plants.	In some animals.
87.63	1.407 "	**Strontium** [1]	Sr	In a few plants.	
65.37	1.301 "	**Zinc** [1]	Zn	In a few plants.	In a few animals; traces in some corals.

The exceedingly rare occurrence of **cerium, chromium, didymium, lanthanum, molybdenum,** and **vanadium** is in all probability merely adventitious.

[1] Commonly regarded as poisons when present in *mineral* (ionic) forms, even in small proportions.

Pg 66-67

of a bird, the Turaco. Although among the rare life elements it ranks first in toxic action upon fungi, algæ, and in general upon all plants, yet it is occasionally found in the tissues of trees growing in copper-ore regions.[1]

In general most of the metallic compounds and several of the non-metallic compounds are toxic or destructive to life when present in large quantities. All the mineral elements of high atomic weight are toxic in comparatively minute proportions, while the essential life elements of low atomic weight are toxic only in comparatively large proportions. Toxicity depends largely upon the liberation of ions, and non-ionized and non-ionizable organic compounds—such as hemoglobin containing non-ionizable iron—are wholly non-toxic.

Pure Speculation as to the Primary Physicochemical Stages of Life

The mode of the origin of life is a matter of pure speculation, in which we have as yet little observation or uniformitarian reasoning to guide us, for all the experiments of Bütschli and others to imitate the original life process have proved fruitless. We shall, however, from our knowledge of bacteria (see Chap. III) put forward five hypotheses in regard to it, *considering the life process as probably a gradual one, marked by short leaps or accessions of energy, and not as a sudden one.*

First: We may advance the hypothesis that an early step in the organization of living matter was the assemblage one by one of several of the ten elements now essential to life, namely, hydrogen, oxygen, nitrogen, carbon, phosphorus, sulphur, potassium, calcium, magnesium, and iron (also perhaps silicon), which are present in all living organisms, with the exception of some of the most primitive forms of bacteria which may

[1] M. A. Howe, letter of February 24, 1916.

lack magnesium, iron, and silica. Of these the four most important elements were obtained from their previous combination in water (H_2O), from the nitrogen compounds of volcanic emanations or from the atmosphere[1] consisting largely of nitrogen, and from atmospheric carbon dioxide (CO_2). The remaining six elements, phosphorus, sulphur, potassium, calcium, magnesium, and iron, came from the earth.

Second: Whether there was a sudden or a more or less serial grouping of these elements, one by one, we are led to a second hypothesis that they were gradually bound by a new form of mutual attraction whereby the actions and reactions of a group of life elements established a new form of unity in the cosmos, an organic unity, an *individual* or *organism* quite distinct from the larger and smaller aggregations of inorganic matter previously held or brought together by the forces of gravity. Some such stage of mutual attraction may have been ancestral to the cell, the primordial unity and individuality of which we shall describe later.

Third: This leads to the hypothesis that this grouping occurred in the gelatinous state described as "colloidal" by Graham.[2] Since all living cells are colloidal, it appears probable that this grouping of the "life elements" took place in a state of colloidal suspension, for it is in this state that the life elements best display their incessant action, reaction, and interaction. Bechhold[3] observes that "Whatever the arrangement of matter in living organisms in other worlds may be, it must be of colloidal nature. What other condition except the

[1] Ammonia is also formed by electrical action in the atmosphere and unites with the nitric oxides to form ammonium nitrate or nitrite; these compounds fall to earth in rain. —F. W. Clarke.

[2] Over fifty years ago Thomas Graham introduced the term "colloid" (L. *colla*, glue) to denote non-crystalloid indiffusible substances, like gelatine, a typical colloid, as distinguished from diffusible crystalloids. Proteins belong to that class of colloids which, once coagulated, cannot, as a rule, be redissolved in water.

[3] Bechhold, Heinrich, 1912, p. 104.

colloidal could develop such changeable and plastic forms, and yet be able, if necessary, to preserve these forms unaltered?"

Fourth: As a fourth hypothesis relating to the origin of organisms, we may advocate the idea that the evolution and specialization of various "chemical messengers" known as catalyzers (including enzymes or "unformed ferments") has proceeded step by step with the evolution of plant and animal functions. In the evolution from the single-celled to the many-celled forms of life and the multiplication of these cells into hundreds of millions, into billions, and into trillions, as in the larger plants and animals, biochemical coordination and correlation became increasingly essential. This cooperation was also an application of energy new to the cosmos.

Fifth: With this assemblage, mutual attraction, colloidal condition, and chemical coordination, a fifth hypothesis is that there arose the rudiments of competition and Natural Selection which tested all the actions, reactions, and interactions of two competing individuals. Was there any stage in this grouping, assemblage, and organization of life forms, however remote or rudimentary, when the law of natural selection did not operate between different unit aggregations of matter? Probably not, because *each of the chemical life elements possesses its peculiar properties which in living compounds best serve certain functions.*

Evolution of New Organic Compounds

Special actions and reactions appear to be characteristic of each of the life elements, issuing in new compounds.

The central idea in our five hypotheses (see p. 67) of successive physicochemical stages is that in the origin and early evolution of the life organism there was a gradual attraction and grouping of the ten chief life elements, followed by the grouping of the nineteen or more chemical elements which were subsequently added. The creation of new chemical compounds may have been analogous to the successive addition of new characters and functions, such as we now observe through palæontology in the origin and development of the higher plants and animals, resembling a series of inventions and discoveries by the organism.

Conceivable steps in the process were as follows: From earth, air, and water there may have been an early grouping of oxygen, nitrogen, hydrogen, and carbon, such as we witness in the lowliest bacterial stages of life. Even those lifeless compounds which contain neither hydrogen, carbon, nor oxygen, make up but a very small percentage of the substance of known bodies. The compounds of carbon, hydrogen, and oxygen (C, H, O)[1] constitute a unique ensemble of fitness among all the possible chemical substances for the exchange of matter and energy within the life organism and between it and its environment. As the higher forms of life are constituted to-day, water and the carbon dioxide of the atmosphere are the chief materials of the complicated life compounds, and also the common end products of the materials yielding energy to the body. Proteins are made from materials containing nitrogen in addition.

Thus may have arisen the utilization of the binary compounds of carbon and oxygen (CO_2), and of hydrogen and oxygen (H_2O), to the attractive power of which Henderson[2] has especially drawn our attention. It is this attractive power of oxygen or of hydrogen or of both elements combined which is now bringing, and in the past may have brought into the life organism other elements useful to it in its various func-

[1] Henderson, Lawrence J., 1913, pp. 71, 194, 195, 207, 231, 232.
[2] *Op. cit.*, pp. 230, 240.

tions. Thus in the origin of life hydrogen and oxygen, elements unrivalled in chemical activity, functioned as "attractive" agents to enable the life organism to draw in other chemical elements to serve new purposes and functions.

Through such attraction or other means the incorporation of the active metals—potassium, sodium, calcium, magnesium, iron, manganese, and copper—into the substance of living organisms may have occurred in the order of their utility in capturing energy from the environment and storing it within the organism. For example, an immense period of geologic time may have elapsed before the addition of magnesium and iron to certain hydrocarbons enabled the plant to draw upon the energy of solar light. This marked the appearance of chlorophyll in the earliest algal stage of plant life.

Evolution of Interactions

The organism as a whole is made a harmonious unit through *interaction*. Its actions and reactions must be regulated, balanced, coordinated, correlated, protected from foreign invasion, accelerated, retarded. This harmony seems in large part to be due to the principle that every action and reaction sends off as a by-product a "chemical messenger" which sooner or later produces an interaction at some more or less distant point.

The *regulating* and *balancing* of actions and reactions within the organism was provided for by the presence in the fluid circulation of outside chemical agents, for many of the primordial actions and reactions are known to give rise to chemical by-products which circulate throughout the life organism. Among such regulating and balancing influences we observe that exerted by the phosphates upon the acidifying tendency of carbon dioxide;[1] in respiration carbon dioxide raises the hydrogen concentration of the blood; the phosphates restrain this tendency, while the breathing apparatus, in response to stimuli from the respiratory centres irritated by the hydrogen, throws out the excess of this element.

Thus there evolved step by step the function of *coordinating* and *correlating* the activities of various parts of the life organism remote from each other by means of chemical messengers adapted to effect not only a *general interaction* between general parts, but also *special interactions* between special parts; for it is now known that, as Huxley prophesied (see p. 57), certain chemical messengers do reach particular groups of living elements and leave others entirely untouched. For example, the enzyme developed in the yeast ferment produces a different result in each one of a series of closely related carbohydrates.[2]

These chemical messengers are doubtless highly diversified: they are now known to exist in at least three or four forms, as follows:

First: The simplest forms of such chemical messengers are those which originate as *by-products of single chemical reactions.* For example, the carbon dioxide (CO_2) liberated in the cell by the reactions of respiration acts at a distance on other portions of the cell and of the organism. Thus every cell of the body furnishes in the carbon dioxide which it eliminates a chemical messenger,[3] since under normal conditions the carbon dioxide of the blood is one of the chief regulators of the respiratory centre, influencing this centre by virtue of its acidic properties.

Second: Of prime importance among the various "chemical messengers" are the *organic catalyzers*[4] *known as enzymes*, the

[1] W. J. Gies.
[2] Moore, F. J., 1915 p 170; Loeb, Jacques, 1906, pp. 21, 22.
[3] Abel, John J., 1915, p. 168.
[4] Loeb, Jacques, 1906, pp. 8, 28.

action of which has already been described (see p. 57). They appear to be present in all cells, and in most cases the activity of the cell itself depends upon them.[1] These enzymes are very probably of a protein nature and are readily destroyed by heat in the presence of water. The active agents of the external secretions when present are always of the nature of a ferment or enzyme. Driesch[2] has suggested that the nucleus of the cell is a storehouse of these ferments which pass out into the protoplasm tissues and there set up specific activities.

Third: *Antigens, antibodies including the agents of immunity.*[3] The active and inactive protein compounds termed *antigens* include certain known proteins and possibly a few other compounds of kindred nature. Among the *active* protein compounds are certain enzymes, bacterial poisons, snake venoms, spider poisons, and some vegetable poisons; antigens of this class are all powerfully active and possess properties which suggest that they may eventually be classed as enzymes. On the invasion of an organism by any foreign protein of this class in any region except the interior of the alimentary canal it would seem that certain chemical messengers called *antibodies* arise which are especially fitted to protect the tissues of the body against such invasion; these antibodies are true *agents of immunity* and serve to increase the resistance of the organism to any future attack of the invading antigen; it is to this formation of neutralizing antibodies, known as antitoxins, that the curative powers for such infections as diphtheria and tetanus are due.

There are also antigens of another kind, consisting of *inactive* protein compounds, which, when they invade an organism, induce the formation of antibodies acting in an entirely dif-

[1] Schäfer, Sir Edward A., 1916, pp. 4, 5. [2] Wilson, Edmund B., 1906, p. 427.
[3] Zinsser, Hans, 1915, pp. 223–226, 247, 248.

ferent manner from the antitoxins. While antibodies of this kind tend to assimilate or remove the invading antigen, they do not confer immunity against a future invasion: on the contrary, they render the organism increasingly susceptible. Experiments on animals show that, while the first injection of such inactive proteins may be entirely harmless, subsequent injections may result in severe injury or even death.

It is, therefore, evident that the invasion of an organism either by a powerfully active or by an inactive antigen causes changes of a physicochemical nature which appear to originate in the body cell itself, resulting in the formation of chemical messengers known as antibodies which appear in the circulating blood.

Fourth: Of vital importance to the life organism are those chemical messengers known as *internal secretions*, due for the most part to the so-called endocrine (Gr. ἔνδον, within, and κρίνω, to separate) organs or ductless glands, which liberate some specific substance within their cells that passes directly into the blood stream and has a stimulating or inhibiting effect upon other organs. To certain of these stimulating internal messengers Starling applied the term "hormone" (Gr. ὁρμάω, to awaken, to stir up). Recently Schäfer,[1] in reviewing all the organs of internal secretion, has proposed the opposite term "chalone" (Gr. χαλάω, to make slack) for those messengers which depress, retard, or inhibit the activity of distant parts of the body. The *interactions* between different parts of the organism produced by these chemical messengers depend upon a simpler chemical constitution than that of the enzymes,[2] as hormones and chalones, for the most part, are not rendered inactive, even by prolonged boiling.

We may suppose that in the course of evolution certain

[1] Schäfer, Sir Edward A., 1916, p. 5. [2] *Loc. cit.*

special cells and, finally, special groups of cells gave rise to the glands, and none of the discoveries we have hitherto described throws greater illumination on the whole process of building up an elaborate life organism than those connected with the products of internal secretion. Among the special glands of internal secretion known in man are the thyroids, parathyroids, thymus, suprarenals, pituitary body, and pineal gland, rudiments of which doubtless occur in the very oldest vertebrates and even among their invertebrate ancestors; although their functions have been discovered chiefly through experiment upon the lower mammals and man.

Of the chemical messengers produced by these glands some affect the growth of the entire organism, while others affect only certain parts of the organism; some arrest growth entirely, others stimulate growth at certain points only, and others again entirely change the proportions of certain parts of the body. Thus an injury to the pituitary body, which lies beneath the vertebrate brain, results in stunted stature, marked adiposity, and delayed or imperfect sexual development; on the other hand, a diseased condition of the pituitary body, rousing it to excessive function, is followed by a great increase in the general size of the head, as well as by a complete change in the proportions of the face from broad to long and narrow, and an abnormal growth of the long limb-bones, while at the same time the proportions of the hands are changed from normal to the short and broad condition known as brachydactyly.[1] In other words, the regulation and balance resulting in the normal size and proportions of certain parts of the skeleton are dependent upon chemical messengers coming from these glands.

[1] Schäfer, Sir Edward A., 1916, pp. 107, 108, 110. Cushing, Harvey, 1911, pp. 253, 256.

It has also been discovered that the source of such internal secretions is not confined to the ductless glands, but that certain duct-glands, such as the ovaries, testes, and pancreas, serve a double function, for they secrete not only through their ducts, but they also produce an internal secretion which enters the circulation of the blood. It is, of course, a fact known from remote antiquity that removal of the sex

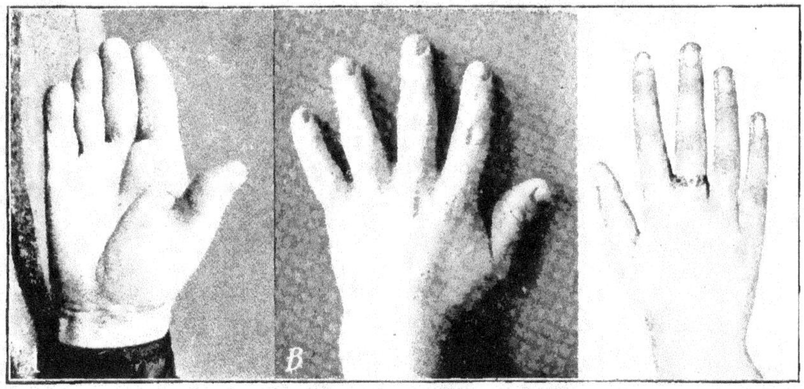

FIG. 10. HAND FORM DETERMINED BY HEREDITY (*A*) AND BY ABNORMAL INTERNAL SECRETIONS (*B*, *C*).

A. Hereditary brachydactyly (partial) attributed to congenital causes. After Drinkwater.

B. Acquired brachydactyly. This abnormally broad and stumpy hand shows one of the results of abnormally excessive secretions of the pituitary gland. After Cushing.

C. Acquired dolichodactyly. This slender hand with tapering fingers shows one of the results of abnormally insufficient secretions of the pituitary gland. After Cushing.

glands from a young animal of either sex not only inhibits the development of all the so-called secondary sexual characters, but favors the development of characters of the opposite sex. During the last and present centuries it has been discovered that all these inhibited characters may be restored by successfully transplanting or grafting into some part of the body the ovary or testicle, either from the same or another individual, thus proving that in both sexes the secondary sexual characters are dependent upon some internal secretion from the ovaries and testes and not upon the normal production of the male and female germ-cells, or ova and spermatozoa.

The classic demonstration of this internal messenger system is that made experimentally by Berthold in fowls. In 1849 he transplanted the testicles of young cocks which afterward developed the masculine voice, comb, sexual desire, and love of combat, thus anticipating the theories of Brown-Sequard, who committed himself to the view that a gland, ductless or not, sends into the circulation substances essential to the normal growth and maintenance of many if not all parts of the body.

With the discovery that the regulating and balancing functions, as well as the accelerating or retarding of the activities of certain characters of organisms, are phenomena of physico-chemical action, reaction, and interaction in individual development, we obtain a distant glimpse of the possible causes of the balance, development, or degeneration of certain parts of organisms through successive generations, and conceivably of the long-sought means of interaction between the actions and reactions of individual development (body-protoplasm and body-chromatin) and of the germ-cells in race development (heredity-chromatin).

In fact, a heredity hypothesis was proposed by Cunningham[1] in 1906 based upon Berthold's discovery that the connection between the germ-cells and the secondary sexual organs of the body was really of a chemical rather than of a nervous nature as had previously been supposed. To paraphrase Cunningham's hypothesis in modern terms, since hormones and chalones issuing as internal secretions from the groups of germ-cells (ovaries and testes) determine the development of many

[1] Cunningham, J. T., 1908, pp. 372-428.

other organs, it is possible that hormones and chalones arising from the various cellular activities of the body itself may act upon the physicochemical elements in the germ-cells which correspond potentially to the tissues from which these hormones and chalones are derived. Cunningham was a strong believer in the Lamarckian explanation (see p. xiii) of evolution, and his heredity hypothesis was designed to suggest a means by which the modifications of the body due to environmental and developmental conditions could so modify the corresponding tissues and physicochemical constitution of the chromatin in the germ-cells as to become hereditary and reappear in subsequent generations.

Physicochemical Differentiation

As the result of recent investigations of cancer, Loeb[1] comes to the following conclusions:

"We must assume that every individual of a certain species differs in a definite chemical way from every other of that species, and that in its chemical constitution an animal of one species differs still more from an animal of another. Every cell of the body has a chemical character in common with every other cell of that body and also in common with the body fluids; and this particular chemical group differs from that of every other individual of the species and to a still greater degree from that of any individual of another group or species. Thus it happens that cells belonging to the same organism are adapted to all the other cells of that organism and also to the body fluids. . . .

"It has been possible to demonstrate by experimental methods that there are fine chemical differences not only between different species and between different individuals of

[1] Loeb, Leo, 1916, pp. 209–226.

the same species, but also between different sets of families which constitute a strain, for certain chemical characters differentiate them from other strains of the same species. It has been shown, for instance, that white mice bred in Europe differ chemically from white mice bred in America, although the appearance of both strains may be identical."

The investigations of Reichert and Brown (cited in Chapter VIII, p. 247) give an insight into the almost inconceivable physicochemical complexity of a single element of the blood, namely, the oxyhemoglobin crystals.

CHAPTER III

ENERGY EVOLUTION OF BACTERIA, ALGÆ, AND PLANTS

Energy and form. Primary stages of biochemical evolution in bacteria. Evolution of protoplasm and chromatin, the two structural components of the living world. Chlorophyll and the energy of sunlight. Evolution of the algæ. Some physicochemical contrasts between plant and animal evolution.

We shall now trace some of the physicochemical principles of action, reaction, and interaction as they actually appear in operation in some of the simpler forms of life, beginning with the bacteria. In the bacterial organisms the capture, storage, release, and interaction of *energy* are what is best known and apparently most important, while their *form* is less known and apparently less important.

Primary Stages of Biochemical Evolution in Bacteria

A bacterialess earth and a bacterialess ocean would soon be uninhabitable either for plants or animals; conversely, it is probable that bacteria-like organisms prepared both the earth and the ocean for the further evolution of plants and animals, and that life passed through a very long bacterial stage.

In the origin of life bacteria appear to lie half-way between our hypothetical chemical precellular stages (pp. 67–71) and the chemistry and definite cell structure of the lowliest plants, or algæ. Owing to their minute size or actual invisibility, bacteria are classified less by their shape than by their chemical actions, reactions, and interactions, the analysis of which is one of the triumphs of modern research.

The size of bacteria is in inverse ratio to their importance in the primordial and present history of the earth. The largest known are slightly above 1/20 of a millimetre in length and 1/200 of a millimetre in width.[1] The smaller forms range from 1/2000 of a millimetre to organisms on the very limit of microscopic vision, 1/5000 of a millimetre in size, and to the bacteria beyond the limits of microscopic vision, the existence of which is inferred in certain diseases. The chemical constitution of these microscopic and ultramicroscopic forms is doubtless highly complex. The number of these organisms is inconceivable. In the daily excretion of a normal adult human being it is estimated that there are from 128,000,000,000 to 33,000,000,000,000 bacteria, which would weigh approximately 5 5/10 grams when dried, and that the nitrogen in this dried mass would be about 0.6 gram, constituting nearly one-half the total intestinal nitrogen.[2]

The discovery of the chemical life of the lowliest bacteria marks an advance toward the solution of the problem of the origin of life as important as that attending the long-prior discovery of the chemical action of chlorophyll in plants.

In their power of finding energy or food in a lifeless world the bacteria known as *prototrophic*, or "primitive feeders," are not only the simplest known organisms, but it is probable that they represent the survival of a primordial stage of life chemistry. These bacteria derive both their energy and their nutrition directly from inorganic chemical compounds: such types were thus capable of living and flourishing on the lifeless earth even before the advent of continuous sunshine and long

[1] The influenza bacillus, 5/10 × 2/10 of a micron (1/1000 mm.) in size, and the germ of infantile paralysis, measuring 2/10 of a micron, are on the limit of microscopic vision. Beyond these are the ultramicroscopic bacteria, beyond the range of vision, some of which can pass through a porcelain filter. See Jordan, Edwin O., 1908, pp. 52, 53.

[2] Kendall, A. I., 1915, p. 209.

before the first chlorophyllic stage (Algæ) of the evolution of plant life. Among such bacteria, possibly surviving from Archæozoic time, is one of these "primitive feeders," namely, the *Nitroso monas* of Europe.[1] For combustion it takes in oxygen directly through the intermediate action of iron, phosphorus, or manganese, each of the single cells being a powerful little chemical laboratory which contains oxidizing catalyzers, the activity of which is accelerated by the presence of iron and of manganese. Still in the primordial stage, *Nitroso monas* lives on ammonium sulphate, taking its energy (food) from the nitrogen of ammonium and forming nitrites. Living symbiotically with it is *Nitrobacter*, which takes its energy (food) from the nitrites formed by *Nitroso monas*, oxidizing them into nitrates. Thus these two species illustrate in its simplest form our law of the *interaction of an organism (Nitrobacter) with its life environment (Nitroso monas)*.[2]

These organisms are wide-spread: *Nitroso monas* is found in Europe, Asia, and Africa, while *Nitrobacter* appears to be almost universally distributed.

These "primitive feeders" are classed among the *nitrifying bacteria* because they take up the nitrogen of ammonia compounds. Heraeus and Hüppe (1887) were the first to observe these nitrifiers in action in the soils and to prove that prechlorophyllic organisms were capable of development, with ammonium and carbon dioxide as their only sources of energy. Nine chemical "life elements" are involved in the life reactions of these organisms, namely, sodium, potassium, phosphorus, magnesium, sulphur, calcium, chlorine, nitrogen, and carbon. This discovery was confirmed by Winogradsky (1890, 1895), who showed that the above two symbiotic groups existed; one the *nitrite* formers, *Nitroso monas*, and the other the

[1] Fischer, Alfred, 1900, pp. 51, 104.

[2] Jordan, Edwin O., 1908, pp. 492–497.

nitrate formers, *Nitrobacter*. These bacteria are not only independent of life compounds, but even small traces of organic carbon and nitrogen compounds are injurious to them. Later Nathanson (1902) and Beyjerinck (1904) showed that certain sulphur bacteria possess similar powers of converting ferrous to ferric oxide, and H_2S to SO_2.

Such bacterial organisms may have flourished on the lifeless earth and chemically prepared both the earth and the waters for the lowly forms of plant life. The relation of the *nitrifying bacteria* to the decomposition of rocks is well summarized by Clarke in the following passage:[1] "Even forms of life so low as the bacteria seem to exert a definite influence in the decomposition of rocks. A. Müntz has found the decayed rocks of Alpine summits, where no other life exists, swarming with the nitrifying ferment. The limestones and micaceous schists of the Pic du Midi, in the Pyrenees, and the decayed calcareous schists of the Faulhorn, in the Bernese Oberland, offer good examples of this kind. The organisms draw their nourishment from the nitrogen compounds brought down in snow and rain; they convert the ammonia into nitric acid, and that in turn corrodes the calcareous portions of the rocks. A. Stützer and R. Hartleb have observed a similar decomposition of cement by nitrifying bacteria. The effects thus produced at any one point may be small, but in the aggregate they may become appreciable. J. C. Branner, however, has cast doubts upon the validity of Müntz's argument, and further investigation of the subject seems to be necessary."

It is noteworthy that it is the *nitrogen derived from waters and soils*, rather than from the atmosphere, which plays the chief part in the life of these organisms; in a sense they represent an early carbon stage of chemical evolution, since carbon

[1] Clarke, F. W., 1916, p. 485.

is not their prime constituent, also adaptation to an earth-and-water environment rather than to an atmospheric one.

In our portrayal of the chemistry of the lifeless earth it is shown how the chief life elements essential for the energy and nutrition of the nitrifying bacteria, namely, sodium, potassium, calcium, and magnesium, with potassium nitrite and ammonium salts as a source of nitrogen, may have accumulated in the waters, pools, and soils. These bacteria were at once the soil-forming and the soil-nourishing agents of the primal earth; they throve in the presence of energy-liberating compounds of extremely primitive character. It is important to note that water and air are essential to vigorous ammonium reactions, whether at or near the surface. In arid regions at the present time the ammonifying bacteria do not exist on the dry surface rocks, but act vigorously in the soils, not only at the surface, but also in the lower layers at depths of from six to ten feet, where moisture is constant and the porous soil well aërated,[1] thus giving rise to a nitrogen-nourished substratum, which explains the deep rooting of desert-dwelling plants.

A second point of great significance is that these nitrifying organisms are *heat-loving* and *light-avoiding;* they are dependent on the heat of the earth or of the sun, for, like all other bacteria, they carry on their activities best in the absence of sunshine, direct sunlight being generally fatal. The sterilizing effect of sunlight is due partly to the coagulation of the bacterial colloids by the rays of ultra-violet light. The sensitiveness of bacteria to sunlight cannot, however, be viewed as evidence against their geologic antiquity, because their undifferentiated structure and their ability to live on inorganic foodstuffs *even without the aid of sunshine* seem to favor the idea that they represent a very primitive form of life.[2]

[1] Lipman, Charles B., 1912, pp. 7, 8, 16, 17, 20.

[2] I. J. Kligler.

The great geologic antiquity even of certain lower forms of bacteria which feed on nitrogen is proved by the discovery, announced by Walcott[1] in 1915, of a species of pre-Palæozoic

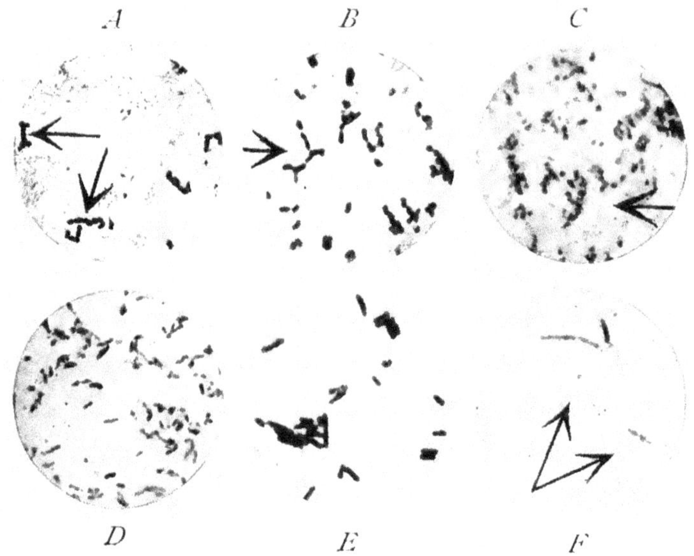

FIG. 11. FOSSIL AND LIVING BACTERIA COMPARED.

Extremely ancient fossil bacteria (*A*) compared with similar types of living bacteria (*B–F*).

A. Fossil bacteria from the pre-Cambrian Newland limestone (Algonkian), after Walcott.

B. Existing nitrifying bacteria found in soils—the arrow indicates a chain series similar to that of Walcott's fossil bacteria.

C. A more complex type of nitrifying bacteria found in soils.

D. Nitrogen-fixing bacteria from the root nodules of legumes. Note the granular structure of the supposed "chromatin."

E. Denitrifying bacteria found in soil and water.

F. Bacteria stained to bring out the chromatin granules or "nuclei" in the centre of each rod-like bacterial cell.

fossil bacteria attributed to "*Micrococcus*," but probably related rather to the existing *Nitroso coccus*, which derives its nitrogen from ammonium salts.

These fossil bacteria were found in a section of a chlorophyll-

[1] Walcott, Charles D., 1915, p. 256.

bearing algal plant from the Newland limestone of the Algonkian of Montana, the age of which is estimated to be about 33,000,000 years. They point to a very long antecedent stage of bacterial evolution. In this section (Fig. 11, *A*), at the points indicated by the arrows, there is a little chain of cells closely similar to those in the existing species of *Azotobacter*, an organism that fixes atmospheric nitrogen and converts it into a form utilizable by the plant. The Algonkian form is related to the other nitrifiers, *Nitroso coccus*, *Nitroso monas*, and to *Nitrobacter* which lives on simple salts with carbon dioxide (CO_2) as a source of carbon.

The gradual evolution of a cellular structure in these organisms can be partly traced despite their excessively minute size. The cell structure of the Algonkian and of the recent *Nitroso coccus* bacteria (Fig. 11, *A*, *B*) is very primitive and uniform in appearance, the protoplasm being naked or unprotected; this primitive structure is also seen in *C*, another type of nitrogen-fixer of the soil, which is chemically more complex because it can obtain its nitrogen either from the inorganic nitrogen compounds or from the organic nitrogen compounds (amino-acids), which are fatal to the *Nitroso monas* and the *Nitrobacter* forms. The arrow points to a group of cells similar in appearance to those in *B*. A higher stage of granular structure appears in *D*, a nitrogen-fixer from the root nodules of legumes, which like *B* and *C* lives on inorganic chemical compounds, but draws upon the atmosphere for nitrogen and upon sugar for its carbon; we observe an uneven granular structure in this cell. This may be an illustration of an early type of parasitic adaptation. The next type of bacterium (*E*) is a *denitrifier*, which derives its oxygen from the nitrates, reducing them to nitrites and free nitrogen and ammonia. A further stage of structural and chemical evolution is seen (*F*) in four elongated bacteria, each showing a rod-like but cellular form with a deeply staining chromatin or nuclear mass; the arrows point to cells showing these chromatin granules. This organism is chemically more complex in that it can secrete a powerful tryptic-like enzyme which enables it to utilize complex polypeptids and proteins (casein). Also it is an obligatory aërobic type, being unable to function in the absence of free oxygen.

It was only after the chlorophyllic, carbon-storing true plants had evolved that the second great group of parasitic nitrifying bacteria arose to develop the power of capturing and storing the *nitrogen of the atmosphere through life association or symbiosis with plants*, also of deriving their carbon, not from inorganic compounds, but from the carbohydrates of plants. Such users of atmospheric nitrogen and of plant carbon include three general types: *B. radicicola*, associated with the root formation of legumes (compare *D*, Fig. 11), *Clostridium* (anaërobic, *i. e.*, independent of free oxygen), and *Azotobacter* (aërobic, *i. e.*, requiring free oxygen).[1]

It seems that the early course of bacterial evolution was in the line of developing a variety of complex molecules for performing a number of metabolic functions, and that the visible cell differentiation came later.[2] Step by step the chemical evolution and addition of increasingly complex actions, reactions, and interactions appear to correspond broadly with the structural evolution of the bacterial organism in its approach to the condition of a typical cell with its cell-wall, protoplasm, and chromatin nucleus.

To sum up, the existing bacteria exhibit a series of primordial physicochemical phases in the capture, storage, and utilization of energy, and in the development of products useful to themselves and to other organisms and of by-products which

[1] Jordan, Edwin O., 1908, pp. 484–491.

[2] I. J. Kligler.

as chemical messengers cause interactions in other organisms. With the simplest bacteria which live directly on the lifeless world we find that most of the fundamental chemical energies of the living world are already established, namely:

(*a*) the colloidal cell interior, with all the adaptations of colloidal suspensions, including

(*b*) the stimulating electric action and reaction of the metallic on the non-metallic elements; for example, the accelerations by iron, manganese, and other metals. Some bacteria carry positive, others negative ion charges;

(*c*) the catalytic messenger, or enzyme action, both within and without the organism;

(*d*) the protein and carbon energy storage, the primary food supply of the living world.

Thus the chemical reactions of bacteria are analogous to those of the higher plant and animal cells.

Considering bacteria as the primordial food supply, it is the invariable presence of nitrogen which distinguishes the bacteria making up their proteins; nitrogen is also a large constituent of all animal proteins.

PERCENTAGE OF ELEMENTS IN THE PROTEINS [1]

Carbon	50.0–55.0
Hydrogen	6.9– 7.3
Oxygen	19.0–24.0
Nitrogen	18.0–19.0
Sulphur	0.3– 2.4

Bacterial suspensions manifest the characteristics of colloidal suspensions, namely, of fluids containing minute gelatinous particles which are kept in motion by molecular move-

[1] Moore, F. J., 1915, p. 199. Nucleic proteins contain a notable amount of phosphorus as well.

ment: these colloidal substances have the food-value of protein and form the primary food of many Protozoa, the most elementary forms of animal life. Chemical messengers in the form of enzymes of three kinds exist, proteolytic, oxidizing, and synthetic.[1] The proteolytic enzymes are similar to the tryptic enzymes of animals, being able to digest only the proteoses and simple proteins (casein, albumin) but not the complex proteins. Powerful oxidizing enzymes are present, but their character is not known. Synthetic enzymes, bringing together *new living chemical compounds*, must also exist, though as yet there is no positive information concerning them.

Armed with these physicochemical powers, which may have been acquired one by one, the primordial bacteria begin to mimic the subsequent evolution of the higher plant and animal world by an adaptive radiation into groups which respectively seek new sources of energy, either directly from the inorganic world or parasitically from the developing organic bacterial and plant foods in protein and carbohydrate form, the different groups living together in large communities and interacting chemically upon one another by the changes produced in their environment.

The parasitic life of bacteria, beginning with their symbiotic relations with other bacteria, was extended into intimate relations with the plants and finally with the entire living world.

Like other forms of life, bacteria need oxygen for combustion in their intracellular actions and reactions; but free oxygen is not only unnecessary but actually toxic to the anaërobic bacteria, discovered by Pasteur in 1861, which derive their oxygen from inorganic and organic compounds. There is, however, a transitional group of bacteria, known as the *facultative anaërobes*, which can use either free or combined oxygen,

[1] I. J. Kligler.

thus forming a link to all the higher forms of life in which free oxygen is an absolute essential. There is a group of the higher spore-forming bacteria which must have free oxygen. These constitute probably a late stage in bacterial evolution and form the link to the higher forms.

The iron bacteria discovered by Ehrenberg in 1838 obtain their energy from the oxidation of iron compounds, the insoluble oxide remaining stored in the cell and accumulating into iron as the bacteria die.[1] In general the beds of iron ore found in certain of the pre-Cambrian stratified rocks, which have an estimated age of 60,000,000 years, are believed to be of bacterial origin. Sulphur bacteria similarly obtain their energy from the oxidation of hydrogen sulphide.

Bacteria in the Balance of Life

Bacteria thus anticipate the plant world of algæ, diatoms, and carbon-formers, as well as the animal world of Protozoa and Mollusca, by playing an important rôle in the formation of the new crust of the earth. This is observed in the primordial limestone depositions composed of calcium carbonate formed by bacterial action on the various soluble salts of calcium present in solution in sea-water, a process exemplified to-day[2] in the Great Bahama Banks, where chalk mud is now precipitated through accumulation by *B. calcis*. Doubtless in the shallow continental seas of the primal earth such bacteria swarmed, as in the shallow coastal seas of to-day, having both the power of secreting and precipitating lime and, at the same

[1] It is claimed that iron bacteria play an important part in the formation of numerous small deposits of bog-iron ore, and it seems possible that their activities may be responsible for extensive sedimentary deposits as well. Further, the fact of finding iron bacteria in underground mines opens the possibility that certain underground deposits of iron ore may have been formed by them.—Harder, E. C., 1915, p. 311.

[2] Drew, George H., 1914, p. 44.

time, of converting nitrogen combinations. In the warm oceanic waters the amount of lime deposited is larger and the *variety* of living forms is greater; but the *number* of living forms which depend for food on the algæ is less because the denitrifying bacteria which flourish in warm tropical waters deprive the algæ of the nitrates so necessary for their development. Again, where algal growth is scarce, the protozoic unicellular and multicellular life (plankton) of the sea, which lives upon the algæ, is also less abundant. This affords an excellent illustration of the great law of *the balance of the life environment through the equilibrium of supply of energy*, one aspect of the interaction of organisms with their life environment. The denitrifying bacteria rob the waters of the energy needed for the lowest forms of plants, and these in turn are not available for the lowest forms of animal life. Thus in the colder waters of the oceans, where the denitrifying bacteria do not exist, the number of living forms is far greater, although their variety is far less.[1]

The so-called luminous bacteria also anticipate the plants and animals in light production,[2] which is believed to be connected with the oxidation of a phosphorescing substance in the presence of water and of free oxygen.

Evolution of Protoplasm and Chromatin, the Two Structural Components of the Living World

It is still a matter of discussion[3] whether any bacteria, even at the present time, have reached the evolutionary stage of the typical cell with its cell-wall, its contained protoplasm, and its distinct nuclear form and inner substance known as chromatin. Some bacteriologists (Fischer) maintain that bacteria

[1] Pirsson, Louis V., and Schuchert, Charles, 1915, p. 104.
[2] Harvey, E. Newton, 1915, pp. 230, 238.
[3] I. J. Kligler.

have neither nucleus nor chromatin; others admit the presence of chromatin, but deny the existence of a formal nucleus; others contend that the entire bacterial cell has a chromatin content; while still others claim the presence of a distinctly differentiated nucleus containing chromatin. Most of them, however, are agreed as to the presence in bacteria of granules of a chromatin nature, while they leave as an open question the presence or absence of a structurally distinct nucleus. This conservative point of view is borne out by the fact that all the common bacteria have been found to contain *nuclein*, the specific nuclear protein complex. Nuclei and chromatin were ascribed to the Cyanophyceæ, by Kohl[1] as early as 1903 and by Phillips[2] and by Olive[3] in 1904.

It is also a matter of controversy among bacteriologists whether protoplasm or chromatin is the more ancient. Cell observers (Boveri, Wilson, Minchin), however, are thoroughly agreed on this point. Thus Minchin is unable to accept any theory of the evolution of the earliest forms of living beings which assumes the existence of forms of life composed entirely of protoplasm without chromatin.[4] All the results of modern investigations—the combined results, that is to say, of cytology and protistology—appear to him to indicate that the chromatin elements represent the primary and original living units or individuals, and that the protoplasm represents a secondary product. As to whether chromatin or protoplasm is the more ancient, Boveri suggests that true cells arose through symbiosis between protoplasm and chromatin, and that the chromatin elements were primitively independent, living symbiotically with protoplasm. The more probable view is that of Wilson, that chromatin and protoplasm are coexistent in cells

[1] Kohl, F. G., 1903. [2] Phillips, O. P., 1904. [3] Olive, E. W., 1904.
[4] Minchin, E. A., 1916, p. 32.

from the earliest known stages, in the bacteria and even probably in the ultramicroscopic forms.

The development of the cell theory after its enunciation in 1838 by Schleiden and Schwann followed first the differentia-

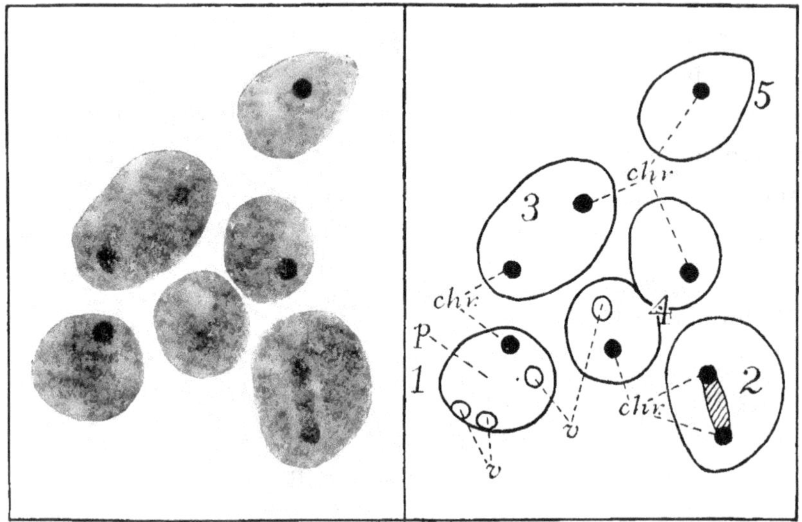

FIG. 12. PROTOPLASM (GRAY) AND CHROMATIN (BLACK) OF *Amœba*, A TYPICAL PROTOZOAN.

A group of six specimens of *Amœba limax* magnified 1000 diameters; *p*=protoplasm; *chr.*=chromatin substance of nucleus; *v*=vacuoles.

1 and 5. Two amœbæ with the chromatin nucleus (*chr.*) in the "resting stage."
2. An amœba with the chromatin nucleus dividing into two chromatin nuclei.
3. A parent amœba with chromatin nuclei completely separated.
4. Protoplasm and chromatin nuclei separated to form two young amœbæ.

After a photograph by Gary N. Calkins.

tion of protoplasmic structure in the cellular tissues (histology). Since 1880 it has taken a new direction in investigating the *chemical and functional separation of the chromatin.* As protoplasm is now known to be the *expression*, so chromatin is now known to be the *seat* of heredity which Nägeli (1884) was the first to discuss as having a physicochemical basis; the "idioplasm" postulated in his theory being realized in the actual

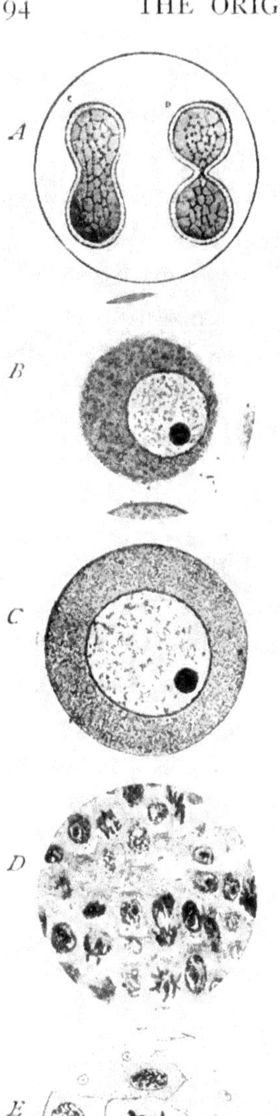

structure of the chromatin as developed in the researches of Hertwig, Strasburger, Kölliker, and Weismann, who independently and almost simultaneously (1884, 1885) were led to the conclusion that the nucleus of the cell contains the physical basis of inheritance and that the chromatin is its essential constituent.[1] In the development from unicellular (Protozoa) into multicellular (Metazoa) organisms the chromatin is distributed through the nuclei to all the cells of the body, but Boveri has demonstrated that all the body-cells lose a portion of their chromatin and only the germ-cells retain the entire ancestral heritage.

Chemically, the most characteristic peculiarity of chromatin (Fig. 13), as

[1] Wilson, E. B., 1906, p. 403.

Fig. 13. The Two Structural Components of the Living World.

Protoplasm or cytoplasm represents the *chief visible form* or substance of the cell in the growing condition. Chromatin is the *chief visible centre* of heredity; there are doubtless other visible and invisible centres of energy concerned in heredity.

Protoplasm (grayish dotted areas) and Chromatin (black, waving rods, threads, crescents, and paired spindles) in single cells (*A–C*) and in clusters of cells (*D, E*).

A. *Achromatium*, bacteria-like organisms with network of chromatin threads and dots.

B, *C*. Single-cell eggs in the ovaries of a sea-urchin (resting stage), the chromatin concentrated into a small black sphere within the nucleolus (inner circle).

D. Many cells in the root-tip of an onion. Chromatin (division stage) in black, wavy lines and threads.

E. Many cells in the embryo of the giant redwood-tree of California. Chromatin (division stage) in black, waving rods, threads, crescents, and spindles. The cell boundaries in thin black lines and the dotted protoplasm are clearly shown. After Lawson.

contrasted with protoplasm, is its phosphorus content.[1] It is also distinguished by a strong affinity for certain stains which cause its scattered or collected particles to appear intensely dark (Fig. 13, *A–E*). Nuclein, which is probably identical with chromatin, is a complex albuminoid substance rich in phosphorus. The chemical, or molecular and atomic, constitution of chromatin infinitely exceeds in complexity that of any other form of matter or energy known. As intimated above (pp. 6, 77), it not improbably contains undetected chemical elements. Experiments made by Oskar, Gunther, and Paula Hertwig (1911–1914) resulted in the conclusion that in cells exposed to radium rays the seat of injury is chiefly, if not exclusively, in the chromatin:[2] these experiments point also to the separate and distinct chemical constitution of the chromatin.

The principle formulated by Cuvier, that the distinctive property of life is the maintenance of the individual specific form throughout the incessant changes of matter which occur in the inflow and outflow of energy, acquires wider scope in the law of the continuity of the germ-plasm (*i. e.*, chromatin) announced by Weismann in 1883, for it is in the heredity-chromatin[3] that the ideal form is not only preserved, but through subdivision carried into the germ-cells of all the present and succeeding generations.

It would appear, according to this interpretation, that the continuity of life since it first appeared in Archæozoic time is the continuity of the physicochemical energies of the chromatin; the development of the individual life is an unfolding of the energies taken within the body under the directing agency

[1] Minchin, E. A., 1916, pp. 18, 19. [2] Richards, A., 1915, p. 291.

[3] The term "chromatin" or "heredity-chromatin" as here used is equivalent to the "germ-plasm" of Weismann or the "stirp" of Galton. It is the *visible centre* of the energy complex of heredity, the larger part of which is by its nature *invisible.* Chromatin, although within our microscopic vision, is to be conceived as a gross manifestation of the infinite energy complex of heredity, which is a cosmos in itself.

FIG. 14. BULK OF CHROMATIN IN SEQUOIA AND TRILLIUM COMPARED.

Chromatin rods in an embryonic cell of the *Sequoia* compared with those in an embryonic cell of the small wood-plant known as the Trinity-flower (*Trillium*). The chromatin of *Sequoia* (*Sc.*), which contains all the characters, potential and casual, of the giant tree, is less in bulk than the chromatin of *Trillium* (*Tc.*).

S. *Sequoia washingtonia*, or *gigantea*, the Big Tree of California. The tree known as "General Sherman," shown here, is $270\frac{9}{10}$ feet high above ground, its largest circumference is $102\frac{3}{5}$ feet, and its greatest diameter is $36\frac{1}{2}$ feet.

Sc. Part of the germ cell of the nearly allied species, *Sequoia sempervirens*, the redwood, with the darkly stained chromatin rods in the centre. About 1,000 times actual size. The redwood is but little inferior in size to the "Big Tree." After Goodspeed.

T. *Trillium*.

Tc. Part of the germ cell of *Trillium sessile*, showing the darkly stained chromatin rods in the same phase and with the same magnification as in the cell of *Sequoia*. After Goodspeed.

of the chromatin; and the evolution of life is essentially the evolution of the chromatin energies. It is in the inconceivable physicochemical complexity of the microscopic specks of chromatin that life presents its most marked contrast to any of the phenomena observed within the lifeless world.

Although each organism has its specific constant in the cubic content of its chromatin, the bulk of this content bears little relation to the size of the individual. This is illustrated by a comparison of the chromatin content of the cell-nucleus of *Trillium*, a plant about sixteen inches high, with that of *Sequoia sempervirens*, the giant redwood-tree of California, which reaches a height of from 200 to 340 feet[1] and attains an age of several thousand years (Fig. 14); we observe that the chromatin bulk in *Sequoia* is apparently less than that in *Trillium*.

The chromatin content of such a nucleus is measured by the bulk of the chromosome rods of which it is composed. In the sea-urchin the size of the sperm-nucleus, the most compact type of chromatin, has been estimated as about 1/100,000,000 of a cubic millimetre, or 10 cubic microns, in bulk.[2] Within such a chromatin bulk there is yet ample space for an incalculable number of minute particles of matter. According to the figures given by Rutherford[3] in the first Hale Lecture the diameter of the sphere of action of an atom is about 1/100,000,000

[1] Jepson, Willis Linn, 1911, p. 23. [2] E. B. Wilson, letter of June 28, 1916.

[3] It is necessary, observes Rutherford, to be cautious in speaking of the diameter of an atom, for it is not at all certain that the actual atomic structure is nearly so extensive as the region through which the atomic forces are appreciable. The hydrogen atom is the lightest known to science, and the average diameter of an atom is about 1/100,000,000 of a centimetre; but the negatively charged particles known as electrons are about 1/1800 of the mass of the hydrogen atom. . . . These particles travel with enormous velocities of from 10,000 to 100,000 miles a second. . . . The alpha particles produce from the neutral molecules a large number of negatively charged particles called ions. The ionization due to these alpha particles is measurable. . . . In the phosphorescence of an emanation of pure radium the atoms throw off the alpha particles with velocities of 10,000 miles a second, and each second five billion alpha particles are projected.—Rutherford, Sir Ernest, 1915, pp. 113, 128.

of a centimetre, or 1/10,000,000 of a millimetre, or 1/10,000 of a micron—the unit of microscopic measurement. The electrons released from atoms of matter are only 1/1800 of the mass of the hydrogen atom, the lightest known to science, and thus the mass of an electron would be only 1/18,000,000 of a micron.

These figures help us in some measure to conceive of the chromatin as a microcosm made up of an almost unlimited number of mutually acting, reacting, and interacting particles; but while we know the heredity-chromatin to be the physical basis of inheritance and the presiding genius of all phases of development, we cannot form the slightest conception of the mode in which the chromatin speck of the germ cell controls the destinies of *Sequoia gigantea* and lays down all the laws of its being for its long life period of five thousand years.

In observing the trunk of "General Sherman" (Fig. 14), the largest and oldest living thing known, one finds that an active regeneration of the bark and woody layers is still in progress, tending to heal scars caused by fire many centuries ago. This regeneration is attributable to the action of the heredity-chromatin in the plant tissues.

We are equally ignorant as to how the chromatin responds to the actions, reactions, and interactions of the body cells, of the life environment, and of the physical environment, so as to call forth a new adaptive character,[1] unless it be through some infinitely complex system of chemical messengers and other catalytic agencies (p. 77). Yet in pursuing the history of the evolution of life upon the earth we may constantly keep before us our fundamental biologic law[2] that the causes of evolution are to be sought within four complexes of energies, which are partly visible and partly invisible, namely:

[1] Wilson, E. B., 1906, p. 434. [2] Osborn, H. F., 1912.2.

1. Physicochemical energies in the evolution of the physical environment;
2. Physicochemical energies in the individual development of the organism, namely, of its protoplasm controlled and directed by its chromatin;
3. Physicochemical energies in the evolution of the heredity-chromatin with its constant addition of new powers and energies;
4. Physicochemical energies in the evolution of the life environment, beginning with the protocellular chemical organisms, and such intermediate organisms as bacteria, and followed by such cellular and multicellular organisms as the higher plants and animals.

Selection and Elimination

Incessant competition, selection, intraselection (Roux), and elimination between all parts of organisms in their chromatin energies, in their protoplasmic energies, and in their actions, reactions, and interactions with the living environment and with the physical environment.

Chlorophyll and the Energy of Sunlight

As bacteria seek their energy in the geosphere and hydrosphere, chlorophyll is the agent which connects life with the atmosphere, disrupting and collecting the carbon from its union with oxygen in carbon dioxide. The utilization of the energy of sunlight in the capture of carbon from the atmosphere through the agency of chlorophyll in algæ marked the second great phase in the evolution of life, following the first bacterial phase. This capture of atmospheric carbon, the chief energy element of plants, always takes place in the presence of sunlight; while the chief energy elements of bacteria, nitrogen and (less frequently) carbon, are captured through molecule-splitting in the presence of heat, but without the powerful aid of sunlight.

It is the metamorphosed, fossilized tissue of plants which leads us to the conclusion that the agency of chlorophyll is also extremely ancient. Near the base of the Archæan rocks[1] graphites, possibly formed from fossilized plant tissue, are observed in the Grenville series and in the Adirondacks. The very oldest metamorphosed sedimentaries are mainly composed of shales containing carbon which may have been deposited by plants.

As a reservoir of life energy which is liberated by oxidation, hydrogen exceeds any other element in the heat it yields, namely, 34.5 calories per gram, while carbon yields 8.1 calories per gram.[2] Since the carbohydrates constitute the basal energy-supply of the entire plant and animal world,[3] we may, with reference to the laws of action and reaction, examine the process even more closely than we have done above (p. 51). The results of the most recent researches are presented by Wager:[4]

"The plant organ responds to the directive influence of light by a curvature which places it either in a direct line with the rays of light, as in grass seedlings, or at right angles to the light, as in ordinary foliage leaves." "Of the light that falls upon a green leaf a part is reflected from its surface, a part is transmitted, and another part is absorbed. That which is reflected and transmitted gives to the leaf its green color; that which is absorbed, consisting of certain red, blue, and violet rays, is the source of the energy by means of which the leaf is enabled to carry on its work.

"The extraordinary molecular complexity of chlorophyll has recently been made clear to us by the researches of Willstätter and his pupils; Usher and Priestley and others have shown us something of what takes place in chlorophyll when light acts upon it; and we are now beginning to realize more fully what a very complex photosensitive system the chlorophyll must

[1] Pirsson, Louis V., and Schuchert, Charles, 1915, p. 545.
[2] Henderson, Lawrence J., 1913, p. 245.
[3] Moore, F. J., 1915, p. 213.
[4] Wager, Harold, 1915, p. 468.

be, and how much has yet to be accomplished before we can picture to our minds with any degree of certainty the changes that take place when light is absorbed by it. But the evidence afforded by the action of light upon other organic compounds, especially those which, like chlorophyll, are fluorescent, and the conclusion according to modern physics teaching that we may regard it as practically certain that the first stage in any photochemical reaction consists in the separation, either partial or complete, of negative electrons under the influence of light, leads us to conjecture that, when absorbed by chlorophyll, the energy of the light-waves becomes transformed into the energy of electrified particles, and that this initiates a whole train of chemical reactions resulting in the building up of the complex organic molecules which are the ultimate products of the plant's activity."

Chlorophyll absorbs most vigorously the rays between *B* and *C* of the solar spectrum,[1] which are the most energizing; the effect of the rays between *D* and *E* is minimal; while the rays beyond *F* again become effective. As compared with the primitive bacteria in which nitrogen figures so largely, chlorophyllic plant tissues consist chiefly of carbon, hydrogen, and oxygen, the chief substance being cellulose ($C_6H_{10}O_5$),[2] while in some cases small amounts of nitrogen are found, and also mineral substances—potassium, magnesium, phosphorus, sulphur, and manganese. Chlorophyllic algal life is thus in contrast with bacterial life, the prime function of which is to capture nitrogen.

Evolution of the Algæ

Closest to the bacteria in their visible structure are the so-called "blue-green algæ" or Cyanophyceæ, found almost every-

[1] Loeb, Jacques, 1906, p. 115.
[2] Pirsson, Louis V., and Schuchert, Charles, 1915, p. 164.

where in fresh and salt water and even in hot springs, as well as on damp soil, rocks, and bark. The characteristic color of the Red Sea is due to a free-floating form of these blue-green algæ, which in this case are red. Unlike the true algæ, the cell-nucleus of the Cyanophyceæ ordinarily is not sharply limited by a membrane, and there is no evidence of distinct chlorophyll bodies, although chlorophyll is present. In the simpler of the unicellular Cyanophyceæ the only method of reproduction is that known as vegetative multipli-

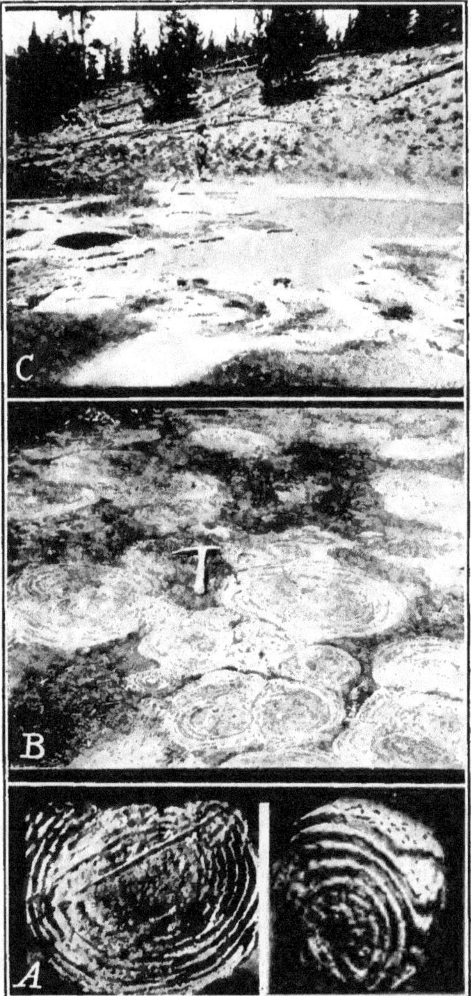

FIG. 15. FOSSIL AND LIVING ALGÆ COMPARED

C. A living algal pool colony near the Great Fountain Geyser, Yellowstone Park. After Walcott.

B. Fossil calcareous algæ, *Cryptozoon proliferum* Hall, from the Cryptozoon Ledge in Lester Park near Saratoga Springs, N. Y. These algæ, which are among the oldest plants of the earth, grew in cabbage-shaped heads on the bottom of the ancient Cambrian sea and deposited lime in their tissue. The ledge has been planed down by the action of a great glacier which cut the plants across, showing their concentric interior structure. Photographed by H. P. Cushing.

A. Fossil algæ, *Newlandia concentrica*, *Newlandia frondosa*, from the Algonkian Belt Series of Montana. After Walcott.

cation, in which an ordinary working cell (individual) divides to form two new individuals. In certain of the higher forms, in which there is some differentiation of connected cells and in which we seem justified in considering the "individual" to be multicellular, multiplication is accomplished through the agency of cells of special character known as the spores. No evidences of sexual reproduction have been observed in the Cyanophyceæ. The sinter deposits of hot springs and geysers in Yellowstone Park are attributed to the presence of Cyanophyceæ.[1]

With the appearance of the true algæ the earth-forming powers of life become still more manifest, and few geologic discoveries of recent times are more important than those growing out of the recognition of algæ as earth-forming agents. As early as 1831 Lyell remarked their rock-forming powers. It is now known that there are formations in which the algæ rank first among the various lower organisms concerned in earth-building. In a forthcoming work by F. W. Clarke and W. C. Wheeler, they remark upon these earth-building activities as follows: "The calcareous algæ are so important as reef-builders that, although they are not marine invertebrates in the ordinary acceptance of the term, it seemed eminently proper to include them in this investigation. In many cases they far outrank the corals in importance, and of late years much attention has been paid to them. On the atoll of Funafuti, for example, the algæ *Lithothamnium* and *Halimeda* rank first and second in importance, followed by the foraminifera, third, and the corals, fourth."

Algæ are probably responsible for the formation of the very ancient limestones; those of the Grenville series at the very base of the pre-Cambrian are believed to be over 60,000,000 years of age. The algal flora of the relatively recent Al-

[1] Coulter, John Merle, 1910, pp. 10–14.

gonkian time,[1] together with calcareous bacteria, developed the massive limestones of the Tetons. Clarke observes: "We are now beginning to see where the magnesia of the limestones comes from and the algæ are probably the most important contributors of that constituent."

Thus representatives of the Rhodophyceæ contribute as high as 87 per cent of calcium carbonate and 25 per cent of magnesium carbonate. Species of *Halimeda*, however, calcified algæ belonging to the very different class Chlorophyceæ, are important agents in reef-building and land-forming, yet are almost non-magnesian.[2]

The Grenville series at the base of the Palæozoic is essentially calcareous, with a thickness of over 94,000 feet, nearly eighteen miles, more than half of which is calcareous.[3] Thus it appears probable that the surface of the primordial continental seas swarmed with these minute algæ, which served as the chief food magazine for the floating Protozoa; but it is very important to note that algal life is absolutely dependent upon phosphorus and other earth-borne constituents of sea-water, as well as upon nitrogen, also earth-borne, and due to bacterial action; for where the denitrifying bacteria rob the sea-water of its nitrogen content the algæ are much less numerous.[4] Silica is also an earth-borne, though mineral, constituent of sea-water which forms the principal skeletal constituent of the shells of diatoms, minute floating plants especially characteristic of the cooler seas, which form the siliceous ooze of the sea-bottoms.

[1] Walcott, Charles D., 1914.
[2] M. A. Howe, letter of February 24, 1916.
[3] Pirsson, Louis V., and Schuchert, Charles, 1915, pp. 545, 546.
[4] *Op. cit.*, p. 104.

Some Physicochemical Contrasts Between Plant and Animal Evolution

In their evolution, while there is a continuous specialization and differentiation of the modes of obtaining energy, plants may not attain a higher chemical stage than that observed among the bacteria and algæ, except in the parasitic forms which feed both upon plant and animal compounds. In the energy which they derive from the soil plants continue to be closely dependent upon bacteria, because they derive their nitrogen from nitrates generated by bacteria and absorbed along with water by the roots. In reaching out into the air and sunlight the chlorophyllic organs differentiate into the marvellous variety of leaf forms, and these in turn are supported upon stems and branches which finally lead into the creation of woody tissues and the clothing of the earth with forests. Through the specialization of leaves in connection with the germ-cells flowers are developed, and plants establish a marvellous series of balanced relations with their life environment, first with the developing insect life, and finally with the developing bird life.

The main lines of the ascent and classification of plants are traced by palæobotanists partly from their structural evolution, which is almost invariably adapted to keep their chlorophyllic organs in the sunlight[1] in competition with other plants, and partly from the evolution of their reproductive organs, which pass through the primitive spore stage into various forms of sexuality, with, finally, the development of the seed habit and the dominance of the sporophyte.[2] It is a striking peculiarity of plants that the powers of motion evolve chiefly in connection with their reproductive activities, namely, with

[1] Wager, Harold, 1915, p. 408. [2] M. A. Howe.

the movements of the germ cells. We follow the development of a great variety of automatic migrating organs, especially in the seed and embryonic stages, by which the germs, or chromatin bearers, are mechanically propelled through the air or water. Plants are otherwise dependent on the motion of the atmosphere and of animals to which they become attached for the migration of their germs and embryos and of their adult forms into favorable conditions of environment. In these respects and in their fundamentally different sources of energy they present the widest contrast to animal evolution.

In the absence of a nervous system the remarkable actions and reactions to environmental stimuli which plants exhibit are purely of a physicochemical nature. The interactions between different tissues of plants, which become extraordinarily complex in the higher and larger forms, are probably sustained through catalysis and the circulation through the tissues of chemical messengers analogous to the enzymes, hormones (accelerators), and chalones (retarders) of the animal circulation. It is a very striking feature of plant development and evolution that, although entirely without the coordinating agency of a nervous system, all parts are kept in a condition of perfect correlation. This fact is consistent with the comparatively recent discovery that a large part of the coordination of animal organs and tissues which was formerly attributed to the nervous system is now known to be catalytic.

Throughout the evolution of plants the fundamental distinctions between the heredity-chromatin and the body-protoplasm are sustained exactly as among animals.

It would appear from the researches of de Vries[1] and other botanists that the sudden hereditary alterations of plant structure and function which may be known as *mutations of de*

[1] De Vries, Hugo, 1901, 1903, 1905.

Vries[1] are of more general occurrence among plants than among animals. Such mutations are attributable to sudden alterations of molecular and atomic constitution in the heredity-chromatin, or to the altered forms of energy supplied to the chromatin during development. Sensitiveness to the biochemical reactions of the physical environment should theoretically be more evident in organisms like plants which derive their energy directly from inorganic compounds that are constantly changing their chemical formulæ with the conditions of moisture, of aridity, of temperature, of chemical soil content, than in organisms like animals which secure their food compounds ready-made by the plants and possessing comparatively similar and stable chemical formulæ. Thus a plant transferred from one environment to another may exhibit much more sudden and profound changes than an animal, for the reason that all the sources of plant energy are profoundly changed while the sources of animal energy in a new environment are only slightly changed. The highly varied chemical sources of plant energy are in striking contrast with the comparatively uniform sources of animal energy which are primarily the starches, sugars, and proteins formed by the plants.

In respect to *character origin,* or the appearance of new characters, therefore, plants may in accordance with the de Vries mutation hypothesis exhibit discontinuity or sudden changes of form and function more frequently than animals. In respect to *character coordination,* or the harmonious relations of all their parts, plants are inferior to animals only in their sole dependence on catalytic chemical messengers, while animal characters are coordinated both through catalytic chemical messengers and through the nervous system.

In respect to *character velocity,* or the relative rates of move-

[1] As distinguished from the earlier defined *Mutations of Waagen* (see p. 138).

ment of different parts of plants in individual development and in evolution, plants appear to agree very closely with animals. In both we observe that some characters *evolve* more rapidly or more slowly than others in geologic time; also that some characters *develop* more rapidly or slowly than others in the course of individual growth. This may be termed character motion or character velocity.

This law of changes in character velocity, both in individual development (ontogeny) and in racial evolution (phylogeny), is one of the most mysterious and difficult to understand in the whole order of biologic phenomena. One character is hurried forward so that it appears in earlier and earlier stages of individual development (Hyatt's law of acceleration), while another is held back so that it appears in later and later stages (Hyatt's law of retardation). Osborn has also pointed out that corresponding characters have different velocities in different lines of descent—a character may evolve very rapidly in one line and very slowly in another. This is distinctively a heredity-chromatin phenomenon, although visible in protoplasmic form. Among plants it is illustrated by the recent observations of Coulter on the relative time of appearance of the archegonia in the two great groups of gymnosperms (*i. e.*, naked-seeded plants), the Cycads (sago-palms, etc.) and the Conifers (pines, spruces, etc.), as follows: In the Cycads, which are confined to warmer climates, the belated appearance of the archegonium persists; in the Conifers, in adaptation to colder climates and the shortened reproductive season, the appearance of the archegonium is thrust forward into the early embryonic stages. Finally, in the flowering plants (Angiosperms) with their brief reproductive season, the forward movement of the archegonium continues until the third cellular stage of the embryo is reached. This is but one illustration among hundreds which might be chosen to show how character velocity in plants follows exactly the same laws as in animals, namely, characters are accelerated or retarded in race evolution and in individual development in adaptation to the environmental and individual needs of the organism.

We shall see this mysterious law of character velocity beautifully illustrated among the vertebrates, where of two characters, lying side by side, one exhibits inertia, the other momentum.

It is difficult to resist the speculation that character velocity in individual development and in evolution is also a phenomenon of physicochemical interaction in some way connected with and under the control of chemical messengers which are circulating in the system.

PART II. THE EVOLUTION OF ANIMAL FORM

CHAPTER IV

THE ORIGINS OF ANIMAL LIFE AND EVOLUTION OF THE INVERTEBRATES

Evolution of single-celled animals or Protozoa. Evolution of many-celled animals or Metazoa. Pre-Cambrian and Cambrian forms of Invertebrates. Reactions to climatic and other environmental changes of geologic time. The mutations of Waagen.

A prime biochemical characteristic in the origin of animal life is the derivation of energy neither directly from the water, from the earth, nor from the earth's or sun's heat, as in the most primitive bacterial stages; nor from sunshine, as in the chlorophyllic stage of plant life; but from its stored form in the bacterial and plant world. All animal life is chemically dependent upon bacterial and plant life.

Many of the single-celled animals like the single-celled bacteria and plants appear to act, react, and interact directly with their lifeless and life environment, their protoplasm being relatively so simple. We do not know how far this action, reaction, and interaction affects the protoplasm only, and how far it affects both protoplasm and chromatin. It would seem as if even at this early stage of evolution the organism-protoplasm was sensitive while the heredity-chromatin was relatively insensitive to environment, stable, and as capable of conserving and reproducing hereditary characters true to type as in the many-celled animals in which the heredity-chromatin is deeply buried within the tissues of the organism remote from direct environmental reactions.

Evolution of Single-Celled Animals or Protozoa

We have no idea when the first unicellular animals known as Protozoa appeared. Since the Protozoa feed freely upon bacteria, it is possible they may have evolved during the bacterial epoch; it is known that Protozoa are at present one of the limiting factors of bacterial activity in the soil, and it is even claimed[1] that they have a material effect on the fertility of the soil through the consumption of nitrifying bacteria.

On the other hand, it may be that the Protozoa appeared during the algal epoch or subsequent to the chlorophyllic plant organisms which now form the primary food supply of the freely floating and swimming protozoan types. A great number of primitive flagellates are saprophytic, using only dissolved proteids as food.[2]

Apart from the parasitic mode of deriving their energy, even the lowest forms of animal life are distinguished both in the embryonic and adult stages by their locomotive powers. Heliotropic or sun reactions, or movements toward sunlight, are manifested at an early stage of animal evolution. In this function there appear to be no boundaries between animals and the motile spores, gametes, and seedlings of certain plants.[3] As cited by Loeb and Wasteneys, Paul Bert in 1869 discovered that the little water-flea *Daphnia* swims toward the light in all parts of the visible spectrum, but most rapidly in the yellow or in the green. More definitely, Loeb observes that there are two particular regions of the spectrum, the rays of which are especially effective in causing organisms to turn, or to congregate, toward them; these regions lie (1) in the blue, in the

[1] Russell, Edward John, and Hutchinson, Henry Brougham, 1909, p. 118; 1913, pp. 191, 219.

[2] Gary N. Calkins.

[3] Loeb, Jacques, and Wasteneys, Hardolph, 1915.1, pp. 44–47; 1915.2, pp. 328–330.

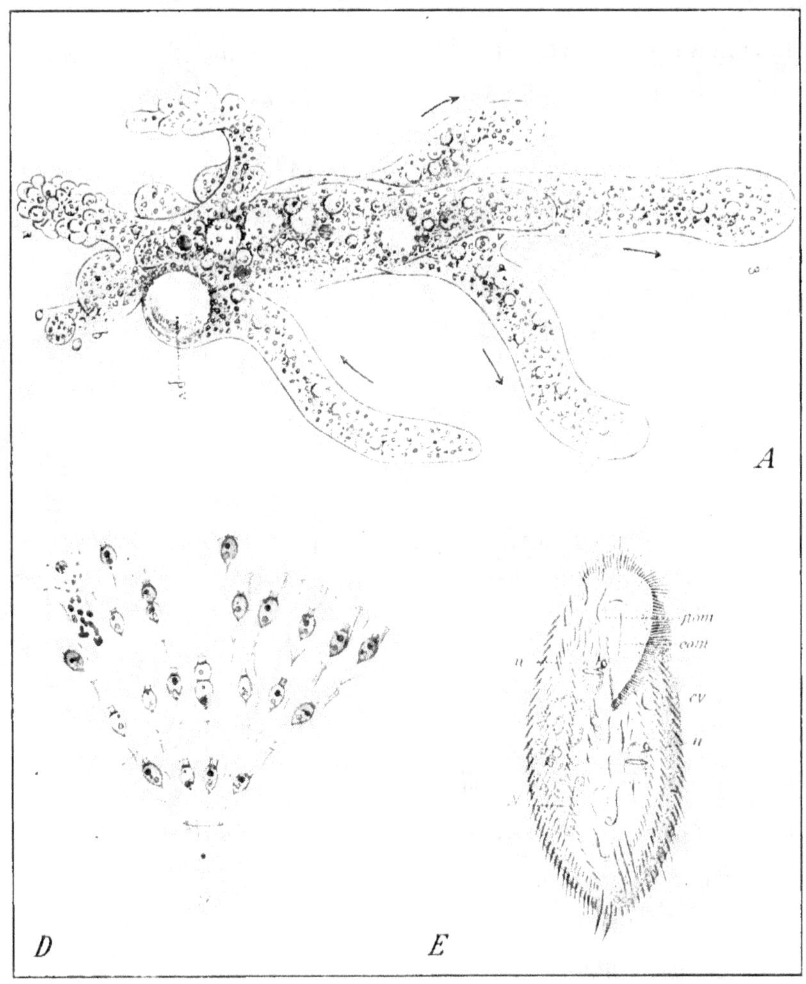

Fig. 16. Typical Forms of Protozoa or Single-Celled Organisms.

A. *Amœba proteus*, one of the soft, unprotected, jelly-like organisms which rank among the simplest known animals. They are continually changing form by thrusting out or withdrawing the lobe-like projections known as pseudopodia, which are temporary prolongations of the cell-body for purposes of locomotion or food capture. Any part of the body may serve for the purpose of food ingestion, which is accomplished by simply extending the body so as to surround the food. Magnified 200 times life-size. After Leidy.

D. A colony of flagellates or Mastigophora, showing a number of individuals in various stages of their life history. They are distinguished by one or more whip-like prolongations which serve chiefly for purposes of locomotion. As contrasted with the *Amœba*, many of the flagellates have definite, characteristic body forms, and have the function of food ingestion limited to a special area of the body. Magnified 285 times life-size. Photographed from a model in the American Museum.

E. A typical ciliate, one of the most highly organized single-celled forms, distinguished by a multitude of fine hair-like cilia, distributed over the whole or a part of the body, which are used for locomotion and for the capture of food. In some forms these cilia are grouped or specialized for further effectiveness. After Bütschli Magnified 180 times life-size.

neighborhood of a wave-length of 477 $\mu\mu$, and (2) in the yellowish-green, in the region of $\lambda = 534\ \mu\mu$; and these two wave-lengths affect different organisms, with no very evident relation to the nature of these latter. Thus the blue rays (of 477 $\mu\mu$) attract the protozoan flagellate *Euglena*, the hydroid

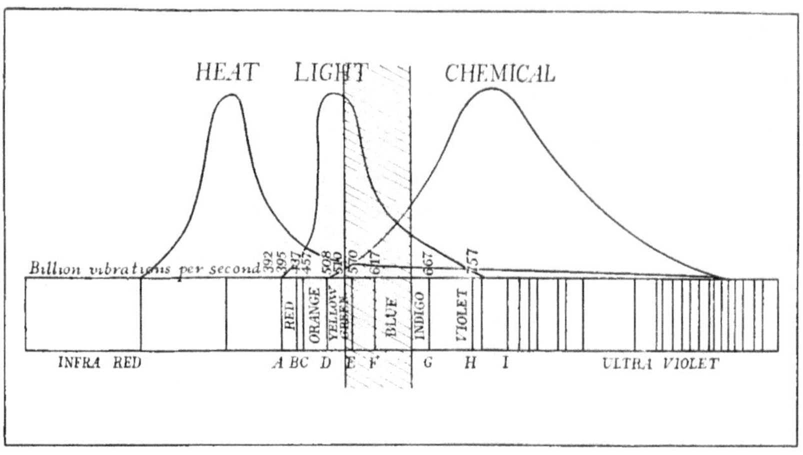

FIG. 17. LIGHT, HEAT, AND CHEMICAL INFLUENCE OF THE SUN.

Diagram showing the increase, maximum, and decrease of heat, light, and chemical energy derived from the sun. The shaded area represents that portion of the spectrum included in the phosphorescent light emitted by our common fire-flies. It is probable that it corresponds more closely with the light sensitiveness of the fire-fly's eye than with that of the human eye as represented by the wave marked "Light." After Ulric Dahlgren.

cœlenterate *Eudendrium*, and the seedlings of oats; while the yellowish-green rays (of 534 $\mu\mu$) in turn affect the protozoan *Chlamydomonas*, the crustacean *Daphnia*, and the crustacean larvæ of barnacles.

Aside from these heliotropic movements which they share with plants, animals show higher powers of individuality, of initiation, of experiment, and of what Jennings cautiously terms "a conscious aspect of behavior." In his remarkable studies this author traces the genesis of animal behavior to reaction and trial. Thus the behavior of organisms is of such a character as to provide for its own development. Through the principle of the production of varied movements and that of the resolution of one physiological state into another, anything that is possible is tried and anything that turns out to be advantageous is held and made permanent.[1] Thus the subpsychic stages when they evolve into the higher stages give us the rudiments of discrimination, of choice, of attention, of desire for food, of sensitiveness to pain, and also give us the foundation of the psychic properties of habit, of memory, and of consciousness.[2] These profound and extremely ancient powers of animal life exert indirectly a *creative influence* on animal form, whether we adopt the Lamarckian or Darwinian explanation of the origin of animal form, or find elements of truth in both explanations.[3] The reason is that choice, discrimination, attention, desire for food, and other psychic powers are constantly acting on individual development and directing its course. Such action in turn controls the habits and migrations of animals, which finally influence the laws of *adaptive radiation*[4] and of selection. In this indirect way these psychic powers are creative of new form and new function.

In the evolution of the Protozoa[5] the starting-point is a simple cell consisting of a small mass of protoplasm containing a nucleus within which lies the heredity-chromatin (Fig. 12). This passes into the plasmodial condition of the *Rhizopods*, in which the protoplasm increases enormously to form the relatively large, unprotected masses adapted to

[1] Jennings, H. S., 1906, pp. 318, 319.

[2] *Op. cit.*, pp. 329–335.

[3] These two explanations are fully set forth below (see pp. 143–146) in the introduction to the evolution of the vertebrates.

[4] *Adaptive radiation*—the development of widely divergent forms in animals ancestrally of the same stock or of related stocks, as a result of bodily adaptation to widely different environments (see p. 157).

[5] Minchin, E. A., 1916, p. 277.

the creeping or semiterrestrial mode of life. From these evolve the forms specialized for the floating pelagic habit, namely, the *Foraminifera* and *Radiolaria*, protected by an excessive development and elaboration of their skeletal structures.[1] Less cautious observers[2] than Jennings find in the

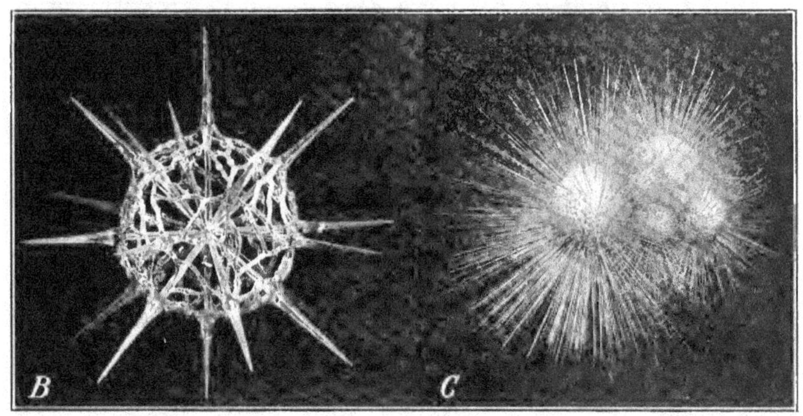

FIG. 18. SKELETONS OF TYPICAL PROTOZOA.

B. Siliceous skeleton or shell of a typical radiolarian, *Stauraspis stauracantha* Haeckel, 170 times the actual size. Owing to their vast numbers, these microscopic, glassy skeletons are an appreciable factor in earth-building. A large part of the island of Barbados is formed of radiolarian ooze. Photographed from a model in the American Museum.

C. Calcareous skeleton or shell of a typical foraminifer, *Globigerina bulloides* d'Orbigny, 30 times the actual size. As the animal increases in size it forms successively larger shells adjoining the earlier ones until, as shown in the figure, a cluster of shells of increasing size is formed. The name foraminifer refers to the many minute openings, plainly seen in this figure, through which the pseudopodia can pass. Photographed from a model in the American Museum. (Compare Fig. 16, p. 112.)

Foraminifera the rudiments of the highest functions and the most intelligent behavior of which undifferentiated protoplasm has been found capable. In the *Mastigophora* the body develops flagellate organs of locomotion and food-capture. As an offshoot from the ancestors of these forms arose the *Ciliata*, the most highly organized unicellular types of living beings,

[1] *Op. cit.*, p. 278. [2] Heron-Allen, Edward, 1915, p. 270.

for a Ciliate, like every other protozoan, is a complete and independent organism, and is specialized for each and all of the vital functions performed by the higher multicellular organisms as a whole.

In the chemical life of the Protozoa[1] (*Amœba*) the protoplasm is made up of colloidal and of crystalloidal substances of different density, between which there is a constant, orderly chemical activity. The relative speed of these orderly processes is attributed to specific catalyzers which control each successive step in the long chain of chemical actions. Thus in the breaking-down process (destructive metabolism) the by-products act as poisons to other organisms or they may play an important part in the vital activities of the organism itself, as in the phosphorescence of *Noctiluca*, or as in reproduction and regeneration. Since regrowth or regeneration[2] takes place in artificially separated fragments of cells in which the nuclear substance (chromatin) is believed to be absent, the formation of new parts may be due to a specific enzyme, or perhaps to some chemical body analogous to hormones and formed as a result of mutual interaction of the nucleus and the protoplasm. Reproduction through cell-division is also interpreted theoretically as due to action set up by enzymes or other chemical bodies produced as a result of interaction between the nucleus and cell body. The protoplasm is regenerated, including both the nuclei and the cell-plasm, by the distribution of large quantities of nucleoproteins, the specific chemical substance of chromatin.

The latest word as to the part played by natural selection in the heredity-chromatin is that of Jennings[3] who, after many years of experiment, has proved that the congenital charac-

[1] Calkins, Gary N., 1916, p. 260. [2] *Op. cit.*, pp. 261–264, 266.
[3] Jennings, H. S., 1916, pp. 522–526.

ters arising from the heredity-chromatin are changed by long-continued selection through a great number of generations in the form of slow gradations which would not be revealed by imperfect selection for a few generations. This is doubtless the way in which nature works. In the protozoan known as *Difflugia* the inherited changes produced by selection seem as gradual as could well be observed. Large steps do occur, but much more frequent is the slow alteration of the stock with the passage of generations. The question is asked whether even such slight and seemingly gradual hereditary changes may not really be little jumps or mutations, since all chemical change is discontinuous. In reply, Jennings observes that it is highly probable that every inherited variation does involve a chemical change, for there is no character change so slight that it may not be chemical in nature. In the relatively immense organic molecule, with its thousands of groups, the simple transfer of one atom, one ion, perhaps one electron, is a chemical change and, in this sense, discontinuous even though its effect is below our powers of perception with the most refined instruments.

Through this modern chemical interpretation of the protozoan life cycle we may conceive how the laws of thermodynamics may be applied to single-celled organisms, and especially our fundamental biologic law of action, reaction, and interaction. By far the most difficult problem in biologic evolution is the mode of working of this law among the many-celled organisms (Metazoa) including both invertebrates and vertebrates.

Evolution of Many-Celled Animals or Metazoa

It is possible that during the long period of pre-Cambrian time, which, from the actual thickness of the Canadian pre-Cambrian rocks, is estimated at not less than thirty million years, some of the simpler Protozoa gave rise to the next higher stage of animal evolution and to the adaptive radiation on land and sea of the Invertebrata.

We are compelled to assume that the *physicochemical actions, reactions, and interactions* were sustained and became step by step more complex as the *single-celled* life forms (Protozoa) evolved into organisms with groups of cells (Metazoa), and these into organisms with two chief cell-layers (Cœlenterata), and later into organisms with three chief cell-layers.

Phyla of Fossil Invertebrata

Protozoa,
Porifera,
Cœlenterata,
Molluscoida,
Echinodermata,
Annulata,
Arthropoda,
Mollusca.

The metamorphosis by heat and pressure of the pre-Cambrian rocks has for the most part concealed or destroyed all the life impressions which were undoubtedly made in the various continental or oceanic basins of sedimentation. Indirect evidences of the long process of life evolution are found in the great accumulations of limestone and in the deposits of iron and graphite[1] which, as we have already observed, are considered proofs of the existence at enormously remote periods of limestone-forming algæ, of iron-forming bacteria, and of a variety of chlorophyll-bearing plants. These evidences begin with the metamorphosed sedimentaries overlying the basal rocks of the crust of the primal earth.

Pre-Cambrian and Cambrian Forms of Invertebrates

The discovery by Walcott[2] of a world of highly specialized and diversified invertebrate life in the Middle Cambrian seas completely confirms the prophecy made by Charles Darwin in

[1] Joseph Barrell. See Pirsson, Louis V., and Schuchert, Charles, 1915, p. 547.
[2] Walcott, Charles D., 1911, 1912.

1859[1] as to the great duration that must be assigned to pre-Cambrian time to allow for the evolution of highly specialized life forms.

By Middle Cambrian time the adaptive radiation of the Invertebrata to all the conditions of life—in continental waters,

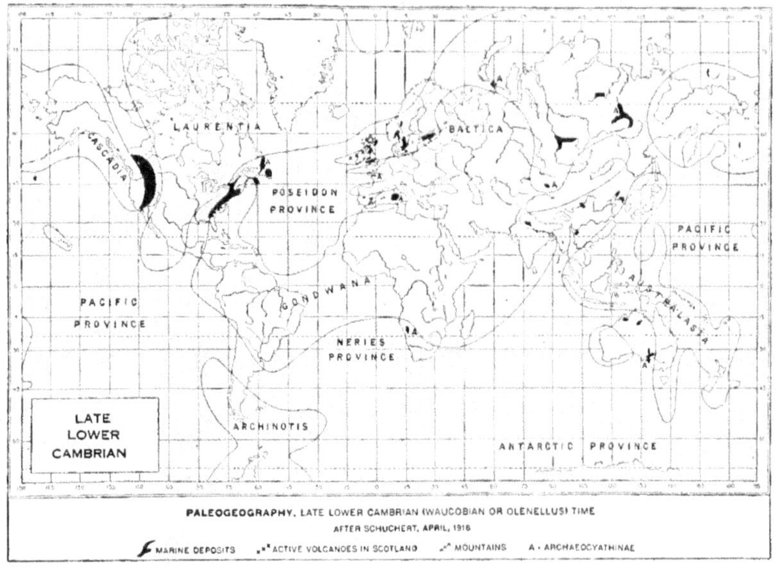

FIG. 19. THEORETIC WORLD ENVIRONMENT IN LATE LOWER CAMBRIAN TIME.

This period corresponds with that of the first well-known marine fauna with trilobites and brachiopods as the dominant forms. No land life of any kind is known, and the climate appears to have been warm and equable the world over. After Schuchert.

along the shore-lines, and in the littoral and pelagic environment of the seas—appears to have been governed by mechanical and chemical principles fundamentally similar to those observed among the Protozoa, but distributed through myriads of cells and highly complicated tissues and organs, instead of being differentiated within a single cell as in the ciliate Protozoa. Among the elaborate functions thus evolved, showing

[1] Darwin, Charles, 1859, pp. 306, 307.

a more complicated system of action, reaction, and interaction with the environment and within the organism, were, first, a more efficient locomotion in the quest of food, in the capture of food, and in the escape from enemies, giving rise in some cases to skeletal structures of various types; second, the evolution of offensive and defensive weapons and armature; third, various chemical modes of offense and defense; fourth, protection and concealment by methods of burrowing.[1]

There are heavy protective coverings for slowly moving and sessile animals. In contrast we find swiftly moving types (*e. g.*, *Sagitta* and other chætognaths) with the lines of modern submarines, whose mechanical means of propulsion resemble those of the most primitive darting fishes. Other types, such as the Crustacea, have skeletal parts for the triple purposes of defense, offense, and locomotion, some being adapted to less swift motion. In Palæozoic time they include the slowly moving, bottom-living, armored types of trilobites. Then there are other slowly moving, bottom-living forms, such as the brachiopods and gastropods, with very dense armature of phosphate and carbonate of lime. Finally, there are pelagic or surface-floating types, such as the jellyfishes, which are chemically protected by the poisonous secretions of their "sting-cells."

This highly varied life of mid-Cambrian time affords abundant evidence that in pre-Cambrian time certain of the invertebrates had already passed through first, second, and even third phases of form in adaptation to as many different life zones.

Our first actual knowledge of such extremely ancient adaptations dates back to the pre-Cambrian and is afforded by Walcott's discovery[2] in the Greyson shales of the Algonkian Belt

[1] R. W. Miner.

[2] Walcott, Charles D., 1899, pp. 235–244.

Series of fragmentary remains of that problematic fossil, *Beltina danai*, which he refers to the Merostomata and near to the eurypterids, thus making it probable that either eurypterids, or forms ancestral both to trilobites and eurypterids existed in pre-Cambrian times. More extensive adaptive radiations are found in the Lower Cambrian life period of *Olenellus*. This trilobite is not primitive but a compound phase of evolution, and represents the highest trilobite development. Trilobites are beautifully preserved as fossils because of their dense chitinous armature, which protected them and at the same time admitted of considerable freedom of motion. The relationships of the trilobites to other invertebrates have long been in dispute, but the discovery of the ventral surface and appendages in the mid-Cambrian *Neolenus serratus* (Fig. 20) seems to place the trilobites definitely as a subclass of the Crustacea, with affinities to the freely swimming phyllopods, which swarm on the surface of the existing oceans.

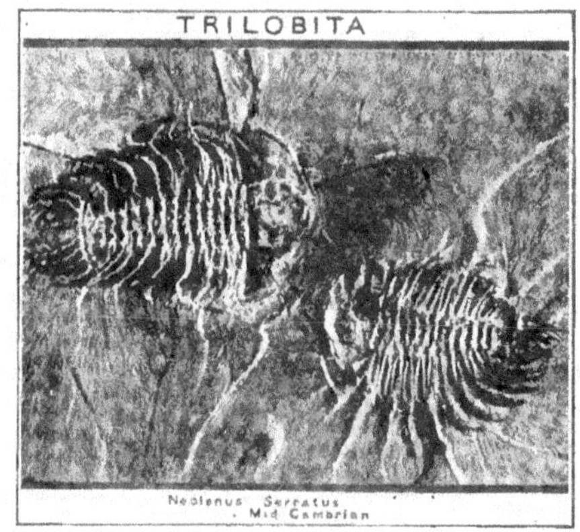

FIG. 20. A MID-CAMBRIAN TRILOBITE.
Neolenus serratus (Rominger). After Walcott.

A most significant biological fact is that certain of the primitively armored and sessile brachiopods of the Cambrian seas have remained almost unchanged generically for a period of nearly thirty million years, down to the present time. These animals afford a classic illustration of the rather exceptional condition known to evolutionists as "balance," resulting in absolute stability of type. One example is found in *Lingulella* (*Lingula*), of which the fossil form, *Lingulella acuminata*, characteristic of Cambrian and Ordovician times, is closely similar to that of *Lingula anatina*, a species living to-day. Representatives of the genus *Lingula* (*Lingulella*) have persisted from Cambrian to Recent times. The great antiquity of the brachiopods as a group is well illustrated by the persistence of *Lingula* (Cambrian—Ordovician—Recent), on the one hand, and of *Terebratula* (Devonian—Recent), belonging to a widely differing family, on the other. These lamp-shells are thus characteristic of all geologic ages, including the present. Reaching their maximum radiation during the Ordovician and Silurian, they gradually lost their importance during the Devonian and Permian, and at the present time have dwindled into a relatively insignificant group, members of which range from the oceanic shore-line to the deep-sea or abyssal habitat.

By the Middle Cambrian the continental seas covered the whole region of the present Cordilleras of the Pacific coast. In the present region of Mount Stephen, B. C., in the unusually favorable marine oily shales of the Burgess formation, the remarkable evolution of invertebrate life prior to Cambrian time has been revealed through Walcott's epoch-making discoveries between 1909 and 1912.[1] It is at once evident (Figs. 20–27) that the seashore and pelagic life of this time exhibits types as widely divergent as those which now occur among the aquatic Invertebrata; in other words, the extremes of invertebrate evolution in the seas were reached some thirty million years ago. Not only are the characteristic external features of these soft-bodied invertebrates evident in the fossil remains, but in some cases (Fig. 22) even the internal organs show through the imprint of the transparent integument. Walcott's researches on this superb series have brought out two important points: First, the great antiquity of the chief

[1] Walcott, Charles D., 1911, 1912.

aquatic invertebrate groups and their high degree of specialization in Early Cambrian times, which makes it necessary to look for their origin far back in the pre-Cambrian ages; and, second, the extraordinary persistence of type, not only among the lamp-shells (brachiopods) but among members of all the invertebrate phyla from the mid-Cambrian to the present

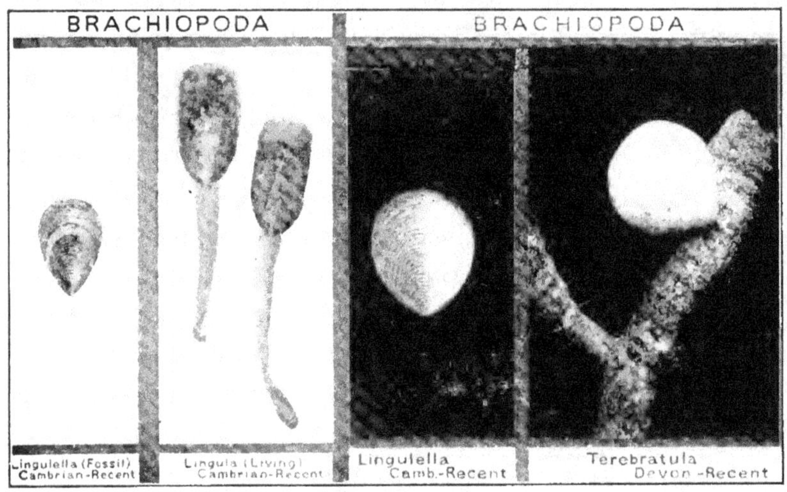

FIG. 21. BRACHIOPODS, CAMBRIAN AND RECENT.

Lingulella (*Lingula*) *acuminata*, a fossil form ranging from Cambrian to Ordovician, and the very similar existing form, *Lingula anatina*, which shows that the genus has persisted from Cambrian times down to the present day.

Lingulella (fossil), Cambrian to Ordovician, contrasted with a living specimen of the widely differing *Terebratula*, which ranges from Devonian to recent times.

time, so that sea forms with an antiquity estimated at twenty-five million years can be placed side by side with existing sea forms with very obvious similarities of function and structure, as in the series arranged for these lectures by Mr. Roy W. Miner, of the American Museum of Natural History (Figs. 21, 22, 24–27).

Except for the trilobites, the existence of Crustacea in Cambrian times was unknown until the discovery of the primitive shrimp-like form, *Burgessia bella* (Fig. 22), a true crustacean, which may be compared with *Apus lucasanus*, a member of the most nearly allied recent group. We observe a close correspondence in the shape of the chitinous shield (carapace), in the arrangement of the leaf-like locomotor appendages at the base of the tail, and in the clear internal impres-

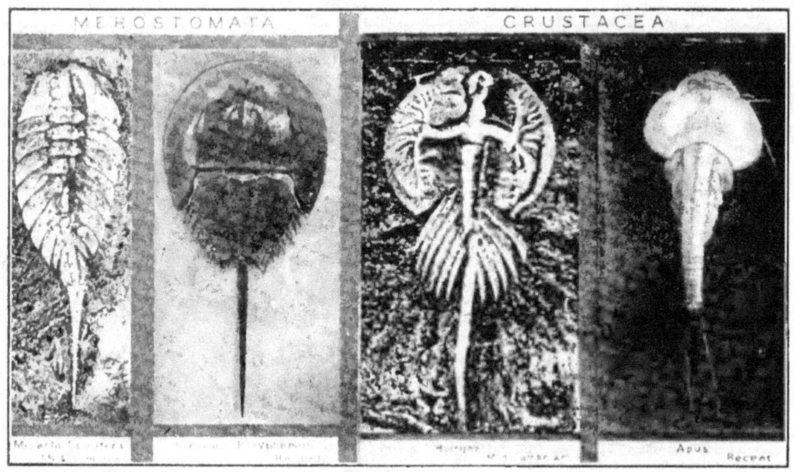

Fig. 22. Horseshoe Crab and Shrimp, Cambrian and Recent.

Molaria spinifera, a mid-Cambrian merostome (after Walcott), compared with the recent "horseshoe crab," *Limulus polyphemus*.

Burgessia bella, a shrimp-like crustacean of the Middle Cambrian (after Walcott), compared with the very similar *Apus lucasanus* of recent times.

sions in *Burgessia* of the so-called "kidneys," with their branched tubules. The position of these organs in *Apus* is indicated by the two light areas on the carapace. Other specimens of *Burgessia* found by Walcott show that the tapering abdominal region and tail are jointed as in *Apus*.

The age of the armored merostome arthropods is also thrust back to mid-Cambrian times by the discovery of several genera of Aglaspidæ, the typical species of which, *Molaria spinifera* Walcott, may be compared with that "living fossil," the horseshoe crab (*Limulus polyphemus*), its nearest modern relative, which is believed to be not so closely related to the phyllopod crustaceans as would at first appear, but rather to the Arachnida through the eurypterids and scorpions. *Molaria* and *Limulus* are strikingly similar in their cephalic shield,

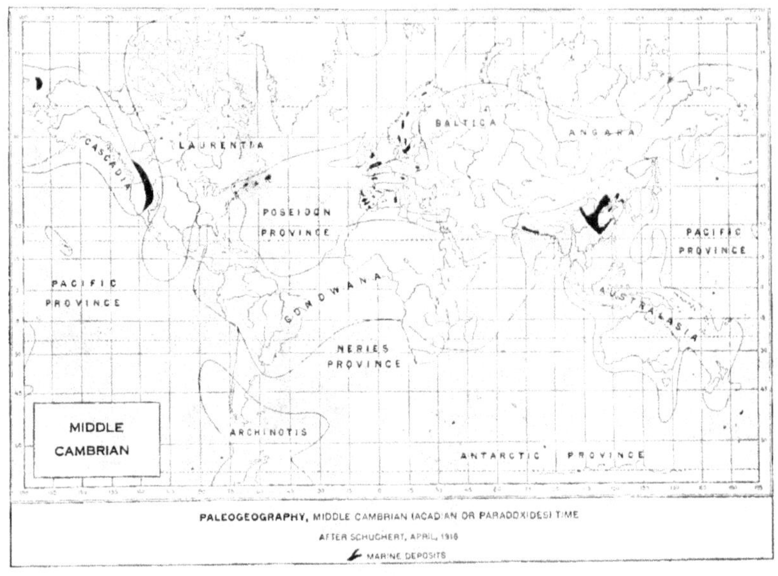

FIG. 23. THEORETIC WORLD ENVIRONMENT IN MIDDLE CAMBRIAN TIME.
The period of the trilobite *Paradoxides*. This shows the theoretic South Atlantic continent "Gondwana" of Suess, connecting Africa and South America.

segmentation, and telson; but the latter shows an advance upon the earlier type in the coalescence of the abdominal segments into a single abdominal shield-plate. The trilobate character of the cephalic shield in *Molaria* is an indication of its trilobite affinities; hence we apparently have good reason to refer both the merostomes and phyllopods to an ancestral trilobite stock.

Another mode of defense is presented by some of the sessile, rock-clinging sea-cucumbers (Holothuroidea) protected not only by their habit of hiding in crevices, but by their leathery epidermis, in which are scattered a number of calcareous plates, as among certain members of the modern edentate mammals. Fossils of this group have been known heretofore only through scattered spicules and calcareous plates dating back no earlier than Carboniferous times (Goodrich); therefore Walcott's holothurian material from the Cambrian constitutes new records for invertebrate palæontology, not only for the preservation of the soft parts, but for the great antiquity of these Cambrian strata. In *Louisella pedunculata* (Fig. 24) we observe the preservation of a double row of tube-feet, and the indication at the top of oral tentacles around the mouth like those of the modern Elpidiidæ. A typical rock-clinging holothurian is the recent *Pentacta frondosa.*

Besides these sessile, rock-clinging forms, the adaptive radiation of the holothurians developed burrowing or fossorial types, an example of which is the mid-Cambrian *Mackenzia costalis* (Fig. 24) which strikingly suggests one of the existing burrowing sea-cucumbers, *Synapta girardii.* The characteristic elongated cylindrical body-form with longitudinal muscle-bands is clearly preserved in the fossil, while around the mouth is a ring of tubercles interpreted by Walcott as calcareous ossicles from above which the oral tentacles have been torn away.

A remarkable and problematic mid-Cambrian fossil, *Eldonia ludwigi* (Fig. 24), is regarded by Walcott as a free-swimming or pelagic animal. It bears a superficial resemblance to a medusa, or jellyfish, while the lines radiating from a central ring suggest the existence of a water vascular system; but the cylindrical body coiled around the centre shows a spiral intestine through its transparent body-wall, and it is therefore considered to be a swimming holothurian, or sea-cucumber, with a medusa-like umbrella. The existing holothuroid *Pelagothuria natatrix* Ludwig, shown at the right, is somewhat analogous,

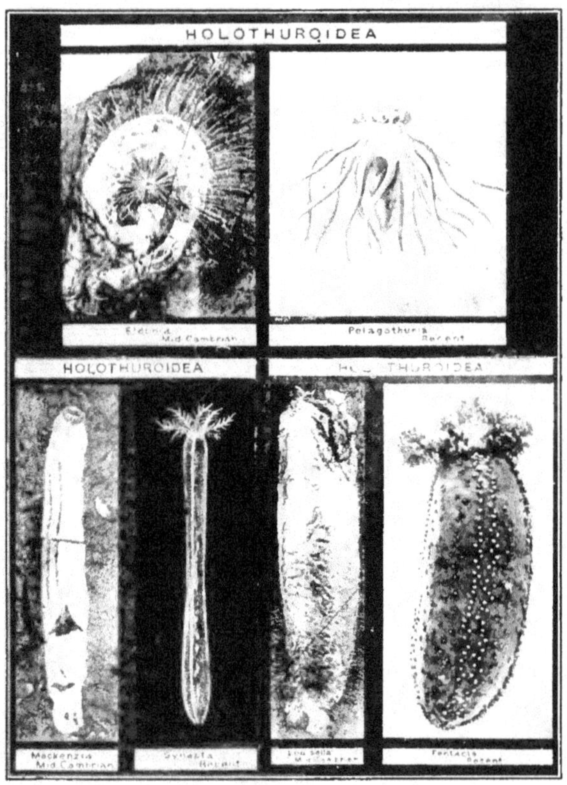

FIG. 24. SEA-CUCUMBERS OF CAMBRIAN AND RECENT SEAS.

Eldonia ludwigi of the mid-Cambrian (after Walcott), regarded as pelagic and somewhat resembling a jellyfish, is thought rather to be a form analogous to *Pelagothuria natatrix*, a swimming sea-cucumber, although it shows wide differences. The mouth of *Pelagothuria* is above the swimming umbrella, the posterior part of the body and the anal opening are below: in the fossil *Eldonia* both mouth and anus hang below. *Mackenzia costalis*, a mid-Cambrian form (after Walcott), strongly resembling the burrowing sea-cucumbers, a recent form of which, *Synapta girardii*, is shown at the right. *Louisella pedunculata*, another mid-Cambrian form (after Walcott), and a recent rock-clinging form, *Pentacta frondosa*.

although it also displays wide differences of structure. If *Eldonia ludwigi* proves to be a holothurian, we witness in mid-

Cambrian strata members of this order differentiated into at least three widely distinct families.

The worms, including swimming and burrowing annulates, are represented in the Burgess fauna by a very large number of specimens, comprising nineteen species, distributed through eleven genera and six families. Most of these are of the order Polychæta, as, for example, *Worthenella cambria*, in which the head is armed with tentacles, while the segmented body and the continuous series of bilobed parapodia are very clear. When compared with such typical living polychætes as *Nereis virens* and *Arabella opalina* (Fig. 25), we have clear proof of the modern relationships of these mid-Cambrian species, as well as of Cambrian sea-shore and tidal conditions closely similar to those of the present time. A specialization toward the spiny or scaly annulates at this period is emphasized in such forms as *Canadia spinosa* (Fig. 25), a slowly moving form which shows a development of lateral chætæ and

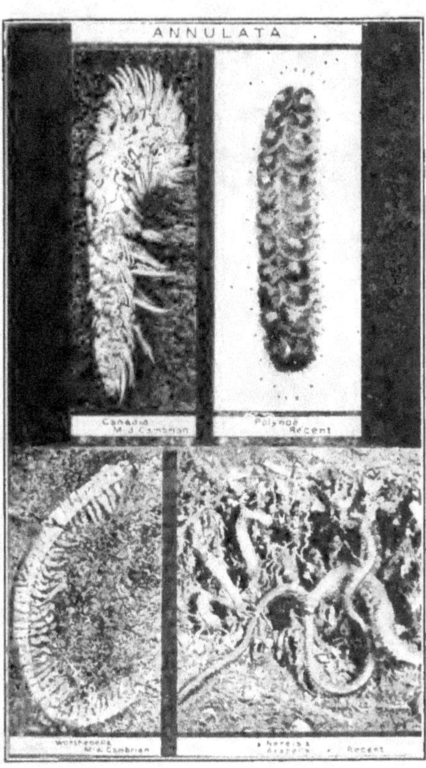

FIG. 25. WORMS (ANNULATA) OF THE MIDDLE CAMBRIAN AND RECENT SEASHORES.

Canadia spinosa, a mid-Cambrian form (after Walcott) with overlapping groups of scale-like dorsal spines, resembling those of the living *Aphroditidæ*, such as *Polynoë squamata*.

Worthenella cambria, a worm of mid-Cambrian times (after Walcott), compared with *Nereis virens* and *Arabella opalina*, recent marine worms.

overlapping groups of scale-like dorsal spines comparable only to those of the living Aphroditidæ. An example of this latter family is *Polynoë squamata*, furnished with dorsal scales. Still other recent forms, such as *Palmyra aurifera* Savigny, have groups of spinous scales closely resembling those of *Canadia*.

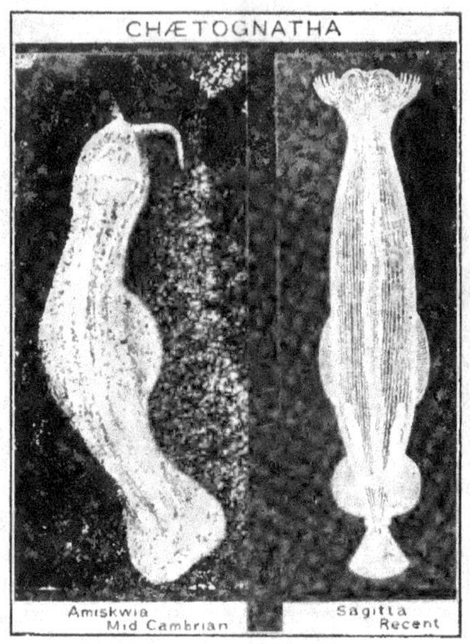

FIG. 26. FREELY SWIMMING CHÆTOGNATHS, CAMBRIAN AND RECENT.

Amiskwia sagittiformis, a mid-Cambrian form (after Walcott), has a body divided into head, trunk, and tail like the recent *Sagitta*, as seen in *S. gardineri*.

Even the modern freely propelled *Chætognatha* have their representatives in the mid-Cambrian, for to no other group of invertebrates can *Amiskwia sagittiformis* Walcott (Fig. 26) be referred, so far as we can judge by its external form. As in the recent *Sagitta* the body is divided into head, trunk, and a somewhat fish-like tail. Its single pair of fins of chætognath type would perhaps give a clearer affinity to the genus *Spadella*. The conspicuous pair of tentacles which surmounts the head is absent in modern chætognaths, although some recent species show a pair of sensory papillæ mounted on a stalk on either side of the head, as in *Spadella cephaloptera* Bush. The digestive canal and other digestive organs appear through the thin walls of the body.

A modern group of jellyfishes, the Scyphomedusæ (Fig. 27), is represented by the Middle Cambrian *Peytoia nathorsti*, the elliptical disk of which is seen from below. Although this fossil species is ascribed by Walcott to the group Rhizostomæ because of a lack of marginal tentacles, the thirty-two radiating lobes which are so beautifully preserved in the fossil correspond closely with those of the existing genus *Dactylometra* of the suborder Semostomæ. It is possible that the marginal tentacles may have been lost in *Peytoia*, as so frequently happens in living jellyfishes when in a dying condition.

From the Burgess fauna it appears that the pre-Cambrian invertebrates had entered and become completely adapted to all the life zones of the continental and oceanic waters, except possibly the abyssal. All the principal phyla—the segmented Annulata, the jointed Arthropoda (including trilobites, merostomes, crustaceans, arachnids, and insects), medusæ and other cœlenterates, echinoderms, brachiopods, molluscs (including pelycypods, gastropods, ammonites, and other cephalopods), and sponges—were all clearly established in pre-Cambrian times. Which one of these great invertebrate divisions gave rise to the vertebrates remains to be determined by future discovery. At present the Annulata, Arthropoda, and Echinodermata all have their advocates as being theoretically related to the ancestors of the vertebrates. The evolution of each of these invertebrate types follows the laws of adaptive radiation, and in the case of the articulates and molluscs extends into the terrestrial and arboreal habitat zones, while many branches of the articulates enter the aërial zone.

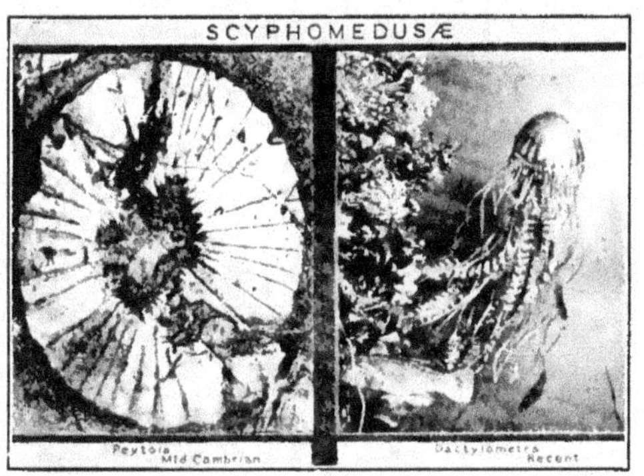

FIG. 27. JELLYFISH, CAMBRIAN AND RECENT.

Peytoia nathorsti, mid-Cambrian (after Walcott), and *Dactylometra quinquecirra*, recent. The thirty-two lobes of the fossil specimen correspond with the same number often observed in *Dactylometra*, and the characteristic marginal tentacles may have been lost in *Peytoia*.

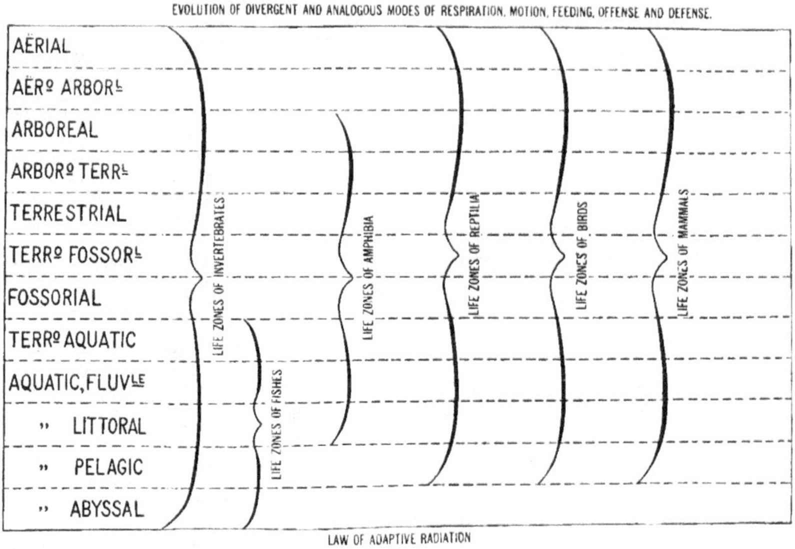

Fig. 28. The Twelve Chief Habitat Zones of Animal Life.

These twelve zones compose the environment, aërial to abyssal, into which the Invertebrata and Vertebrata have adaptively radiated in the course of geologic time. The Invertebrates range from the abyssal to the aërial zones. The fishes, ranging only from the terrestrio-aquatic to the abyssal habitat zones, nevertheless evolve body forms and types of locomotion similar to those observed in the Amphibia, which range from the littoral to the arboreal habitat zones. The reptiles, birds, and mammals, ranging from the aërial to the pelagic habitat zones, independently evolve through the law of adaptive radiation many convergent, parallel, or similar types of body form, as well as similar modes of locomotion and of offense and defense.

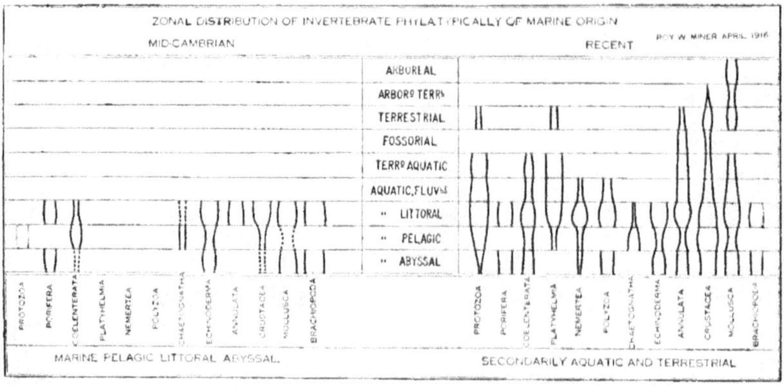

Fig. 29. Life Zones of Cambrian and Recent Invertebrates.

Chart showing in shaded areas the limited habitat zones—Littoral, Pelagic, Abyssal—of the known Cambrian forms (left) compared with the wide adaptive radiation (Abyssal to Arboreal) of recent forms (right). By Roy W. Miner.

The evolution of the articulates[1] is believed to be as follows: From a pre-Cambrian annelidan (worm-like) stock arose the trilobites with their chitinous armature and many-jointed bodies. The same stock gave rise also to the chitin-armored

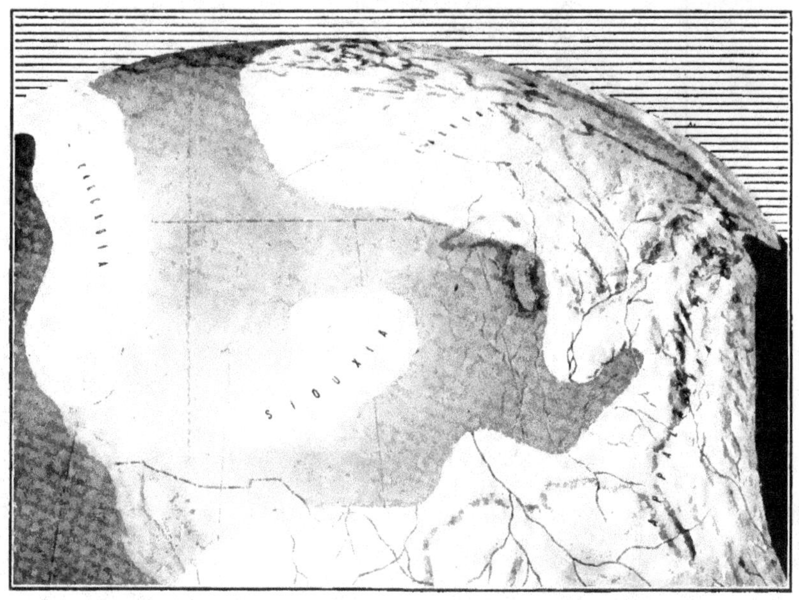

FIG. 30. ENVIRONMENT. NORTH AMERICA IN CAMBRIAN TIMES.

Theoretic restoration of the North American continent (white), continental seas (gray), and ocean (dark gray) in Upper Cambrian (Lower Saint-Croixian) time, during which there occurred the earliest known great invasion of land by the oceans. This period marks the rise of invertebrate gastropods, limulids, eurypterids, and articulate brachiopods, and the greatest differentiation of trilobites. The lands were probably all low and the climate warm. Detail from the globe model in the American Museum by Chester A. Reeds and George Robertson, after Schuchert.

sea-scorpions, or eurypterids, which attained a great size and dominated the seas of Silurian times (Fig. 31). Another line from the same stock is that of the chitin-armored horseshoe crab (*Limulus*). Out of the eurypterid stock of Silurian times may have come the terrestrial scorpions, fossils of which are

[1] Pirsson, Louis V., and Schuchert, Charles, 1915, p. 608.

first known in the Silurian, and through it arose the entire group of arachnoid (spider-like) animals, including the existing scorpions, spiders, and mites. It is also possible that the

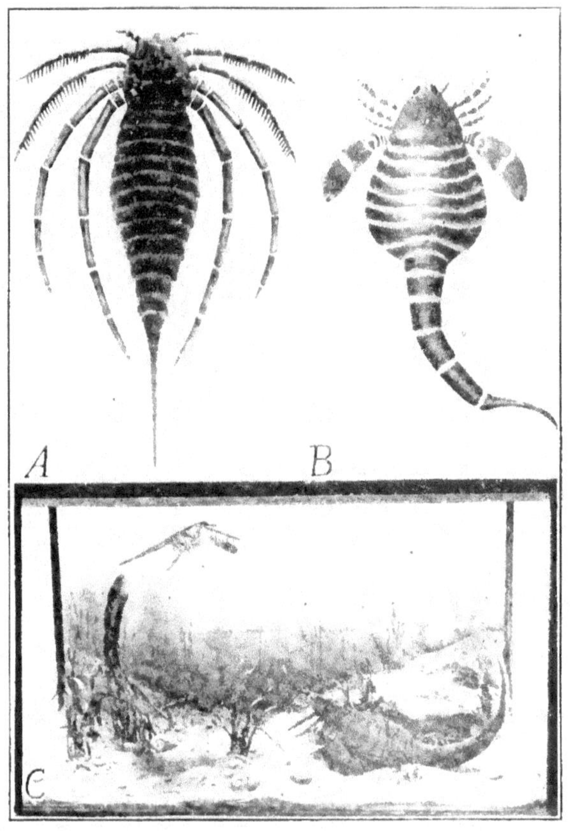

FIG. 31. EURYPTERIDS OR SEA-SCORPIONS OF SILURIAN TIMES.

A. Restoration of the giant eurypterid, *Stylonurus excelsior*, from the Catskill sandstone. Natural length, four feet.

B. Restoration of *Eusarcus*, from the Bertie water-lime. Natural length, three feet.

C. Restoration of *Eusarcus*, age of the Bertie water-lime. (After John M. Clarke.)

amphibious, terrestrial, and aërial Insecta were derived from some Silurian or Devonian chitin-armored articulate. The true Crustacea also have probably developed out of the same pre-Cambrian stock, giving rise to the phyllopods and other true Crustacea of the Cambrian, and to the cirripedes or barnacles of the Ordovician.

FIG. 32. NORTH AMERICA IN MIDDLE DEVONIAN TIMES.

Theoretic restoration of the North American continent (white), continental seas (gray), and ocean (dark gray), in Middle Devonian (Hamilton) time. This period is marked by the last extensive inundation of the Arctic seas, by the rise of the Schickchockian Mountains and many volcanoes in Acadia, and by the beginning of the great Catskill delta built up by rivers from the rising Acadian region. Marine shark and arthrodires become abundant, the American fauna of the Mississippi Sea shows numerous brachiopods and bivalves, and the first evidence of a land flora with large conifers (*Dadoxylon*) is found. Detail from a globe model in the American Museum by Chester A. Reeds and George Robertson, after Schuchert.

REACTIONS TO CLIMATIC AND OTHER ENVIRONMENTAL CHANGES OF GEOLOGIC TIME

Schuchert observes that there is no more significant period in the history of the world than the Devonian[1] (Fig. 32), for at this time the increasing verdure of the land invited the

[1] Pirsson, Louis V., and Schuchert, Charles, 1915, p. 714.

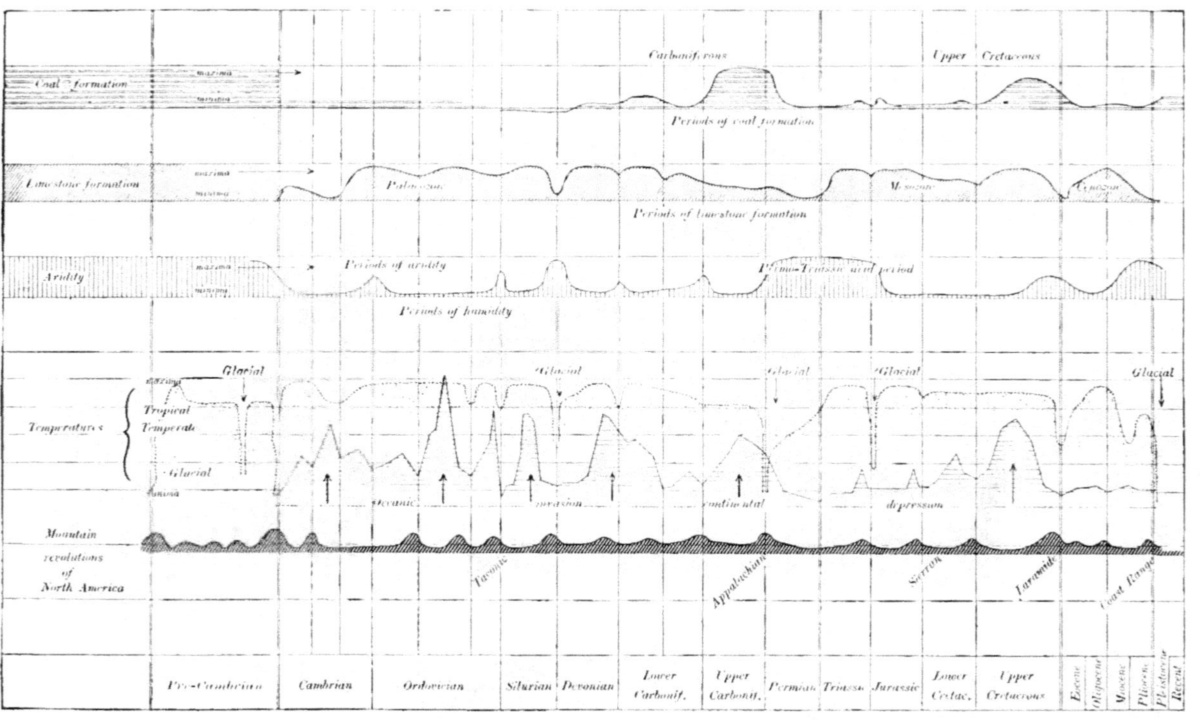

FIG. 33. CHANGING ENVIRONMENT DURING THE PAST FIFTY OR MORE MILLION YEARS.

Theoretic correlation of climatic, continental, oceanic, and life phases. This chart shows the maximum and minimum periods of coal formation, of limestone formation, of aridity and of humidity; also the theoretic and actual epochs of glaciation in the northern and southern hemispheres preceding the final glaciation, periods of maximum continental depression and oceanic invasion, and periods of mountain revolution. Modified from Huntington after Schuchert.

invasion of life from the waters, the first conquest of the terrestrial environment being attained by the scorpions, shell-fish, worms, and insects.

This is an instance of the constant dispersion of animal forms into new environments in search of their food-supply, the chief instinctive cause of all migration. This impulse is constantly acting and reacting throughout geologic time with the migration of the environment, which is graphically presented by Huntington's chart (Fig. 33), from the researches of Barrell, Schuchert, and others. The periodic readjustment of the earth crust of North America[1] is witnessed in fourteen periods of mountain-making (oblique lines), concluding with the Appalachian Range, the Sierra Nevada (Sierran), the Rocky Mountains (Laramide), and the Pacific Coast Range.

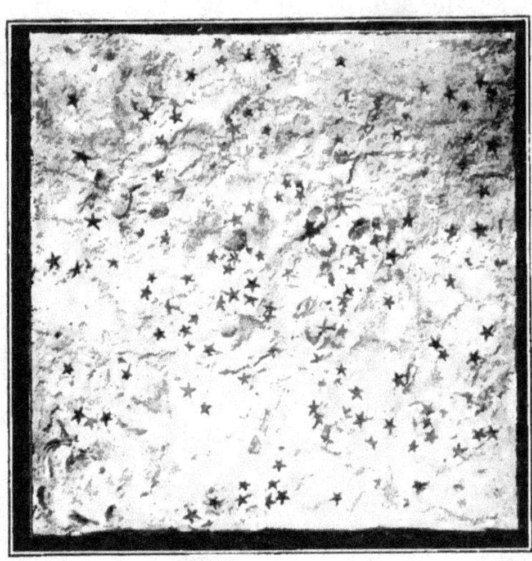

FIG. 34. FOSSIL STARFISHES.

A portion of petrified sea bottom of Devonian age, showing fossil starfishes associated with and devouring bivalves as starfishes attack oyster-beds at the present time. Hamilton group, Saugerties, N. Y. After John M. Clarke.

Between these relatively short periods of mountain upheaval came[2] periods of continental depression and oceanic invasion (horizontal lines) when the continent was more or less flooded by the oceans. There are certainly twelve and probably not less than seventeen periods of continental flood-

[1] Pirsson, Louis V., and Schuchert, Charles, 1915, p. 979.

[2] *Op. cit.*, p. 982.

ing which vary in extent up to the submergence of 4,000,000 square miles of surface.

Each of these changes, which by some geologists are believed to be cyclic, included long epochs especially favorable to certain forms of life, resulting in the majority of cases in high specialization like that of the sea-scorpions (eurypterids) followed by more or less sudden extinction. In the oceans the life most directly influenced was that of the lime-secreting organisms which resulted in maximum and minimum periods of limestone formation (oblique lines) by algæ, pelagic foraminifera, and corals. On land there were two greater (Carboniferous, Upper Cretaceous) and several lesser periods of coal formation.

Changes of environment play so large and conspicuous a part in the selection and elimination of the invertebrates that the assertion is often made that environment is the cause of evolution, a statement only partly consistent with our fundamental biologic law, which finds that the causes of evolution lie within the four complexes of action, reaction, and interaction (see p. 21).

Perrin Smith, who has made a most exhaustive analysis of the evolution of the cephalopod molluscs and especially of the Triassic ammonites, observes that the evolution of form continues uninterruptedly, even where there is no evidence whatever of environmental change. Conversely, environmental change does not necessarily induce evolution—for example, during the Age of Mammals, although the mammals developed an infinite variety of widely divergent forms, the reptiles (p. 231) show very little change.

The Mutations of Waagen

When Darwin published the "Origin of Species," in 1859, *no one had actually observed how one form of animal or plant actually passes into another*, whether according to some definite law or principle, or whether fortuitously or by chance. So far as we know, the honor of first observing how new specific forms arise belongs to Wilhelm Heinrich Waagen.[1] It was among the fossil ammonites of the Jurassic, which are represented by the existing pearly nautilus, that Waagen first observed the actual mode of transformation of one animal form into another, as set forth in his classic paper of 1869, "Die Formenreihe des *Ammonites subradiatus*."[2] The essential feature of the "mutation of Waagen"[3] is that it established the law of minute and inconspicuous changes of form which accumulate so gradually that they are observable only after a considerable passage of time, and which take a definite direction as expressed in the word *Mutationsrichtung*. We now recognize that they represent a true evolution of the heredity-chromatin. This law of definitely directed evolution is illustrated in the detailed structure of the type series of ammonites (Fig. 35) in which Waagen's discovery was made. It has proved to be a fundamental law of the evolution of form, for it is observed alike in invertebrates and vertebrates wherever a closely successive series can be obtained.

Among the fossil invertebrates a mutation series of the brachiopod, *Spirifer mucronatus* of the Middle Devonian or Hamilton time, is one of the most typical (Fig. 36).

The essential law discovered by Waagen is one of the most

[1] Born in 1841, died in 1900. An Austrian paleontologist and stratigraphic geologist.

[2] Waagen, Wilhelm, 1869.

[3] The term "mutation" used in this sense was introduced by Waagen in 1869. Twenty years later the great Austrian palæontologist Neumayr defined the "Mutationsrichtung" as the tendency of form to evolve in certain definite directions. See Neumayr, M., 1889, pp. 60, 61.

important in the whole history of biology. It is that certain new characters arise definitely and continuously, and, as Osborn has subsequently shown,[1] adaptively. This law of the

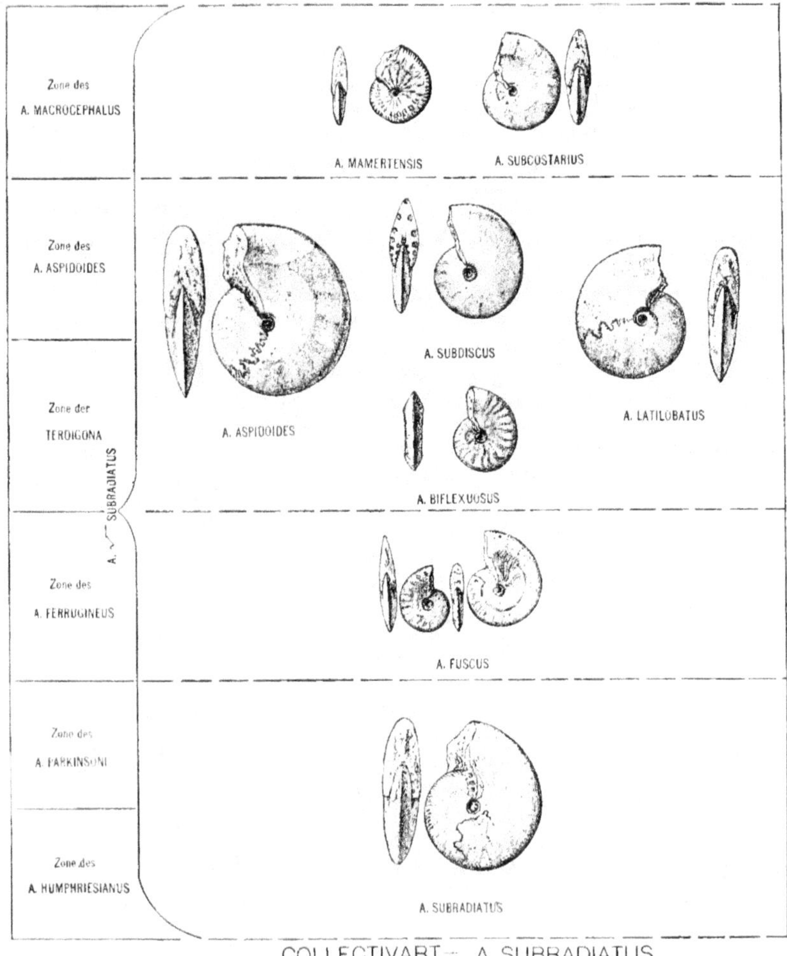

Fig. 35. Continuous Character Changes Known as the Mutations of Waagen. Successive geologic mutations of *Ammonites subradiatus*, drawn and rearranged from the original plates published by Waagen in 1869, showing his type series of the continuous character changes known as the Mutations of Waagen.

[1] Osborn, Henry Fairfield, 1912.1.

gradual evolution of adaptive form is directly contrary to Darwin's theoretic principle of the selection of chance variations. It is unfortunate that the same term, *mutation*, was chosen by the botanist, Hugo de Vries, in 1901, to express his observation that certain characters in plants arise by sudden

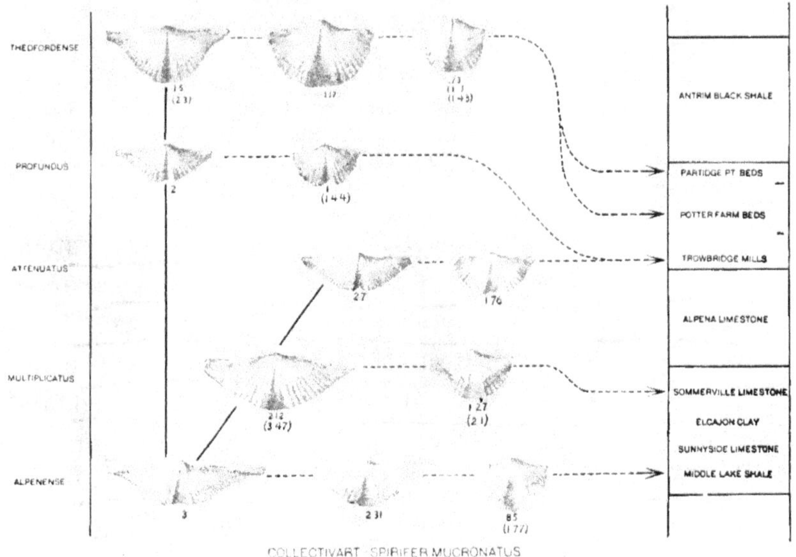

FIG. 36. SUCCESSIVE MUTATIONS OF *Spirifer mucronatus.*

Specimens from the geologic section at Alpena, Mich., on the shore of Lake Huron, and from the corresponding section at Thedford across the lake on the Canadian shore, arranged by A. Grabau to show the relationships of the various mutations. In the scale of strata at the right $8\frac{1}{4}$ mm. equals 100 feet depth.

changes (saltations) or discontinuously, and without any definite direction or adaptive trend (*Mutationsrichtung*). The essential feature of de Vries's observations, in contrast to Waagen's, is that of discontinuous saltations in directions that are entirely fortuitous—that is, either in an adaptive or inadaptive direction, the direction to be subsequently determined by selection—a theoretic principle agreeing closely with that of Darwin.

CHAPTER V

VISIBLE AND INVISIBLE EVOLUTION OF THE VERTEBRATES

Chromatin evolution. Errors and truths in the Lamarckian and Darwinian explanations of the processes of evolution. Character evolution more important than species evolution. Individuality in character origin, velocity, and cooperation. Origin of the vertebrate type. The laws of convergence, divergence, and adaptive radiation of form.

SIMON NEWCOMB[1] considered the concept of the rapid movement of the solar system toward Lyra as the greatest which has ever entered the human mind. He remarks: "If I were asked what is the greatest fact that the intellect of man has ever brought to light, I should say it was this: Through all human history, nay, so far as we can discover, from the infancy of time, our solar system—sun, planets, and moons—has been flying through space toward the constellation Lyra with a speed of which we have no example on earth. To form a conception of this fact the reader has only to look at the beautiful Lyra and reflect that for every second that the clock tells off we are ten miles nearer to that constellation."

The history of the back-boned animals (Vertebrata) as the visible expression of the invisible evolution of the microscopic chromatin presents an equally great concept of the potentialities of matter in the infinitely minute state.

According to this concept our study of the evolution of the back-boned animals at once resolves itself into two parallel lines of inquiry and speculation, which can never be divorced and are always to be followed in observation and inference:

[1] Newcomb, Simon, 1902 (ed. of 1904, p. 325).

The Visible Body	*The Invisible Germ*
The evolution of SOMATIC (*i. e.*, BODILY) FORM and FUNCTION as *observed* in anatomy, embryology, palæontology, and physiology. The rise, differentiation, and change of function in bodily characters.	The evolution of HEREDITY-CHROMATIN as *inferred* from the incessant visible evolution of Form and Function. The rise and decline of potentialities, predispositions, and other germinal characters.

A clear distinction exists between the slow, stable heredity-chromatin, or germ evolution, and the unstable body cell evolution as viewed by the experimental zoologist. The body is unstable because it is immediately sensitive to all variations of environment, growth, and habit, while the chromatin alters very slowly. The peculiar significance of heredity-chromatin, when viewed in the long perspective of geologic time, is its stability in combination with incessant plasticity and adaptability to varying environmental conditions and new forms of bodily action. Chromatin is far more stable than the surface of the earth. Throughout, the potentiality of constant changes of proportion, gain and loss of characters, genesis of new characters, there is always preserved a large part of the history of antecedent form and function. In the vertebrates chromatin evolution is mirrored in the many continuous series of forms which have been discovered, also in the perfection of mechanical detail in organisms of titanic size and inconceivable complexity, like the dinosaurs among reptiles and the whales among mammals, which rank with the *Sequoia* among plants.

Adaptive Characters of Internal-External Action, Reaction, Interaction

Of the causes[1] of this slow but wonderful process of chromatin evolution there are two historic explanations, each adumbrated in the Greek period of inquiry.

[1] See Preface, p. ix.

The older, known as the Lamarckian,[1] expressed in modern terms, is that *the causes of the genesis of new form and new function are to be sought in the body cells (soma)*, on the hypothesis that cellular actions, reactions, and interactions with each other and with the environment are in some way impressed physicochemically upon and are heritable by the chromatin. This idea was originally suggested by the accurate observation of early naturalists and anatomists that bodily function not only controls and perfects form but is generally adaptive or purposive in its effects upon form. According to this Lamarck-Spencer-Cope explanation a change of environment, of habit, and of function should always be antecedent to changes of form in succeeding generations; moreover, if this explanation were the true one, successive changes in evolutionary series would be like growth, they would be observed to follow the direct lines of individual action, reaction, and interaction, and the young would

ADAPTATIONS OF ENVIRONMENTAL CORRELATION:
- RESPIRATORY, OLFACTORY, VISUAL, AUDITORY, THERMAL, GRAVITY FUNCTIONS AND ORGANS
- COORDINATIVE AND CORRELATIVE TO VARIATIONS OF LIGHT, HEAT, HUMIDITY, ARIDITY, CAUSED BY MIGRATIONS OF THE INDIVIDUAL OR OF THE ENVIRONMENT.

ADAPTATIONS OF INTERNAL CORRELATION:
- CORRELATION AND COORDINATION OF THE INTERNAL GROWTH AND FUNCTIONS THROUGH INTERNAL SECRETIONS, ENZYMES, AND THE NERVOUS SYSTEM.

ADAPTATIONS OF NUTRITION
- (1) ON INORGANIC COMPOUNDS.
- (2) ON BACTERIA.
- (3) ON PROTOPHYTA, ALGÆ, ETC.
- (4) ON PROTOZOA.
- (5) ON HIGHER PLANTS, HERBIVOROUS DIET.
- (6) ON HIGHER ANIMALS, CARNIVOROUS DIET.
- (7) PARASITIC, WITHOUT OR WITHIN PLANTS AND ANIMALS.

ADAPTATIONS OF INDIVIDUAL COMPETITION AND SELECTION:
- (A) SELECTION, AFFECTING VARIATION, RECTIGRADATION, MUTATION, ORIGIN, AND DEVELOPMENT OF SINGLE CHARACTERS, PROPORTIONS, ETC.
- (B) AFFECTING ALL REPRODUCTIVE ORGANS, PRIMARY AND SECONDARY.

ADAPTATIONS OF RACIAL COMPETITION AND SELECTION,
- AFFECTING CHIEFLY ALL MOTOR, PROTECTIVE, OFFENSIVE, AND DEFENSIVE STRUCTURES OF THE ENDO- AND EXOSKELETON; ALSO REPRODUCTION RATE.

THE PECULIAR SIGNIFICANCE OF THE HEREDITY-CHROMATIN is its stability in combination with incessant plasticity and adaptability to varying environmental conditions and new forms of bodily action.

[1] *Cf.* Preface, pp. xiii, xiv.

be increasingly similar to the adults of antecedent generations, which is frequently the case but unfortunately for the Lamarckian explanation is not *invariably* the case. In many parts of the skeleton chromatin development and degeneration so obviously follow bodily use and disuse that Cope was led to propose a law which he termed *bathmism* (growth force) and to explain the energy phenomena of use and disuse in the body tissues as the *cause* of the appearance of corresponding energy potentialities in the chromatin. In other words, he believed that the energy of development or of degeneration in the bodily parts of the individual is inherited by corresponding parts in the germ. Similar opinions prevail among most anatomists (*e. g.*, Cunningham) and among many palæontologists and zoologists (*e. g.*, Semon).

The opposed explanation, the pure Darwinian,[1] as restated by Weismann and de Vries, is that *the genesis of new form and function is to be sought in the germ cells or chromatin.* This is based upon an hypothesis which is directly anti-Lamarckian, that the actions, reactions, and interactions which cause certain bodily organs to originate, to develop, or to degenerate, to exhibit momentum or inertia in development, do not give rise to corresponding sets of predispositions in the chromatin, and are thus not heritable. According to this explanation, body cell changes do not exert any corresponding specific influence on the germ cells. All predispositions to new form and function not only begin in the germ cells but are more or less lawless or experimental; they are constantly being tested or tried out by bodily experience, habits, and functions. Technically stated, they are "fortuitous" or chance variations, followed by selection of the fittest variations, and thus giving rise to adaptations. Thus Darwin's disciple, Poulton, also de

[1] *Cf.* Preface, p. xiv.

Vries, who has merely restated in his law of "mutation" Darwin's original principle of 1859, and Bateson, the most radical thinker of the three, hold the opinion that there is no adaptive law observed in germ variation, but that the chromatin is continuously experimenting, and that from these experiments selection guides the organism into adaptive and purposive lines. This is the prevailing opinion among most modern experimental zoologists and many other biologists.

Neither the Lamarckian nor the Darwinian explanation accords with all that we are learning through palæontology and experimental zoology of the actual modes of the origin and development of adaptive characters. That there may be elements of truth in each explanation is evident from the following consideration of our fundamental biologic law. Adaptive characters present three phases: first, *the origin of character form and character function;* second, *the more or less rapid acceleration or retardation of character form and function;* third, *the coordination and cooperation of character form and function.* If we adopt the physicochemical theory of the origin and development of life it follows that the causes of such origin, velocity (acceleration or retardation) and cooperation must lie somewhere within the actions, reactions, and interactions of the four physicochemical complexes, namely, the physical environment, the developing organism, the heredity-chromatin, the living environment, because these are the only reservoirs of matter and energy we know of in life history.

While it is possible that the relations of these four energy complexes will never be fathomed, it is certain that our search for causes must proceed along the line of determining which actions, reactions, and interactions invariably precede and which invariably follow those of the body cells (Lamarckian view) or those of the chromatin (Darwin-Weismann view).

The Lamarckian view that adaptation in the body cells *invariably* precedes similar adaptive reaction in the chromatin is not supported either by experiment or by observation; such precedence, while occasional and even frequent, is by no means invariable. The Darwinian view, namely, that chromatin evolution is a matter of chance and displays itself in a variety of directions, is contradicted by palæontological evidence both in the Invertebrata and Vertebrata, among which we observe that *continuity and law in chromatin evolution prevails over the evidence either of fortuity or of sudden leaps or mutations*, that *in the genesis of many characters there is a slow and prolonged rectigradation or direct evolution of the chromatin toward adaptive ends.* This is what is meant in our introduction (p. 9) by the statement that in evolution law prevails over chance.

Visible Characters, Invisible Chromatin Determiners

The chief quest of evolutionists to-day in every field of observation is *the mode and cause of the origin and subsequent history of single characters.* The quest of Darwin for *the causes of the origin of species* has now become an incidental or side issue, since, given a number of new or modified heredity characters,[1] *presto*, we have a new species. In this present aspect of research the discoveries of modern palæontology are in accord with many of the recently discovered laws of heredity. The palæontologist supports the observer of heredity in demonstrating that every vertebrate organism is a mosaic of an

[1] *Character* (Greek, χαρακτήρ, metaph., a distinctive mark, characteristic, character) is the most elastic term in modern biology; we may apply it to every part and function of the organism, large or small, which may evolve separately and be inherited separately. Mendel has shown that "characters" are far more minutely separable in the invisible chromatin than they are in the visible organism; also that every bodily "character" is a complex of numerous germ "characters," which are technically known as *determiners* or *factors*. For example, such a simple visible character as eye color in the fruit-fly is known to have determiners in the chromatin. Morgan, Thomas Hunt, 1916, pp. 118–124.

inconceivably large number of "characters" or "character complexes," structural and functional, some indissolubly and invariably grouped and cooperating, others singularly independent. For example, the zoologist infers that every one of the most minute scales of a reptile or hairs of a mammal is a "character complex" having its particular chemical formulæ and chemical energies which condition the shape, the color, the function, and all other features of the complex. Through researches on heredity each of these characters and character complexes is now believed to have a corresponding physicochemical *determiner or group of determiners* in the germ-chromatin, the chromatin existing not as a miniature, but as an individual *potential and causal.*

In the course of normal physicochemical environment, of normal life environment, of normal individual development, and of normal selection and competition, an organism will tend to more or less closely reproduce its normal ancestral characters. But a new or abnormal physicochemical intruder either into the environment, the developing individual, the heredity-chromatin or the life environment may produce a new or abnormal visible character type. This quadruple nature of the physicochemical energies directed upon each and every character is *tetrakinetic* in the sense that it represents four complexes of energy; it is *tetraplastic* in the sense that it moulds bodily development from four different complexes of causes. This law largely underlies what we call *variation* of type.

In other words, the normal actions, reactions, and interactions must prevail throughout the whole course of growth from the germ to the adult; otherwise the visible body (phenotype, Johannsen) may not correspond with the normal expression of the potentialities of the invisible germ (genotype, Johannsen).

The *principle of individuality*, namely, of separate development and existence, which we have seen to be the prime characteristic of the first chemical assemblage into an organism (p. 68), also governs each of the character complexes, as observed by the palæontologist. In some vertebrates we observe an infinity of similar character complexes, evolving in an exactly similar manner, as in the beautiful markings of the shell and the exquisite

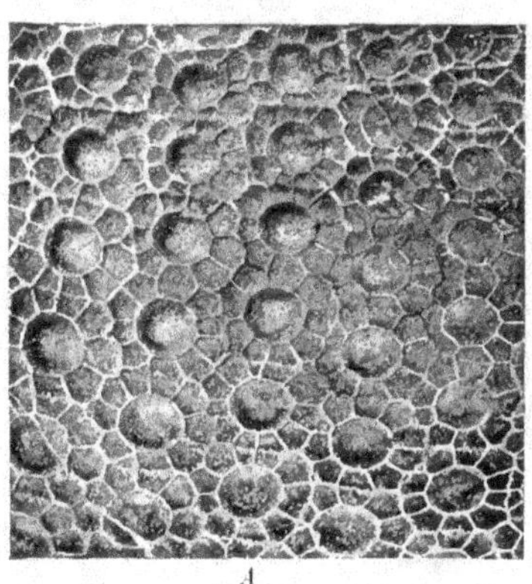

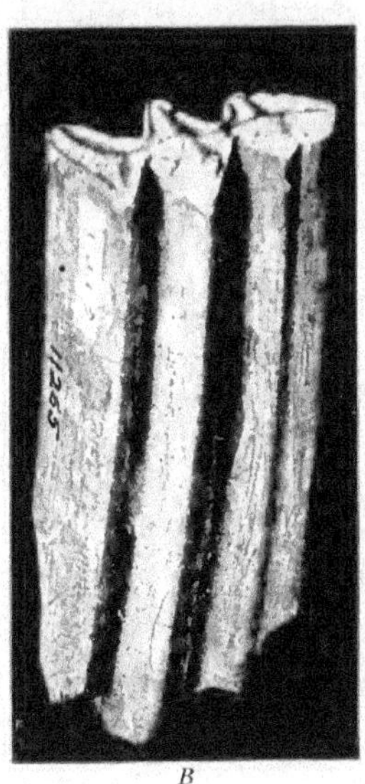

A *B*

FIG. 37. SIMILARLY FORMED CHARACTERS IN THE GLYPTODON.

Shell pattern and tooth pattern of the Glyptodon, a heavily armored fossil armadillo found in North and South America. The entire shell is covered with rosettes, composed of small plates nearly uniform in design, similar to those in the very small section represented (*A*). The entire series of upper and lower teeth bear within a uniform "glyptic" pattern, like that of the tooth shown here (*B*), to which the name Glyptodon refers.

enamel pattern of the teeth of the heavily armored armadillo known as the glyptodon (Fig. 37), in which respectively every portion of the shell evolves similarly and every one of the teeth evolves similarly, from which we might conclude that there is an absence of separability or individuality in form characters and that some homomorphic (similarly formative) impulse is present in all characters of similar chromatin origin. But such a rash conclusion is offset by the existence of other character complexes of similar ancestry in which each character evolves differently and is in a high degree heteromorphic (diversely formative), as, for example, in the grinding teeth of mammals (Fig. 38).

This individuality and separability inherent in character form is equally observed in character velocity and is the basis of the shifting of characters from adult to youthful stages, or *vice versa*, as well as of all the proportionate and quantitative changes which make up four-fifths of vertebrate evolution. Increasing character velocity is a process of *acceleration;* decreasing character velocity is a process of *retardation.* For example, in the evolution of any group of animals, as in plants (p. 108), two character forms side by side, like the fingers of the hand or toes of the foot, may evolve with equal velocity and maintain a perfect symmetry, or one may be accelerated into a very rapid momentum[1] while another may be held in a state of absolute inertia or equilibrium, and a third may be retarded. These are the extremes of character velocity which result in the anatomical or visible conditions respectively known as *development*, *balance*, and *degeneration.*

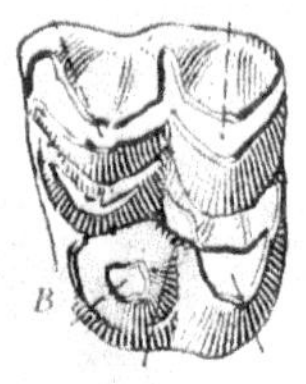

FIG. 38. DISSIMILARLY FORMED CHARACTERS OF SIMILAR ORIGIN.

Surface of the upper grinding teeth of two ancient Eocene mammals. Type *B* is known to be related to type *A*. In *Euprotogonia* (*A*) all the cusps are of a somewhat similar rounded form. In *Meniscotherium* (*B*) each cusp has its own peculiar form.

[1] In physics momentum equals mass × velocity. In biology momentum and inertia refer to the relative rate of character change, both in individual development (ontogeny) and in evolution (phylogeny). *Character parallax* would express the differing velocities of two characters. Thus the character parallax of the right and left horns in the Brontotheriinæ (titanotheres) is very small, *i. e.*, they evolve at nearly or quite the same rate; on the other hand, the character parallax between the first and second premolar teeth in these animals is very great. The character-parallax idea has innumerable applications and can be expressed quantitatively. W. K. Gregory.

The ever changing velocity and changing bodily form and function in character complexes are to be regarded as expressions of physicochemical energy resulting from the actions, reactions, and interactions of different parts of the organism. As we have repeatedly stated, these changes proceed according to some unknown laws. The only vista which we enjoy at present of a possible future explanation of the causes of character origin, character velocity, and character coöperation is through chemical catalysis, namely, through the hypothesis that all *actions* and *reactions* of form and of motion liberate specific catalytic messengers, such as ferments, enzymes, hormones, chalones, and other as yet undiscovered chemical messengers, which produce specific and coöperating *interactions* in every character complex of the organism and corresponding predispositions in the physicochemical energies of the germ; in other words, that the chemical accelerators, balancers, and retarders of body cell development also affect the germ.

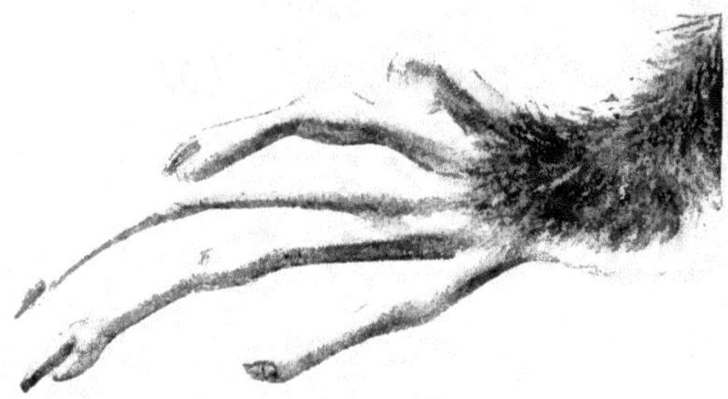

FIG. 39. PROPORTIONAL ADAPTATION IN THE FINGERS OF A LEMUR.

This peculiar hand of the Aye-Aye (*Cheiromys*) of Madagascar affords an excellent example of unequal velocity in the development of adjacent characters. In this hand each finger has its own proportionate rate of evolution. The thumb (upper) is extremely short; the index finger is normal; the middle finger is excessively slender, in adaptation to a very special purpose, namely, for insertion into small spaces and crevices in search of larvæ; the fourth and fifth fingers (two lower) are normal.

In our survey of the marvellous visible evolution of the vertebrates we may constantly keep in our imagination this conception of the invisible actions, reactions, and interactions of the hard parts of the structural tissues, which are preserved in visible form in fossils. In this field of observation the nature of the chemical and physiological influences of the body can only be *inferred*, while *the relations of these physicochemical influences to those of the chromatin are absolutely unknown.*

Such a form of explanation would, however, only apply to a part of the characters of adaptation (table, page 143). The visible and invisible evolution of the hard parts in adaptation resolves itself into six chief and concurrent processes, namely:

Ever changing character form and character function, Ever changing character velocity, acceleration, balance, retardation, in individual development and in the chromatin, Ever changing character cooperation, coordination and correlation, Incessant character origin in the heredity-chromatin, sometimes following, sometimes antecedent to similar character origin in the developing individual, Relatively rapid disappearance of character form and character function in the developing individual, Relatively slow disappearance of the determiners and predispositions of character form and character function in the heredity-chromatin.	Characters and Character Complexes

Changes in the visible bodily hard parts invariably mirror the invisible evolution of the chromatin; in fact, this invisible evolution is nowhere revealed in a more extraordinary manner than in the incessantly changing characters in such structures as the labyrinthine foldings of the deep layers of enamel in the grinding teeth of the horse.

The chromatin as the potential energy of form and function is at once the most conservative and the most progressive centre of physicochemical evolution; it records the body form of past adaptations, it meets the emergencies of the present through the adaptability to new conditions which it imparts to the organism in its distribution throughout every living cell; it is continuously giving rise to new characters and functions.

Taking the whole history of vertebrate life from the beginning, we observe that every prolonged, old adaptive phase in a similar habitat becomes impressed in the hereditary characters of the chromatin. Throughout the development of new adaptive phases the chromatin always retains more or less potentiality of repeating the embryonic, immature, and more rarely some of the mature structures of older adaptive phases in the older environments. This is the basis of the *law of ancestral repetition,* formulated by Louis Agassiz and developed by Haeckel and Hyatt, which dominated biological thought during thirty years of the nineteenth century (1865–1895). It yielded with more or less success a highly speculative solution of the ancestral form history of the vertebrates, through the study of embryonic development and comparative anatomy, long before the actual lines of evolutionary descent were determined through palæontology.

Laws of Form Evolution in Adaptation to the Mechanical and Physicochemical Actions, Reactions, and Interactions of Locomotion, Offense and Defense, and Reproduction

The form evolution of the back-boned animals, beginning with the pro-fishes of Cambrian and pre-Cambrian time, extends over a period estimated at not less than 30,000,000 years. The supremely adaptable vertebrate body type begins to dominate the living world, overcoming one mechanical difficulty after another as it passes through the habitat zones of water, land, and air. Adaptations in the motions necessary for the capture, storage, and release of plant and animal energy continue to control the form of the body and of its appendages, but simultaneously the organism through mechanical and chemical means protects itself either offensively or defensively and also adapts itself to reproduce and protect its kind, according to Darwin's original conception of the struggle for existence as involving both the life of the individual and the life of its progeny. Among all defenseless forms either speed or chemical or electrical protection is a prime necessity, while all heavily armored forms gradually abandon mobility. As among the Invertebrata, calcium carbonate and phosphate and various compounds of keratin and chitin are the chief chemical materials of defensive armature.

Locomotion, as distinguished from that in all invertebrates, is in an elongate body stiffened by a central axis, hence the name *chordate* or *Chordata* for the vertebrate division. The evolution of the cartilaginous skeletal supports (endoskeleton) and of the limbs is generally from the centre of the body toward the periphery, the evolution of the epidermal defensive armature (exoskeleton) is from the periphery toward the centre.

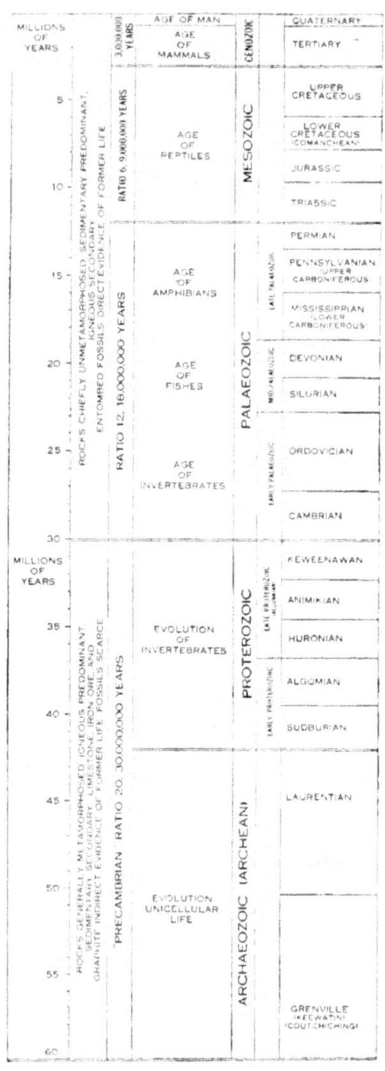

FIG. 40. TOTAL GEOLOGIC TIME SCALE, ESTIMATED AT SIXTY MILLION YEARS.

These estimates are based upon the relative thickness of the pre-Cambrian and post-Cambrian rocks. Prepared by the author and C. A. Reeds after the time estimates of Walcott and Schuchert.

The defensive armature finally through change of function makes important contributions to the inner skeleton.

The chief advance which has been made in the last fifty years is our abundant knowledge of the *modes* of adaptation as contrasted with the very limited knowledge yet attained as to the *causes* of adaptation.

The theoretic application of the fundamental law of action, reaction, and interaction becomes increasingly difficult and almost inconceivable as adaptations multiply and are superposed upon each other with the evolution of the four physicochemical relations, as follows:

Physical environment: succession, reversal, and alternation of habitat zones,

Individual development: succession, reversal, and alternation of adaptive habitat phases, Chromatin evolution: addition of the determiners of new habitat adaptations while preserving the determiners of old habitat adaptations,	Incessant Selection and Competition

Succession of life environments: caused by the migrations of the individual and of the life environment itself.

The Law of Convergence or Parallelism of Form in Locomotor, Offensive, and Defensive Adaptations

There arise hundreds of adaptive parallels between the evolution of the Vertebrata and the antecedent evolution of the Invertebrata. Although the structural body type and mechanism of locomotion is profoundly diverse, the combined necessity for protection and locomotion brings about close parallels in body form between such primitive Silurian eurypterids as *Bunodes* and the vertebrate armored fishes known as ostracoderms, a superficial resemblance which has led Patten[1] to defend the view that the two groups are genetically related.

[1] Patten, Wm., 1912.

It must be the similarity of the internal physicochemical energies of protoplasm, the similarity in the mechanics of motion, of offense and defense, together with the constant similarity of selection, which underlies the law of convergence or parallelism in adaptation, namely, *the production of externally similar forms in adaptation to similar external natural forces*, a law which escaped the keen observation of Huxley[1] in his remarkable analysis of the modes of vertebrate evolution published in 1880.

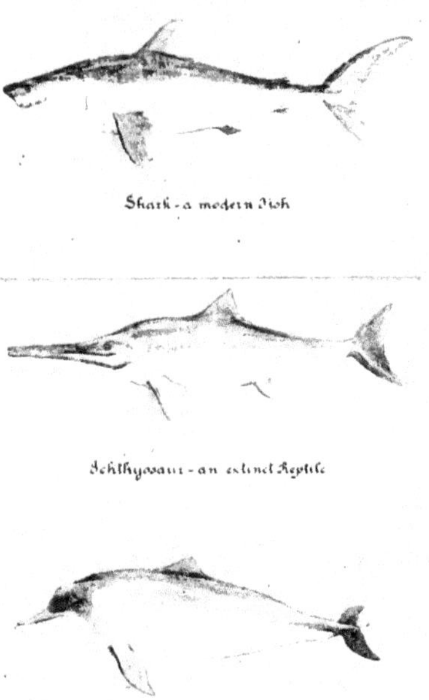

FIG. 41. CONVERGENT ADAPTATION OF FORM IN THREE WHOLLY UNRELATED MARINE VERTEBRATES.

Analogous evolution of the swift-swimming, fusiform body type (upper) in the shark, a fish; (middle) in the ichthyosaur, a reptile; and (lower) in the dolphin, a mammal—three wholly unrelated animals in which the internal skeletal structure is radically different. After Osborn and Knight.

The whole process of motor adaptation in the vertebrates, whether among fishes, amphibians, reptiles, birds, or mammals, is the solution of a series of mechanical problems, namely, of adjustment to gravity, of overcoming the resistance of water or air in the development of speed, of the evolution of the limbs in creating levers, fulcra (joints), and pulleys. The fore and hind fins of fishes and the fore and hind limbs of mammals evolve uniformly where they are homodynamic and divergently where they are heterodynamic. This principle of homodynamy and heterodynamy applies to the body as a whole and to every one of its

[1] Huxley, T. H., 1880.

parts, according to two laws: first, that each individual part has its own mechanical evolution, and, second, that the same mechanical problem is generally solved on the same principle. This, we observe, is invariably the ideal principle, for, unlike man, nature wastes little time on inferior inventions but immediately proceeds to superior inventions.

HABITAT ADAPTATIONS OF THE VERTEBRATES TO THE CHANGES OF ENVIRONMENT

AERIAL
(FLYING, VOLANT TYPES)

AËRO-ARBOREAL
(PARACHUTE, VOLPLANING TYPES)

ARBOREAL
(CLIMBING, LEAPING, AND BRACHIATING TYPES)

ARBOREO-TERRESTRIAL
(WALKING AND CLIMBING, SCANSORIAL TYPES)

TERRESTRIAL
(AMBULATORY, SLOW; CURSORIAL, RAPID; SALTATORY, LEAPING; GRAVIPORTAL, SLOW, CUMBROUS)

TERRESTRIO-FOSSORIAL
(WALKING AND BURROWING TYPES)

FOSSORIAL
(BURROWING TYPES)

TERRESTRIO-AQUATIC
(AMPHIBIOUS TYPES)

AQUATIC

PALUSTRAL, LACUSTRINE
(SURFACE-LIVING, BOTTOM-LIVING)

FLUVIATILE
(FRESH-WATER, SWIFT CURRENT, SLOW-CURRENT; FLUVIO-MARINE TYPES)

MARINE LITTORAL
(SURFACE-LIVING AND BURROWING TYPES)

MARINE PELAGIC
(FREE SURFACE-LIVING, DRIFTING, FLOATING, SELF-PROPELLING TYPES)

MARINE ABYSSAL
(DEEP BOTTOM-LIVING TYPES, SLOW- AND SWIFT-MOVING)

Each of the chief habitat zones may be divided into many subzones. The vertebrates may migrate from one to another of these habitats, or through geophysical changes the environments themselves may migrate. Conditions of locomotion result in forms that are quadrupedal, bipedal, pinnipedal, apodal, etc.

The three mechanical problems of existence in the water habitat are: First, overcoming the buoyancy of water either by weighting down and increasing the gravity of the body or by the development of special gravitating organs, which enable animals to rise and descend in this medium; second, the mechanical problem of overcoming the resistance of water in rapid motion, which is accomplished by means of warped surfaces and well-designed entrant and re-entrant angles of the body similar to the "stream-lines" of the fastest modern yachts; third, the problem of propulsion of the body, which is accomplished, first, by sinuous motion of the entire body, terminating in powerful propulsion by the tail fin; secondly, by supplementary action of the four lateral fins; third, by the horizontal steering of the body by means of the median system of fins.

The terrestrial and aërial evolution of the four-limbed types (Tetrapoda) is designed chiefly to overcome the resistance of gravity and in a less degree the resistance of the atmosphere through which the body moves. When the aërial stage evolves, with increasing speed the resistance of the air becomes only slightly less than that of the water in the fish stage, and the warped surfaces, the entrant and re-entrant angles evolved by the flying body are similar to those previously evolved in the rapidly moving fishes.

In contrast with this *convergence* brought about by the similarity above described of the physicochemical laws of action, reaction, and interaction, and the similarity of the mechanical obstacles encountered by the different races of animals in similar habitats and environmental media, is the law of *divergence*.

Branching or Divergence of Form, the Law of Adaptive Radiation

In general the *law of divergence* of form, perceived by Lamarck and rediscovered by Darwin, has been expanded by Osborn into the modern *law of adaptive radiation*, which expresses the differentiation of animal form radiating in every direction in response to the necessities of the quest for nourishment and the development of new forms of motion in the different habitat zones. The psychic rudiments of this tendency to divergence are observed among the single-celled Protozoa (p. 114). *Divergence* is constantly giving rise to differences in structure, while *convergence* is constantly giving rise to resemblances of structure.

The law of adaptive radiation is a law expressing the modes

of adaptation of form, which fall under the following great principles of convergence and divergence:

Law of Adaptive Radiation in the External Body Form	1. *Divergent adaptation*, by which the members of a primitive stock tend to develop differences of form while radiating into a number of habitat zones. 2. *Convergent adaptation, parallel or homoplastic*, whereby animals from different habitat zones enter a similar habitat zone and acquire many superficial similarities of form. 3. *Direct adaptation*, for example, in primary migration through an ascending series of habitat zones, aquatic to terrestrial, arboreal, aërial. 4. *Reversed adaptation*, where secondary migration takes a reverse or descending direction from aërial to arboreal, from arboreal to terrestrial, from terrestrial to aquatic habitat zones. 5. *Alternate adaptation*, where the animal departs from an original habitat and primary phase of adaptation into a secondary phase, and then returns from the secondary phase of adaptation into a more or less perfect repetition of the primary phase by returning to the primary habitat zone. 6. *Change of adaptation (function)*, by which an organ serving a certain function in one zone is not lost but takes up an entirely new function in a new zone. 7. *Symbiotic adaptation*, where vertebrate forms exhibit reciprocal or interlocking adaptations with the form evolution of other vertebrates or invertebrates.

It is very important to keep in mind that the body and limb form developed in each adaptive phase is the starting point of the next succeeding phase.

Prolonged residence by an animal type in a single habitat zone results in profound alterations in its chromatin and in consequence the history of past phases is more or less clearly recorded.

Among the disadvantages of prolonged existence in one life zone are the following: Through the *law of compensation*, discovered by Geoffroy St. Hilaire early in the last century, every vertebrate, in developing and specializing certain organs sacrifices others; for example, the lateral digits of the foot of the horse are sacrificed for the evolution of the central digit as the animal evolves from tridactylism to monodactylism. These sacrificed parts are never regained; the horse can never regain the tridactyl condition although it may re-enter a habitat zone in which three digits on each foot would serve the purposes of locomotion better than one. In this sense chromatin evolution is irreversible. The extinction of vertebrate races has generally been due to the fact that the various types have sacrificed too many characters in their structural and functional reactions to a particular life habitat zone. A finely specialized form representing a perfect mechanism in itself which closely interlocks with its physical and living environment reaches a *cul-de-sac* of structure from which there is no possible emergence by adaptation to a different physical environment or habitat zone. It is these two principles of too close adjustment to a single environment and of the non-revival of characters once lost by the chromatin which underly the law that the highly specialized and most perfectly adapted types become extinct, while primitive, conservative, and relatively unspecialized types invariably become the centres of new adaptive radiations.

CHAPTER VI

EVOLUTION OF BODY FORM IN THE FISHES AND AMPHIBIANS

Rapid evolution in a relatively constant environment. Mechanism of motion, of offense, and defense. Early armored fishes. Primordial sharks. Rise of existing groups of fishes. Form evolution of the amphibians. Maximum radiation and extinction.

A SIGNIFICANT law of fish evolution is that in a practically unchanging environment, that of salt and fresh water, which is relatively constant both as to temperature and chemical constitution as compared with the variations of the terrestrial environment, it is steadily progressive and reaches the greatest extremes of form and of function. This indicates that a changing physicochemical environment, although important, is not an essential cause of the evolution of form. The same law holds true in the case of the marine invertebrates (p. 137), as observed by Perrin Smith. A second principle of significance is that even the lowliest fishes establish the chief glandular and other organs of action, reaction, and interaction which we observe in the higher types of the vertebrates. Especially the glands of internal secretion (p. 74), the *centres of interaction and coordination*, are fully developed.

MECHANISM OF MOTION, OF OFFENSE, AND DEFENSE

Ordovician time, the early Palæozoic Epoch next above the Cambrian, is the period of the first vertebrates known, namely, the fossil remains of fish dermal defenses found near Cañon City, Col., as announced by Walcott in 1891, and subsequently discovered in the region of the present Bighorn

Mountains of Wyoming and the Black Hills of South Dakota. Small spines referred to acanthodian sharks are also abundant in the Ordovician of Cañon City, Col. Since they were slow-moving types protected with the beginnings of a dorsal armature composed of small calcareous tubercles, to which the

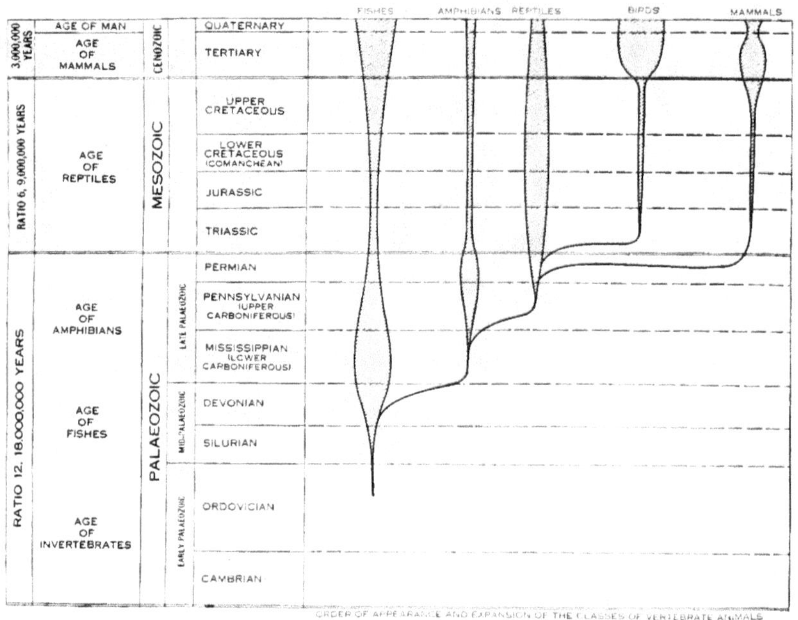

Fig. 42. Chronologic Chart of Vertebrate Succession.

Successive geologic appearance and epochs of maximum adaptive radiation (expansion) and diminution (contraction) of the five classes of vertebrates, namely, fishes, amphibians, reptiles, birds, and mammals.

group name *Ostracoderm* refers, probably these earliest known pro-fishes were not primitive in external form but followed upon a long antecedent stage of vertebrate evolution. In the form evolution of the vertebrates relatively swift-moving, defenseless types are invariably antecedent and ancestral to slow-moving, armored types. Ancestral to these Ordovician chordates there doubtless existed free-swimming, quickly darting types of unarmored fishes. The double-pointed, fusiform body, in which the segmented propelling muscles are external and a stiffening notochord is central, is the fish prototype, which more or less clearly survives in the existing lancelets (*Amphioxus*) and in the larval stages of the degenerate ascidians. These animals also furnish numerous embryonic and larval proofs of descent from nobler types.

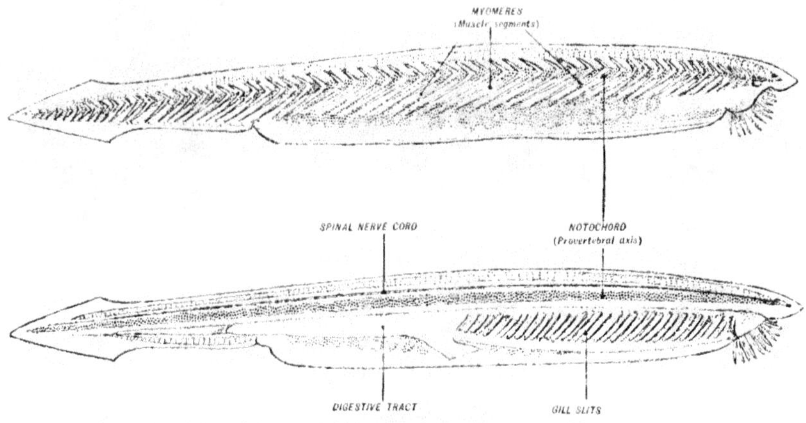

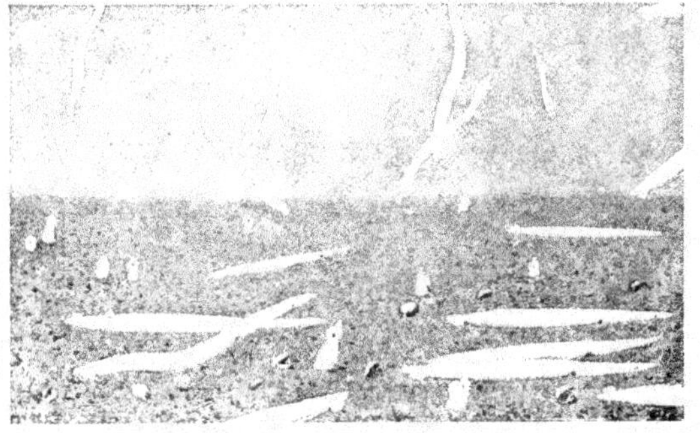

FIG. 43. THE EXISTING LANCELETS (*Amphioxus*).
Fusiform protochordates living in the littoral zone of the ocean shores, sole survivors of an extremely ancient stage of chordate (pro-vertebrate) evolution. The body is fusiform or doubly pointed, hence the name *Amphioxus*. It is stiffened by the continuous central axis (chorda, notochord). All the other organs are more or less sharply segmented. After Willey.

Following the pro-fishes of Ordovician time, the great group of true fishes begins its form evolution with (*A*) active, free-swimming, double-pointed types of fusiform shape, adapted to rapid motion through the water and to predaceous habits in pursuit of swift-moving prey.

From this type there radiated many others: (*B*) the deep, narrow-bodied fishes of relatively slow movements, frequenting the middle depths of the waters; (*D*) the swift-moving, elongate

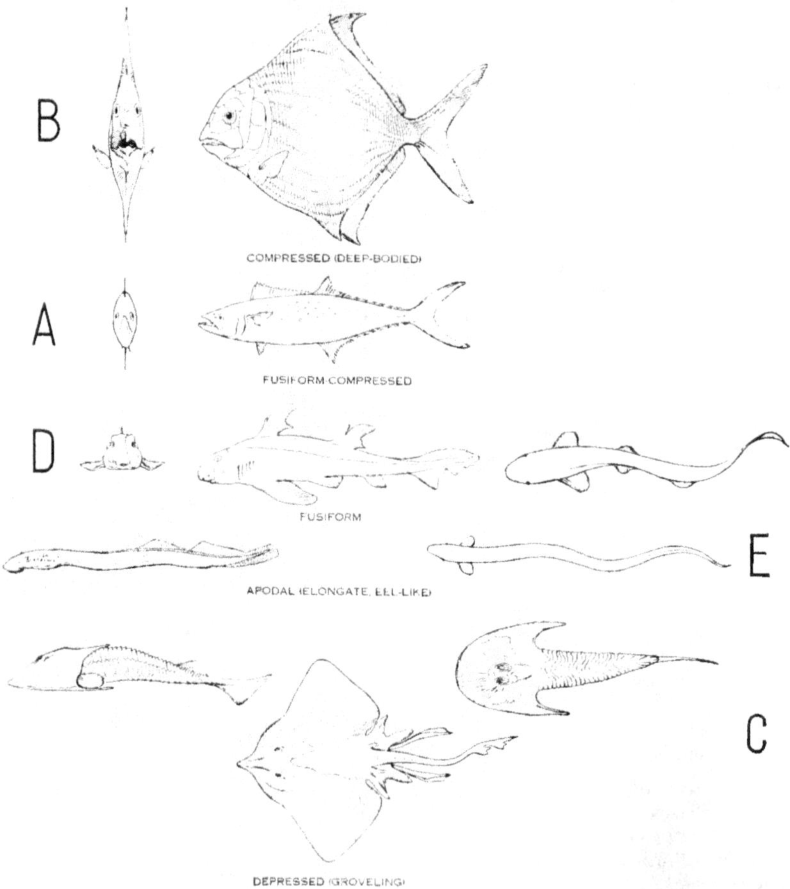

FIG. 44. THE FIVE PRINCIPAL TYPES OF BODY FORM IN FISHES.

These begin with (*A*) the swift-moving, compressed, fusiform types which pass, on the one hand, into (*B*) laterally compressed, slow-moving, deep-bodied types, and, on the other, into (*C*) laterally depressed, round, bottom-dwelling, slow-moving types, also into (*D*) elongate, swift-moving fusiform types which grade into (*E*) the eel-like, swift-moving, bottom-living types without lateral fins. These five types of body form in fishes arise independently over and over again in the various groups of this class of vertebrates. Partially convergent forms subsequently appear among amphibians, reptiles, and mammals. Prepared for the author by W. K. Gregory and Erwin S. Christman.

types which increasingly depend upon lateral motions of the body for propulsion and thus tend to lose the lateral fins and finally to assume (*E*) an elongate, eel shape, entirely finless, for progression along the bottom; (*C*) the bottom-living forms, in which the body becomes laterally broadened, the head very large relatively and covered with protective dermal armature, the movements of the animals becoming slower and slower as the dermal defenses develop. This law applies to all the vertebrates, including man, namely: the development of armor is *pari passu* with the loss of speed. Conversely, the gain of speed necessitates the loss of armor. Smith Woodward[1] has traced similar radiations of body form in the historic evolution of each of the great groups of fishes.

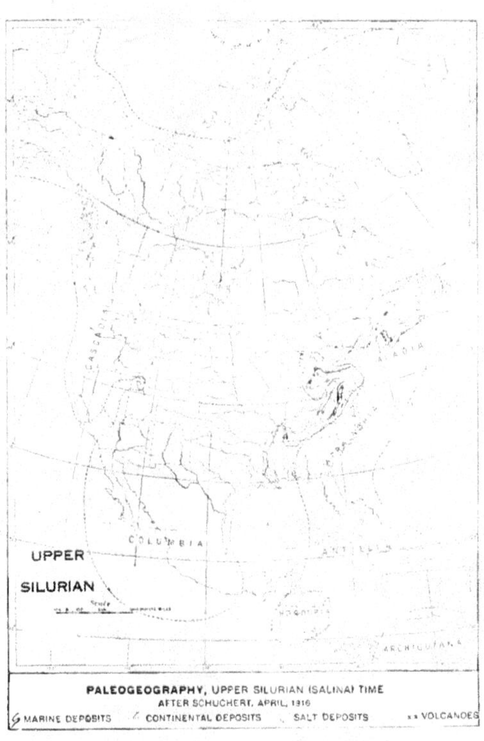

Fig. 45. North America in Upper Silurian Time.

During this period of depression of the Appalachian region and elevation of the western half of the North American continent occurred the maximum evolution of the most primitive armored fishes, known as Ostracoderms, which were widely distributed in Europe, America, and the Antarctic. After Schuchert, 1916.

The interest of this fivefold law of body-form radiation is greatly enhanced when we find it repeated successively under

[1] Smith Woodward, A., 1915.

the law of convergence among the aquatic amphibia, reptiles, and mammals as one of the invariable effects of the *coordination of the mechanism of locomotion with that of offense and defense*. In each of these four or five great radiations of body form, from the swift-moving to the bottom- or ground-living, slow, armored types, there is usually an increase of bodily size, also an increase of specialization, the maximum in both being reached just before the period of extinction arrives.

FIG. 46. THE OSTRACODERM *Palæaspis* OF CLAYPOLE AS RESTORED BY DEAN.

EARLY ARMORED FISHES

The armored Ordovician ostracoderms are very little known. The Upper Silurian ostracoderms enjoyed a wide distribution in Europe and America. They include both the fusiform, free-swimming type (*Birkenia*) and the broadly depressed ray-like types (*Lanarkia*, etc.). Apparently they had not yet acquired cartilaginous lower jaws and were in a lower stage of evolution than the true fishes.

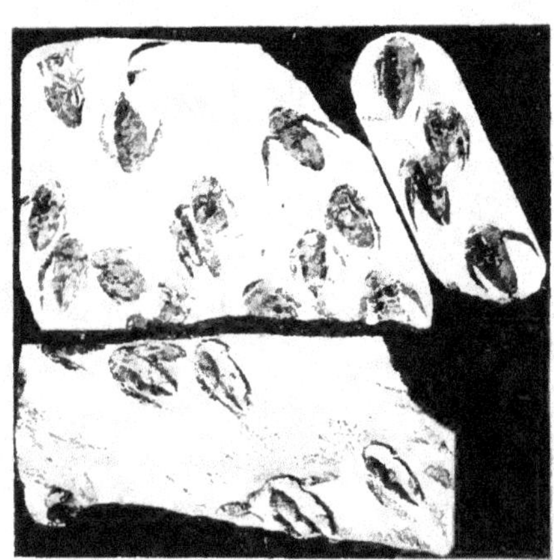

FIG. 47. THE ANTIARCHI.

Armored, bottom-living Ostracoderm type, *Bothriolepis*, from the Upper Devonian of Canada, with chitinous armature and a pair of anterior appendages analogous to those of the eurypterid crustaceans. This cluster of animals was undoubtedly buried simultaneously while headed against the current in search of food or for purposes of respiration. After Patten.

The armature is from the first arranged in shield and plate form, as seen in *Palæaspis*, from the Upper Silurian Salina time of Schuchert. In this epoch we obtain our first glimpses of North American land life in the presence of the oldest known air-breathing animals, the scorpion spiders, also of the first known land plants. There are indications of an arid climate in many parts of the world.

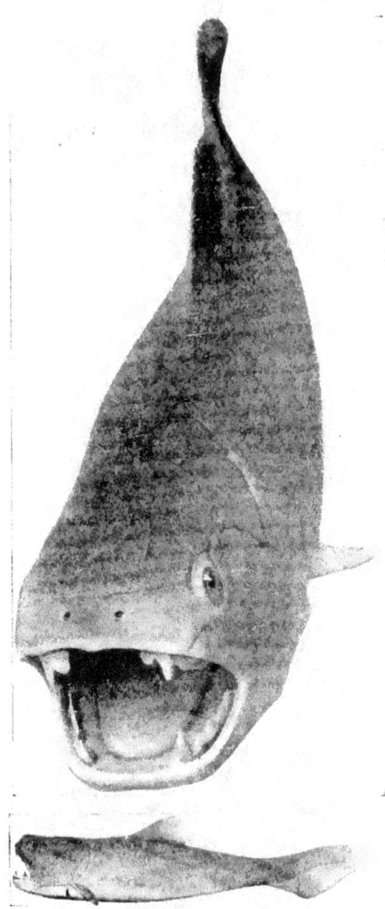

Fig. 48. The Arthrodira.

(Above.) Restoration of the gigantic Middle Devonian Arthrodiran (jointed neck) fish *Dinichthys intermedius*, eight feet in length, of the Cleveland shales (Ohio), showing the bony teeth and bony armature of the head region. (Below.) Lateral view of the same. Model by Dr. Louis Hussakof and Mr. Horter, in the American Museum of Natural History.

In Upper Silurian time the ostracoderms attain the slow, armored, bottom-living stage of evolution, typified in the pteraspidians and cephalaspidians, which were widely distributed in Europe, in America, and possibly in the Antarctic regions, as indicated by recent explorations there. Belonging to another and very distinct order, or subclass (Antiarchi), are certain armored Devonian forms (*Bothriolepis*, *Pterichthys*, etc.), which possessed a pair of jointed lateral appendages. Some of these fishes, which are propelled by a pair of appendages attached to the anterior portion of the body, present analogies to the eurypterids (Merostomata, or Arachnida).

In the fresh-water deposits of Lower Devonian age have been discovered the ancestors of the heavily armored fishes known as the Arthrodira, a group of uncertain relationships. They have many adaptations in common with *Bothriolepis*, such as the jointed neck, dermal jaws, carapace, plastron, and paired appendages (*Acanthaspis*). Some authorities regard the Arthrodira as aberrant lung-fishes. Dean, Hussakof, and others regard the balance of evidence as in favor of relationship with the stem of the Antiarchi (*Bothriolepis*). In the Middle Devonian (the Cleveland shales of Ohio) they attain the formidable size shown in the species *Dinichthys intermedius* (Fig. 48). Like the ostracoderms, these animals are not in the central or main lines of fish evolution but represent collateral lines which early attained a very high degree of specialization which was followed by extinction.

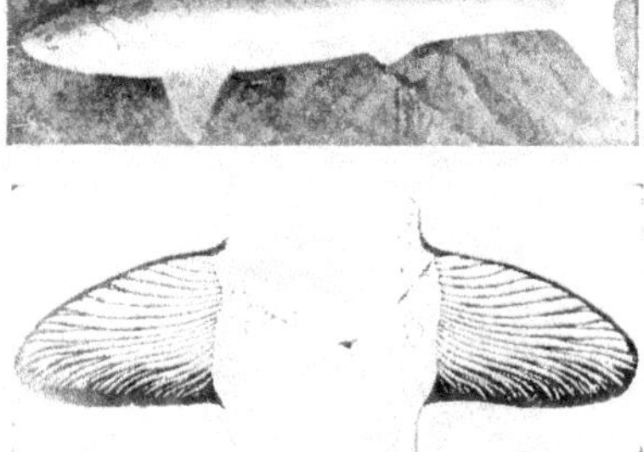

Fig. 40. A Primitive Devonian Shark. (Above.) *Cladoselache*, the type of the primitive Devonian shark of Ohio with paired and median lappet fins provided with rod-like cartilaginous supports, from which type by fusion the limbs of all the higher land vertebrates have been derived. Model by Dean, Hussakof, and Horter from specimens in the American Museum of Natural History. (Below.) The interior structure of the lappet fins of *Cladoselache* showing the cartilaginous rays (white) within the fin (black). After Dean.

Primordial Sharks, Ancestral to Higher Vertebrates

The central line of fish evolution, destined to give rise to all the higher and modern fish types, is found in the typical cartilaginous skeleton and jaws and four fins of the primordial sharks, the primitive fusiform stage of which appears in the spine-finned type (acanthodian, *Diplacanthus*, Fig. 51) of Upper Silurian time. The relatively large-headed, bottom-living types of sharks do not appear until the Devonian, during which epoch the early swift-moving, fusiform, predaceous types through a partly reversed adaptation branch off into the elongated eel-shaped forms of the Carboniferous.

The prototype of the shark group is the *Cladoselache* (Fig. 49), a fish famed in the annals of comparative anatomy since it demonstrates that the fins of fishes arise from lateral skin

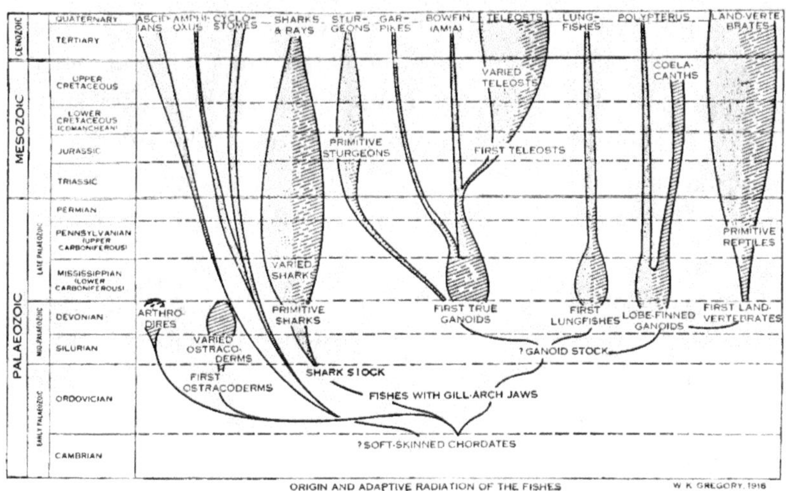

FIG. 50. ORIGIN AND ADAPTIVE RADIATION OF THE FISHES.

This chart shows the now extinct Siluro-Devonian groups, the Ostracoderms and Arthrodires, in relation to the surviving lampreys (Cyclostomes); sharks and rays (Elasmobranchs); sturgeons, garpikes, and bowfins (Ganoids); bony fishes (Teleosts); primitive and recent lung-fishes (Dipnoi); and finally the fringe-finned or lobe-finned Ganoids (Crossopterygii) from the cartilaginous fins of which the fore and hind limbs of the first land-living vertebrates (Tetrapoda) were derived. Dotted areas represent groups which still exist. Hatched areas represent extinct groups. Prepared for the author by W. K. Gregory.

folds of the body, into which are extended internal stiffening cartilaginous rods (Fig. 49). In course of evolution these rods are concentrated to form the central axis of a freely jointed fin, while in a further step of evolution they transform into the cartilages and bones of the limb girdles and limb segments of the four-footed land vertebrates, the Tetrapoda.

The manner of this fin and limb transformation has been one of the greatest problems in the history of the origin of animal form since the earliest researches of Carl Gegenbaur, of Heidelberg, who sought to derive the lateral fins from a modification through a profound change of adaptation (function) of the cartilaginous rods which support the respiratory gill arches. While palæontology has disproved Gegenbaur's hypothesis that the limbs of the higher vertebrates, including those of man, are derived from the cartilaginous gill arches of fishes, it has helped to demonstrate the truth of Reichert's anatomical hypothesis that the bony chain of the middle ear of man has been derived through change of adaptation from a portion of a modified gill arch, namely, the mandibular cartilage of the fish.

The cycle of shark evolution in course of geologic time embraces a majority of the swift-moving, predaceous types, which radiate into the sinuous, elongate body of the frilled shark (*Chlamydoselache*) and into forms with broadly depressed bodies, such as the bottom-living skates and rays. Under the law of adaptive radiation the sharks seek every possible habitat zone except the abyssal in the search for food. The nearest approach to the evolution of the eel-shaped type among the sharks are certain forms discovered in Carboniferous time.

Rise of Modern Fishes

By Upper Devonian time the fishes in general had already radiated into all the great existing groups. The primitive armored arthrodires and ostracoderms were nearing extinction. The sharks were still in the early lappet-fin stage of evolution above described, a common characteristic of the members of this entire order being that they never evolved a solid bony armature, finding sufficient protection in the shagreen covering.

The scaled armature of the first true ganoid, enamel-covered fishes (*Osteolepis, Cheirolepis*) now makes its first appearance. These armored knights of the sea are descended from simpler scaly forms which also gave rise to the rich stock of sturgeons, garpikes, bowfins, and true bony fishes (teleosts) which now dominate all other fish groups both in the fresh

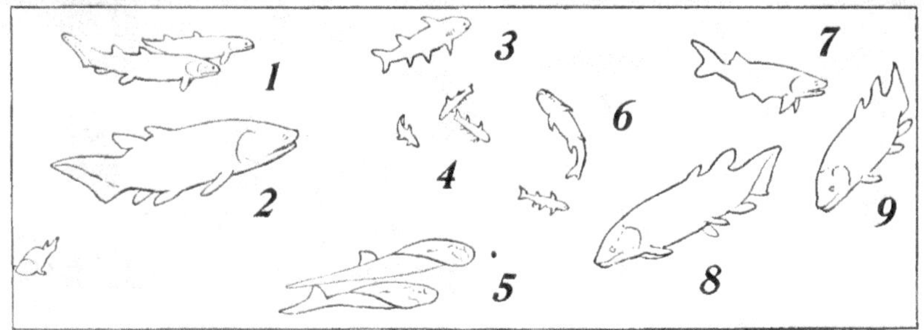

FIG. 51. FISH TYPES FROM THE OLD RED SANDSTONE OF SCOTLAND.

Upper Devonian time. Primitive ganoids, primitive spine-finned sharks, bottom-living Ostracoderms, partly armored ganoids, and the first lung-fishes. 1. *Osteolepis*, primitive lobe-finned ganoid. 2. *Holoptychius*, fringe-finned ganoid. 3, 6. *Cheiracanthus*, spine-finned shark (Acanthodian). 4. *Diplacanthus*, spine-finned shark (Acanthodian). 5. *Coccosteus*, primitive Arthrodiran. 7. *Cheirolepis*, primitive ganoid. 8, 9. *Dipterus*, primitive lung-fish. *Pterichthys*, bottom-living Ostracoderm allied to *Bothriolepis*. Restorations by Dean, Hussakof, and Horter, partly after Traquair. Models in the American Museum of Natural History.

waters and the seas. Remotely allied to this stock are the first air-breathing lung-fishes (Dipnoi), represented by *Dipterus*; also the "lobe-finned," or "fringe-finned" ganoids from which the first land vertebrates were derived. From a single locality, in the Old Red Sandstone of Scotland, Traquair has recovered a whole fossil series of these archaic fish types as they lived together in the fresh water or the brackish pools of Upper Devonian time. (Fig. 51).

In this period the palæogeographers (Schuchert) obtain their first knowledge of the evolution of the terrestrial environment in the indications of the existence of parallel mountain ranges on the British Isles, of active volcanoes in the Gaspé region of

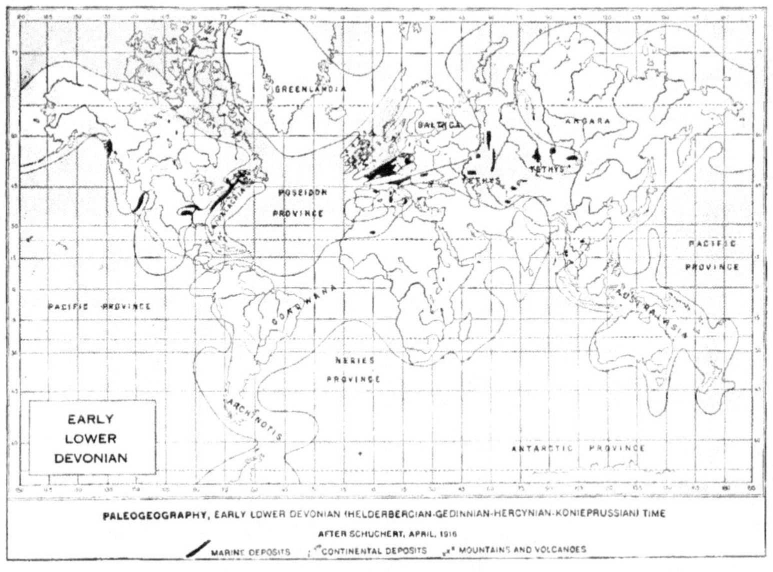

FIG. 52. THEORETIC WORLD ENVIRONMENT IN EARLY LOWER DEVONIAN TIMES. The period of the early appearance of terrestrial invertebrates and vertebrates. This shows the hypothetical South Atlantic continent *Gondwana* and the Eurasiatic inland sea *Tethys*, according to the hypotheses of Suess. Modified after Schuchert, 1916.

New Brunswick, of the mountain formations of South Africa, and of the depressions of the centre of the Eurasiatic continent into the great central Mediterranean Sea, known as the *Tethys* of the great Austrian geologist, Suess. In the seas of this time, as compared with Cambrian seas, we observe that the trilobites are in a degenerate phase, the brachiopods are relatively less numerous, the echinoderms are represented by the bottom-living starfishes, sharks are abundant, and arthrodiran fishes are still abundant in Germany.

It was long believed that the air-and-water-breathing Amphibia evolved from the Dipnoi, the air-breathing fishes of the inland fresh waters, and this hypothesis was stoutly main-

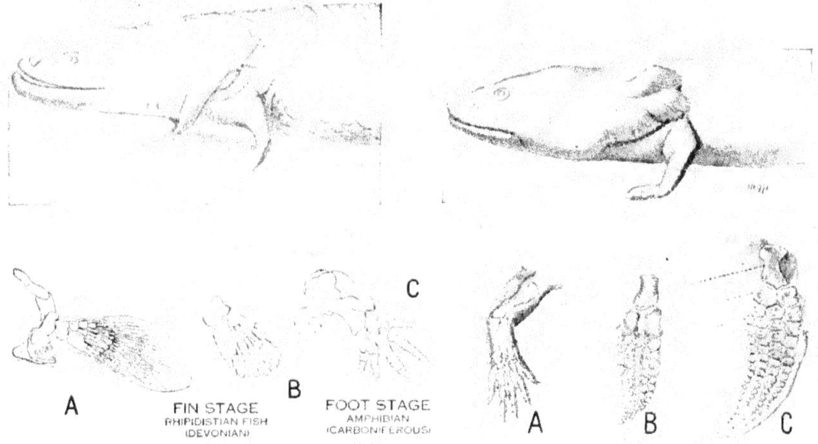

Fig. 53. Change of Adaptation in the Limbs of Vertebrates.

The upper figures represent the theoretic mode of metamorphosis of the fringe-fin of the Crossopterygian fish (left) into the foot of an amphibian (right) through loss of the dermal fringe border and rearrangement of the cartilaginous supports of the lobe. After Klaatsch.

The lower figures represent (left) the theoretic mode of direct original evolution of the bones of the fringe-fin (*A*, *B*) of a Crossopterygian fish—the *Rhipidistia* type of Cope—into the bony, five-rayed limb (*C*) of an amphibian of the Carboniferous Epoch (after Gregory); and (right) the secondary, reversed evolution of the five-rayed limb of a land reptile (*A*) into the fin or paddle (*B*, *C*) of an ichthyosaur (after Osborn).

tained by Carl Gegenbaur, who also upheld what he termed the archipterygian theory of the origin of the vertebrate limb, namely, that the prototype of the modern limbed forms of terrestrial vertebrates is to be found in the fin of the modern Australian lung-fish, *Ceratodus*. This hypothesis of Gegenbaur, which has been warmly supported by a talented group of his students, is memorable as the last of the great hypotheses regarding vertebrate descent to be founded exclusively upon

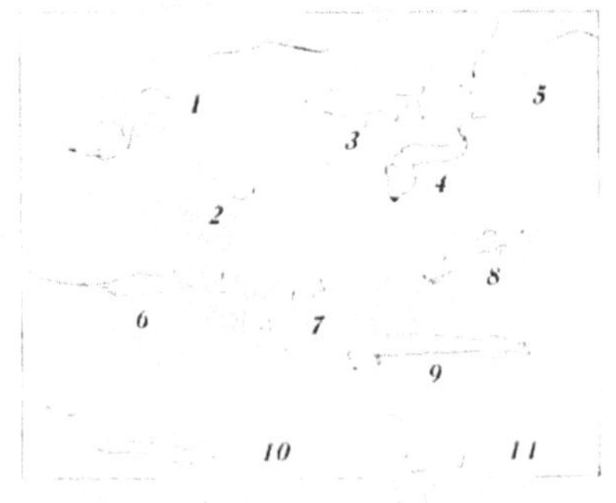

FIG. 54. EXTREMES OF ADAPTATION IN LOCOMOTION AND ILLUMINATION.

Extremes of adaptation in the existing bony fishes (Teleosts) of the Abyssal Zone of the Oceans. Although many different orders of Teleosts are represented, each type has independently acquired phosphorescent organs, affording a fine example of the law of adaptive convergence. The body form in these fishes is of great diversity. 1. Thread-eel, *Nemichthys scolopaceus* Richardson. 2. *Barathronus diaphanus* Brauer. 3. *Neoscopelus macrolepidotus* Johnson. 4, 5. *Gastrostomus bairdi* Gill and Ryder. 6. *Gigantactis vanhoeffeni* Brauer. 7. *Sternoptyx diaphana* Lowe. 8. *Gigantura chuni* Brauer. 9. *Melanostomias melanops* Brauer. 10. *Stylophthalmus paradoxus* Brauer. 11. *Opisthoproctus soleatus* Vaillant. After models in the American Museum of Natural History.

comparative anatomy and embryology as opposed to the triple evidence afforded by these sciences when reinforced by palæontology.

It is through the discovery of primitive types of the fringe-finned ganoids, to which Huxley gave the appropriate name Crossopterygia, in reference to the fringe of dermal rays around a central lobe-fin of cartilaginous rods, that the true ancestry of the Amphibia and of the amphibian limb has been traced. This is now regarded as due to a partial change of adaptation,

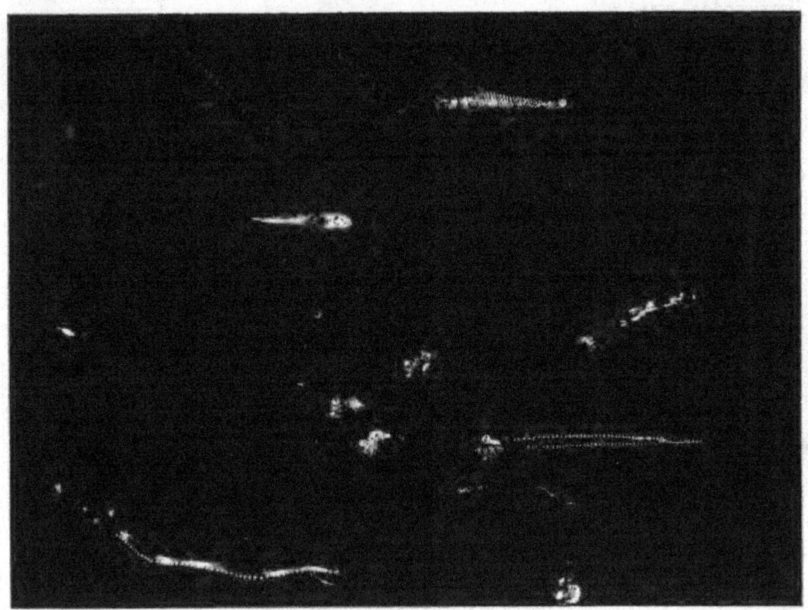

Fig. 55. Phosphorescent Illuminating Organs.

The abyssal fishes represented in Fig. 54 as they are supposed to appear in the darkness of the ocean depths. After models in the American Museum of Natural History.

incident to the passage of the animal from the littoral life zone to the shore zone, whereby the propelling fin was gradually transformed into the propelling limb. This transformation implies a long terrestrio-aquatic phase, in which the fin was partly used for propulsion on muddy surfaces (Fig. 53).

In the reversed parallel retrogressive evolution of the lung-fishes (*Lepidosiren*, *Gymnotus*), of the fringe-finned fishes (*Calamoichthys*) and of the bony fishes (*Anguilla*), the final eel-shaped, finless stage is through convergent adaptation either approached or actually passed.

The bony fishes (teleosts), which first emerge as a distinct group in Jurassic time, radiate adaptively into all the great body-form types which had been previously attained by the older groups, more or less closely imitating each in turn, so that it is not easy to distinguish superficially between the armored catfishes (*Loricaria*) of the existing South American waters and their prototypes (*Cephalaspis*) of the early Palæozoic. The most extreme specialization in the great group of bony fishes is to be found in the radiations of abyssal fishes into slow- and swift-moving forms which inhabit the great depths of the ocean and are adapted to tons of water-pressure, to temperatures just above the freezing point, and to total absence of sunlight which is compensated for by the evolution of a great variety of phosphorescent light-

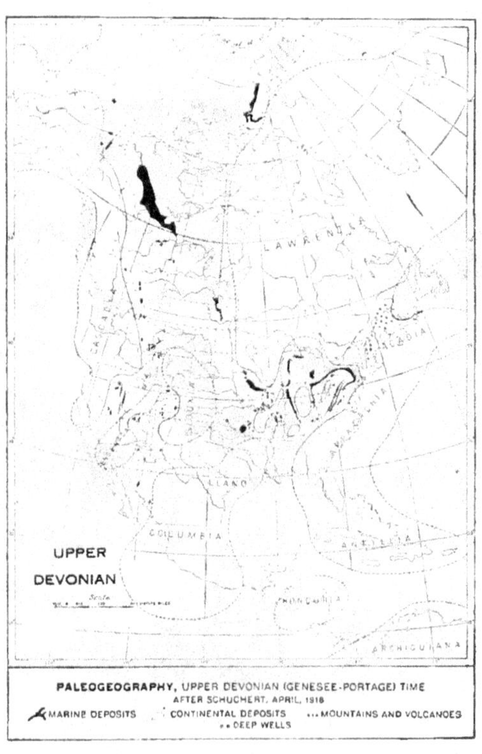

FIG. 56. NORTH AMERICA IN UPPER DEVONIAN TIME.

The maximum evolution of the Arthrodiran fishes (*Dinichthys*, etc.) and of the ganoids of the Upper Devonian of Scotland, the establishment of all the great modern orders of fishes excepting the bony fishes (Teleosts), and the appearance of the first land vertebrates, the amphibians (*Thinopus*), took place during this period of depression of the western centre of the North American continent. Modified after Schuchert.

producing organs in the fishes themselves and in other animals on which they prey.

Another extreme of chemical evolution among the fishes is the production of electricity as a protective function, which is even more effective than bony armature because it does not interfere with rapid locomotion. In only a few of the fishes is electricity generated in sufficient amounts to thoroughly protect the organism. It develops through modified body tissues in the form of superimposed plates (electroplaxes) separated equally from one another by layers of a peculiar jelly-like connective tissue, all lying parallel to each other and at right angles to the direction of discharge.[1] The electric organ is formed from modified muscle and connective tissue and is innervated by motor nerves. The physical principle involved is that of the concentration cell, and the electrolyte used in the process is probably sodium chloride. The theory is that at the moment of discharge a membrane is formed on one surface of the electroplax which prevents the negative ions from passing through while the positive ions do pass through and form the current. The strength of the current varies from four volts in *Mormyrus* up to as much as 250 or more in *Gymnotus*, the electric eel, and consists of a series of shocks discharged 3/1000 of a second apart.

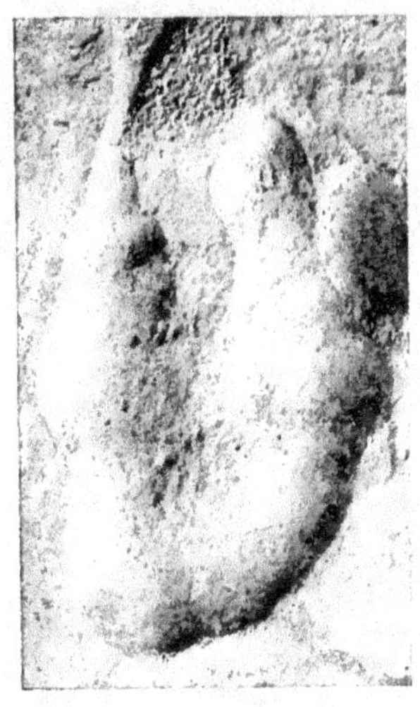

FIG. 57. THE EARLIEST KNOWN LIMBED ANIMAL.
Footprint of *Thinopus antiquus* Marsh, an amphibian from the Upper Devonian of Pennsylvania. Type in the Peabody Museum of Yale University. Photograph of cast presented to the American Museum of Natural History by the Peabody Museum.

[1] Dahlgren, Ulric, 1906, pp. 389–398; 1910, p. 200.

FORM EVOLUTION OF THE AMPHIBIANS

A single impression of a three-toed footprint (*Thinopus antiquus*) in the Upper Devonian shales of Pennsylvania constitutes at present the sole palæontologic proof of the long period of transition of the vertebrates from the fish type to the amphibian type. This transition was a matter of thousands of years. It took place in Lower Devonian if not in Upper Silurian time. Under the influence of the heredity-chromatin it is now rehearsed or recapitulated in a few days in the metamorphosis from the tadpole to the frog.

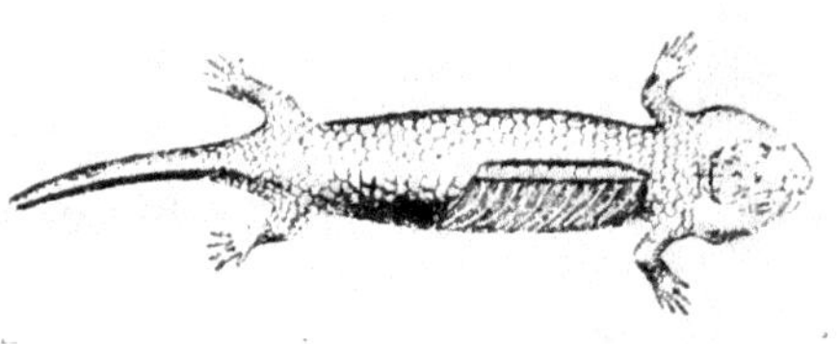

FIG. 58. A PRIMITIVE AMPHIBIAN.
Theoretic reconstruction of a primitive salamander-like type with large, solidly roofed skull, four limbs, and five fingers on each of the fore and hind feet, such as may have existed in Upper Devonian time. After Fritsch.

As compared with fishes, the significant principle of the evolution of amphibians, as the earliest terrestrial vertebrates, is their reaction to marked environmental change. Their entire life responds to the changes of the seasons. They also respond to secular changes of environment in the evolution of types adapted to extremely arid conditions.

The adaptive radiation of the primordial Amphibia probably began in Middle Devonian time and extended through the great swamp, coal-forming period of the Carboniferous, which afforded over vast areas of the earth's surface ideal conditions for amphibian evolution, the stages of which are best preserved in the Coal Measures of Scotland, Saxony, Bohemia, Ohio, and Pennsylvania, and have been revealed through the studies of von Meyer, Owen, Fritsch, Cope, Credner, and Moodie. The earliest of these terrestrio-aquatic types have not only a dual breathing system of gills and lungs, but a dual motor equipment of limbs and of a propelling median fin in the tail region.

So far as known, the primordial Amphibia in their form were chiefly of the small-headed, long-bodied, small-limbed, tail-propelled type of the modern salamander and newt. The large-headed, short-bodied types (*Amphibamus*) were precocious descendants of such primordial forms. In Upper Carbonifer-

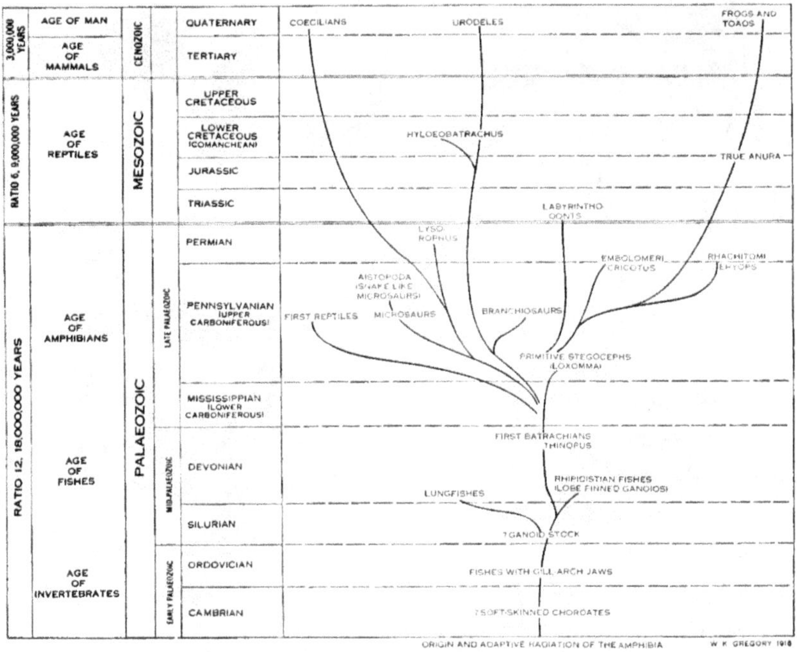

FIG 59. DESCENT OF THE AMPHIBIA

The Amphibia—in which the fin is transformed into a limb (*Thinopus*)—are believed to have evolved from an ancestral ganoid fish stock of Silurian age through the fringe-finned ganoids. From this group diverge the ancestors of the Reptilia and the salamander-like Amphibia which give rise to the various salamander types, also to branches of limbless and snake-like forms (Aistopoda, modern Cœcilians). The other great branch of the solid-skulled Amphibia, the Stegocephalia, was widespread all over the northern continents in Permian and Triassic time (*Cricotus*, *Eryops*), and from this stock descended the modern frogs and toads (Anura). Prepared for the author by W. K. Gregory.

ous and early Permian time the terrestrial amphibians began to be favored by the land elevation and recession of the sea which distinguished the close of the Carboniferous and early Permian time. Under these varied zonal conditions, aquatic, palustral, terrestrio-aquatic, fossorial, and terrestrial, the Am-

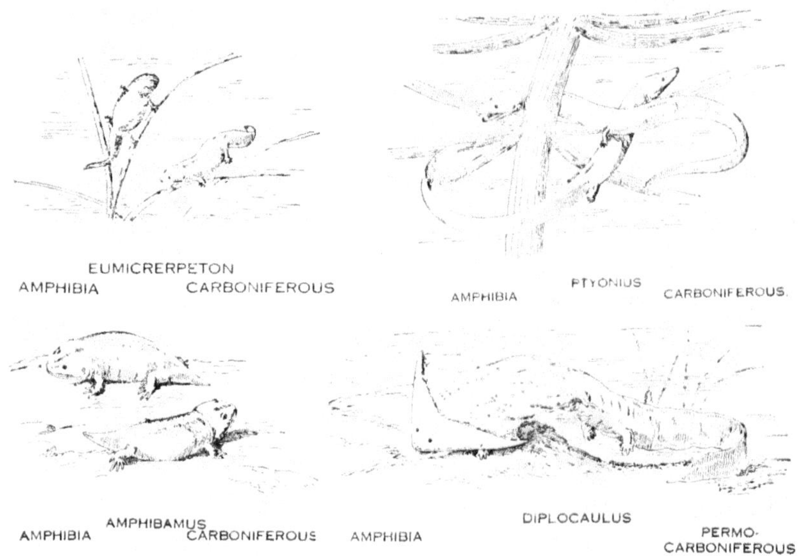

FIG. 60. CHIEF AMPHIBIAN TYPES OF THE CARBONIFEROUS.
Restorations of the early short-tailed, land-living *Amphibamus*, the salamander-like *Eumicrerpeton*, the eel-bodied *Ptyonius*, and the broad-headed, bottom-living *Diplocaulus*. Prepared for the author by W. K. Gregory and Richard Deckert.

phibia began to radiate into several habitat zones and adaptive phases, and thus to imitate the chief types of body form which had previously evolved among the fishes as well as to anticipate many of the types of body form which were to evolve subsequently among the reptiles. One ancestral feature of the amphibians is a layer of superficial body scales in some types, which appear to be derived from those of their lobe-finned fish ancestors; with the loss of these scales most of the Amphibia also lost the power of forming a bony dermal armature.

Recent researches in this country, chiefly by Williston, Case, and Moodie, indicate that the solid-headed Amphibia (Stegocephalia) and primary forms of the Reptilia chiefly belong to late Carboniferous (Pennsylvania) and early Permian time. They are found abundantly in ancient pool deposits, which are now widespread over the southwestern United States and Europe deposited in rocks of a reddish color. This reddish color points to aridity of climate in the northern hemisphere during the period in which the terrestrial adaptive radiation of the Amphibia occurred. These arid conditions continued during the greater part of Permian time, especially in the northern hemisphere.

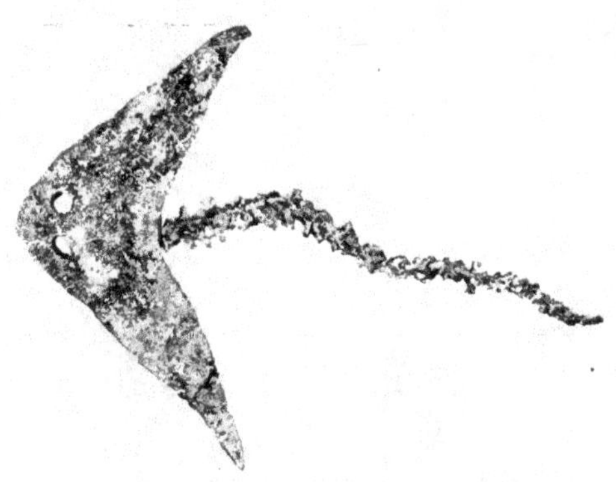

Fig. 61. Skull and Vertebral Column of *Diplocaulus*.

A typical solid-, broad-headed amphibian from the Permian of northern Texas. Specimen in the American Museum of Natural History. (Compare Fig. 60.)

In the southern hemisphere there is evidence, on the contrary, of a period of humidity, cold, and extensive glaciation, which was accompanied by the disappearance of the old lycopod flora (club-mosses) and arrival of the cool fern flora (*Glossopteris*), which appeared simultaneously in South America, South Africa, Australia, Tasmania, and southern India. The widespread distribution of this flora in the southern hemisphere furnishes one of the arguments for the existence of the great South Atlantic continent *Gondwana*, a transatlantic land bridge of animal and plant migration, postulated by Suess and supported by the palæogeographic studies of Schuchert. In North America the glaciation of Permian time is believed to have been only local. The last of the great Palæozoic seas disappeared from the surface of the continents, while the border seas give evidence of the rise of the ammonite cephalopods. Toward the close of Permian time the continent was completely drained. Along the eastern seaboard the Appalachian

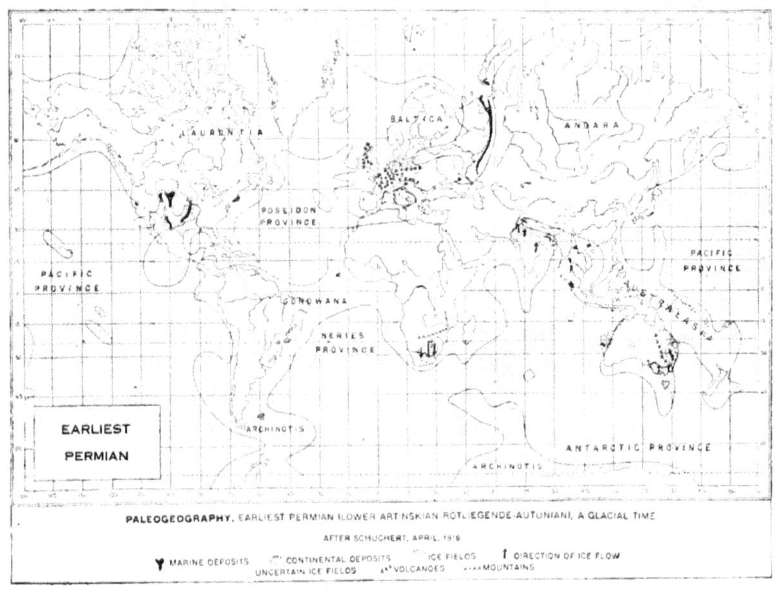

FIG. 62. THEORETIC WORLD ENVIRONMENT IN EARLIEST PERMIAN TIME.

A period of marked glacial conditions in the Antarctic region. Vanishing of the coal floras and rise of the cycad-conifer floras, along with the rise of more modern insects and the beginning of the dominance of reptiles. Modified after Schuchert, 1916.

revolution occurred, and the mountains rose to heights estimated at from three to five miles.

An opposite extreme, of slender body structure, is found in the active predaceous types of water-loving amphibians such as *Cricotus*, of rapid movements, propelled by a long tail fin, and with sharp teeth adapted to seizing an actively moving prey. This type retrogresses into the eel-like, bottom-loving *Lysorophus* with its slender skull, elongate body propelled by lateral swimming undulations, the limbs relatively useless. Corresponding to the bottom-living fishes are the large, sluggish, broad-headed, bottom-living amphibians, such as *Diplocaulus*, with heads heavily armored, limbs small and weak, the body propelled by lateral motions of the tail. There were also

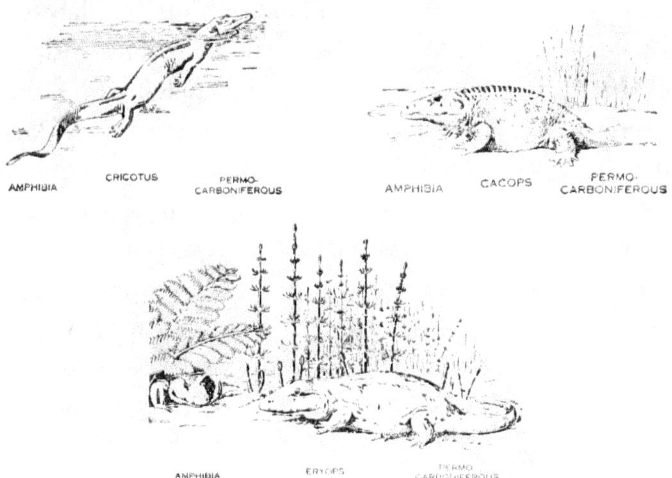

FIG. 63. AMPHIBIA OF THE AMERICAN PERMO-CARBONIFEROUS.

Here are found the free-swimming *Cricotus*, the short-bodied *Cacops*, and abundance of the amphibious terrestrial type, the large, solid-headed *Eryops*. Restorations for the author by W. K. Gregory and Richard Deckert.

more powerful, slow-moving, long-headed, alligator-like, terrestrio-aquatic forms, such as the *Archegosaurus* of Europe and the fully aquatic *Trimerorachis* of America. An extreme stage of terrestrial, ground-living evolution with marked reduction of the use of the tail for propulsion is the large-headed *Cacops*, short-bodied, with limbs of medium size, but with feeble powers of prehension in the feet. Radiating around these animals were a number of terrestrial types exhibiting the evolution of dorsal protective armature and spines (*Aspidosaurus*); other types lead into the pointed-headed structure and pointed teeth of *Trematops*.

The Age of Amphibians passes its climax in Permian time (Fig 63.). In Triassic time there still survive the giant terrestrial forms.

Evidences of extensive intercontinental connections in the northern hemisphere are also found in the similarity of type between the great terrestrial amphibians of such widely separated areas as Texas and Würtemberg, which develop into similar resemblances between the great labyrinthodont amphibians of Lower Triassic times of Europe, North America, and Africa. Ancestral to these Triassic giants is the large, sluggish, water- and shore-living *Eryops* of the Texas Permian, with massive head, depending on its short, powerful limbs and broad, spreading feet for land propulsion, and in a less degree upon its tail for propulsion in the water. This animal may be regarded as a collateral ancestor of the labyrinthodonts; it belongs to a type which spread all over Europe and North America and persisted into the *Metopias* of the Triassic.

FIG. 64. SKELETON OF *Eryops* FROM THE PERMO-CARBONIFEROUS OF TEXAS. A type of the stegocephalian Amphibia which were structurally ancestral to the Labyrinthodonts of the Triassic. Mounted in the American Museum of Natural History.

CHAPTER VII

FORM EVOLUTION OF THE REPTILES AND BIRDS

Appearance of earliest reptile-like forms, the pro-Reptilia, followed by the first higher reptiles. Geologic distribution and environment of the various extinct and existing orders of reptilia. Evolutionary laws exemplified in the origin and development of this great group of animal life. Direct, reversed, alternate, and convergent adaptation. Modes of offense and defense. Terrestrial, fossorial, aquatic, and marine radiation. Aërial adaptation. The Pterosaurs. First appearance of bird-like animals. Theories regarding the evolution of flight in birds. Theories as to the causes of arrested evolution.

The environment of the ancestor of all the reptiles was a warm, terrestrial, and semi-arid region, favorable to a sensitive nervous system, alert motions, scaly armature, slender limbs, a vibratile tail, and the capture of food both by sharply pointed, recurved teeth and by the claws of a five-fingered hand and foot. The mechanically adaptive evolution of the Reptilia from such an ancestor is as marvellous and extreme as the subsequent evolution of the mammals; it far exceeds in diversity the radiation of the Amphibia and extends over a period estimated at from 15,000,000 to 20,000,000 years.

The Permian Reptiles of North America and South Africa

The experiments of the Amphibia in adapting themselves to the Permian continents with their relatively dry surfaces and seasonal water pools and lagoons are contemporaneous with the first terrestrial experiments and adaptive radiations of the Reptilia, a group which was particularly favored in its origin by arid environmental conditions. The result is the creation in Permian time of many externally analogous or convergent groups of amphibians and reptiles which in external appearance are difficult to distinguish. Yet as divergent from the primitive salamander-like Amphibia and clearly of another

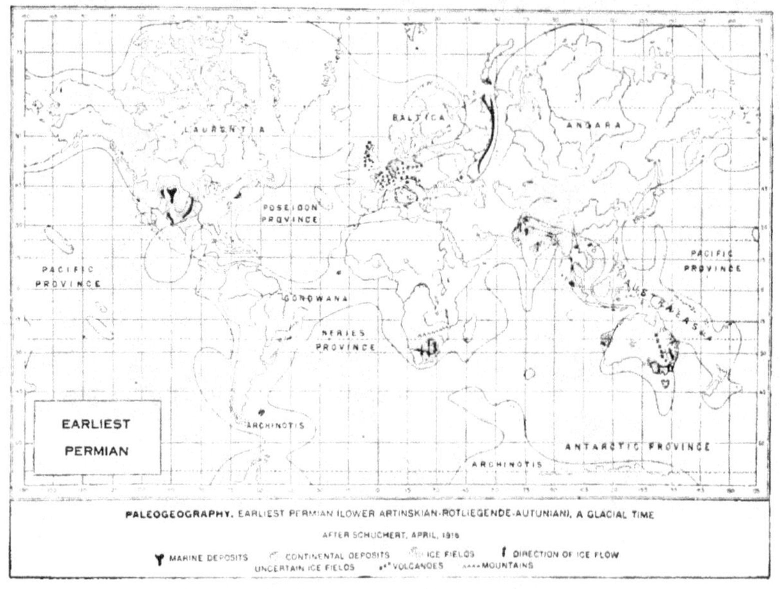

FIG. 65. THEORETIC WORLD ENVIRONMENT IN EARLIEST PERMIAN TIME.

A period of marked glacial conditions in the Antarctic region. Vanishing of the coal floras and rise of the cycad-conifer floras, along with the rise of more modern insects and the beginning of the dominance of reptiles. Modified after Schuchert, 1916.

type these pro-reptiles are different in the inner skeletal structure and in the anatomy of the skull they are exclusively air-breathing, primarily terrestrial in habit rather than terrestrio-aquatic, superior in their nervous reactions and in the development of all the sensory organs, and have a more highly perfected cold-blooded circulatory system. Nevertheless, the most ancient solid-headed reptilian skull type (Cotylosauria, Pareiasauria, of Texas and South Africa, respectively) is very similar to that of the solid-headed Amphibia (Stegocephalia). Bone by bone its parts indicate a common descent from the skull type of the fringe-finned fishes (Crossopterygia, Fig. 53).

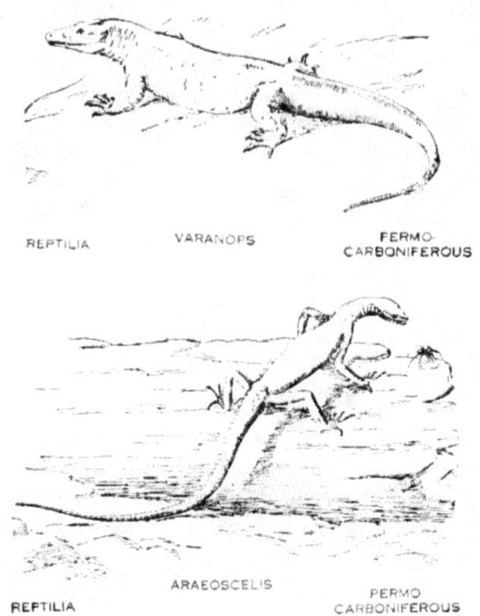

FIG. 66. ANCESTRAL REPTILIAN TYPES.

Two of the defenseless, swift-moving, terrestrial reptilian types, *Varanops* and *Aræoscelis*, of the Permo-Carboniferous period of Texas. The skull and skeleton of *Aræoscelis* foreshadow the existing lizard (Lacertilian) type and Williston regards it as the most nearly related Permian representative known of the true Squamata (ancestors of the lizards, snakes, and mosasaurs). Restorations of *Varanops* and *Aræoscelis* modified from Williston. Drawn for the author by Richard Deckert.

As revealed by the researches of Cope, Williston, and Case, the adaptive radiation of the reptile life of western America in Permian time is as follows: First there is a variety of swift-moving, alert, predaceous forms corresponding to the fusiform, swift-moving stage in the evolution of the fishes. Some of these reptiles (*Varanops*) resemble the modern monitor lizards (*Varanus*); others (*Ophiacodon* and *Theropleura*) are provided with four well-developed limbs and feet, the long tail being utilized as a balancing organ. These were littoral or lowland reptiles, insectivorous or carnivorous in habit. The primitive, lizard-like pelycosaur *Varanops*, with a long tail and four limbs of equal proportions, represents more nearly than any known ancient reptile, apart from certain special characters, a generalized prototype from which all the eighteen Orders of the Reptilia might have descended; its structure could well be ancestral to that of the lizards, the alligators, and the dinosaurs. At present, however, it is not determined whether the primitive ancestors from which the various orders of reptiles descended belong to a single, a double, or a multiple stock.

Passing to the widely different amphibian-like order known as cotylosaurs, we see animals which, on the one hand, grade into the more fully aquatic, paddle-footed, free-swimming *Limnoscelis* with a short, crocodile-like head, which propelled itself by means of its long tail, and, on the other hand, there developed short-tailed, semi-aquatic forms, such as the *Labidosaurus.* In adaptation to the more purely terrestrial habitats there is sometimes a reduction in the length of the tail and greater perfection in the structure of the limbs and the various forms of armature. In *Pantylus* these defenses appear in the form of bony ossicles of the skin and scutes; in *Chilonyx* the skull top is covered with tuberculated defenses; in the slow-moving *Diadectes* the body is partly armored, the animal being proportioned like the existing Gila monster and probably of nocturnal habits, which is inferred from the large size of the eyes.

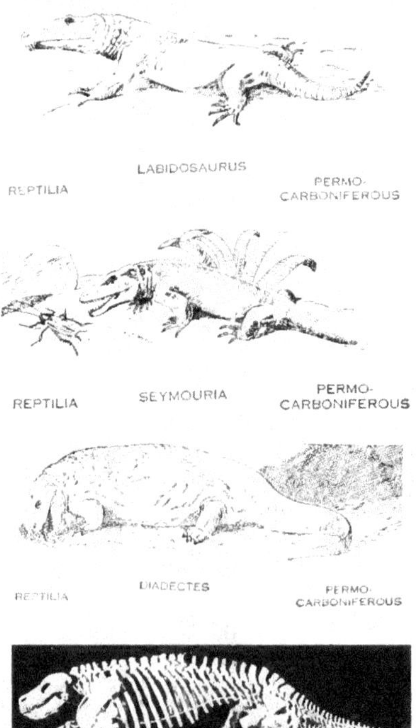

FIG. 67. REPTILES WITH SKULLS TRANSITIONAL IN STRUCTURE FROM THE AMPHIBIAN SKULL.

Typical solid-headed reptiles (Cotylosaurs) characteristic of Permo-Carboniferous time in northern Texas, including the three forms *Seymouria*, *Labidosaurus*, and the powerful *Diadectes*, which resembles the existing Gila monster. The head in the mounted skeleton of *Diadectes* (lower) in the American Museum of Natural History is probably bent too sharply on the neck. Restorations for the author by W. K. Gregory and Richard Deckert. *Labidosaurus* and *Seymouria* chiefly after Williston.

The most remarkable types in this complex reptilian society of Permian Texas are the giant fin-backed lizards, *Clepsydrops, Dimetrodon, Edaphosaurus*, of Cope, probably terrestrial and carnivorous in habit. In these animals the neural spines of the dorsal vertebræ are vertically elongated to support a powerful median membranous fin, the spines of which are sometimes

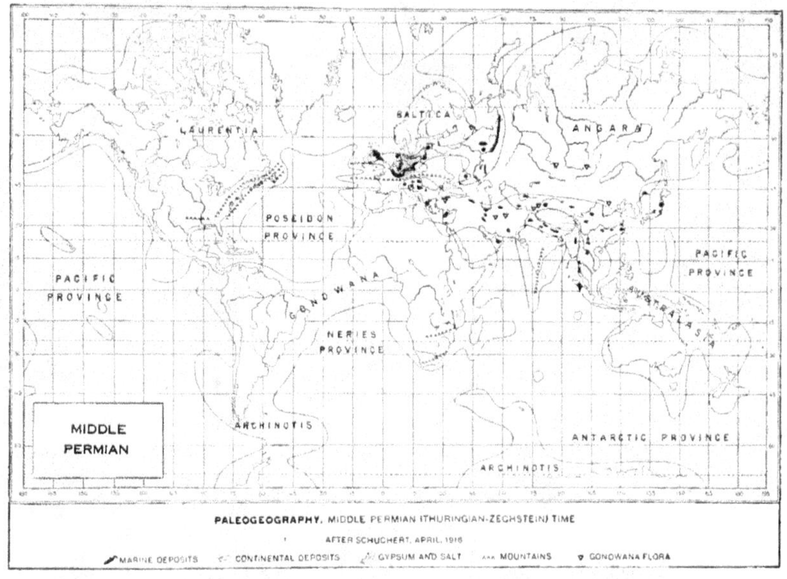

Fig. 68. Theoretic World Environment in Middle Permian Time.
Great extension of the Baltic Sea and of the Eurasiatic Mediterranean *Tethys*. Rise of the Appalachian, Northern European Alps, and many other mountains. Modified after Schuchert.

smooth (*Dimetrodon*), sometimes provided with transverse rods (*Edaphosaurus cruciger*). These structures may have developed through social or racial competition and selection within this reptile family rather than as offensive or defensive organs in relation to other reptile families.

We now glance at the Permian life of another great zoologic region. Africa has been throughout all geologic time the most stable of the continents, especially since the beginning of the Permian Epoch. The contemporaneous evolution of the pro-Reptilia, traced in a continuous earth section from the base of the Permian to the Lower Triassic, as successively explored by Bain, Owen, Seeley, Broom, and Watson, has revealed a far more extensive and more varied adaptive radiation of the reptiles than that which is known on the American continent. Although the adaptations are chiefly terrestrial, we trace certain strong analogies if not actual relationships to the Permo-Triassic reptiles of North America.

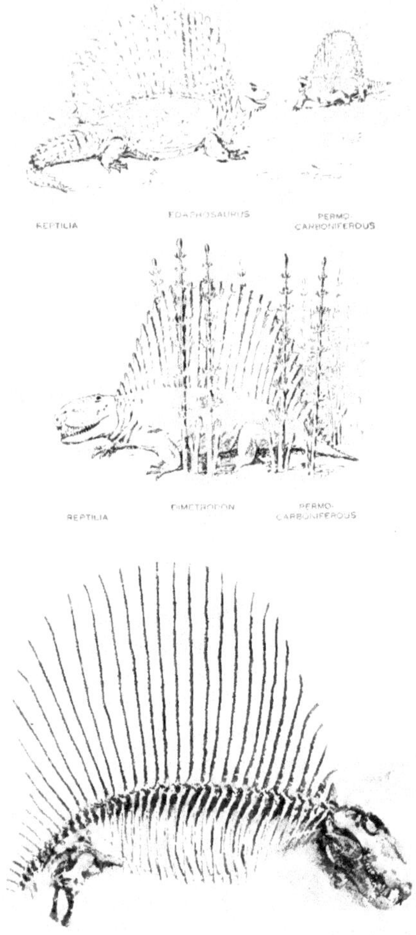

FIG. 69. THE FIN-BACK PERMIAN REPTILES.

Restorations (middle and upper figures) of the giant carnivorous reptiles of northern Texas in Permian time; the large-headed *Dimetrodon* and the contemporary small-headed *Edaphosaurus cruciger*. In both animals the neural spines of the vertebræ are greatly elongated, hence the popular name "fin-back." Skeleton of *Dimetrodon* (lower) in the American Museum of Natural History. Restorations for the author by W. K. Gregory and Richard Deckert.

While the drying pools and lagoons of arid North America were entombing the life of the Permian and Triassic Epochs, there were being deposited in the Karoo series of South Africa some 9,500 feet of strata consisting of shales and sandstones, chiefly of river flood-plain and delta origin, and ranging in time from the basal

Permian into the Upper Triassic. Here, up to the year 1909, twenty-two species of fossil fishes had been recorded, mostly ganoids of Triassic age. The eleven species of amphibians discovered are of the solid-headed (Stegocephalia) type, broadly similar in external appearance to those of the same age discovered in Europe. The one hundred and fifteen species of reptiles described from the Lower and Middle Permian deposits include solid-headed pareiasaurs—great, round-bodied, herbivorous reptiles with massive limbs and round heads—which are allied to the cotylosaurs of the Permo-Carboniferous of America, the agile dromosaurs, similar to the lizard-like reptiles of the Texas Permian, with large eye-sockets, and adapted to swift, cursorial movements, also reptiles known as therocephalians in reference to the analogy which the skull bears to that of the mammals, gorganopsians, and numerous slender-limbed, predatory reptiles with sharp caniniform teeth. The giant predaceous Reptilia of the time are the dinocephalians (*i. e.*, "terrible-headed"), very massive animals with a highly arched back, broad, swollen forehead, short, wide jaws provided with marginal teeth. Surpassing these in size are the anomodonts (*i. e.*, "lawless-toothed") in which the skull ranges from a couple

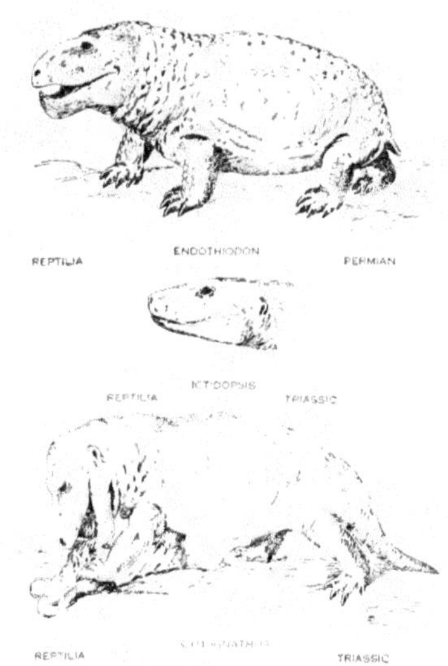

FIG. 70. MAMMAL-LIKE REPTILES OF SOUTH AFRICA.

The relative stability of the African continent favored the early evolution of the free-limbed forms of reptiles known as Anomodonts, including the powerful *Endothiodon*, in which the jaws are sheathed in horn like those of turtles; and also of the Cynodonts (dog-toothed reptiles), including the carnivorous, strongly toothed *Cynognathus* which is allied to the ancestors of the Mammalia. Restorations for the author by W. K. Gregory and Richard Deckert.

of inches to a yard in length, and the toothless jaws are sheathed in horn and beaked like those of turtles. This is a nearly typical social group: large and small, herbivorous, omnivorous, and carnivorous, toothed, toothless and horny-beaked, swift-moving, slow-moving, unarmored, partly armored; it lacks only the completely armored, slow-moving type to be a perfect complex.

In the Upper Permian the fauna includes pareiasaurs and gorganopsians, which are similar to a large group of reptiles of the same geologic age discovered in Russia by Amalitzky.

In Lower and Middle Triassic time the last and most highly specialized of the beaked anomodonts appear together with diminished survivors (*Procolophon*) of the very ancient solid-headed order (Pareiasauria of South Africa, Cotylosauria of Texas). Here also are found the true cynodonts, which are the most mammal-like of all known reptiles. In the Upper Triassic of South Africa occur carnivorous dinosaurs, also crocodile-like phytosaurs (Fig. 75), allied to those of Europe and North America.

Origin of the Mammals and Adaptive Radiation of the Eighteen Orders of Reptiles

The most notable element in this complex reptilian society of South Africa are those remarkable pro-mammalian types of reptiles (cynodont, theriodont), from which our own most remote ancestors, the stem forms of the Mammalia, the next higher class of vertebrates above the Reptilia, were destined to arise. This is another instance where palæontology has dislodged a descent theory based upon anatomy, for at one time from anatomical evidence alone Huxley was disposed to derive the mammals directly from the amphibians.

The question at once arises, why were these particular reptiles so highly favored as to become the potential ancestors of the mammals? At least two reasons are apparent. First, these larger and smaller types of South African pro-mammals exhibit an exceptional evolution of the four limbs, enabling them to travel with relative rapidity, which is connected with ability to migrate, powers doubtless associated with increasing intelligence. Another marked characteristic which favors development of intelligence is the adaptability of their teeth to different kinds of food, insectivorous, carnivorous, and herbivorous, which leads to development and diversity of the powers of observation and choice. In this adaptability they in a limited degree anticipate the evolution of the mammals, for the other reptiles generally are distinguished by a singular arrest or inertia in tooth development. Rapid specialization of the teeth is one of the chief features in the history of the mammals, which display a continuous momentum and advance in tooth structure, associated with specialization of the organs of taste.

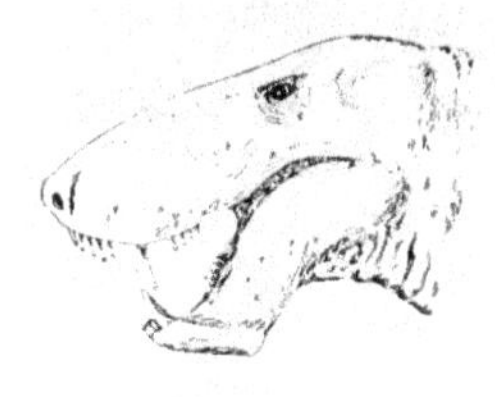

FIG. 71. A SOUTH AFRICAN "DOG-TOOTHED" REPTILE.

Head of one of the South African Cynodonts or "dog-toothed" reptiles, related to the ancestors of the mammals. Restoration for the author by W. K. Gregory and Richard Deckert.

Of greater importance in its influence on the brain evolution of the early pro-mammalian forms is the internal temperature change, whereby a cold-blooded, scaly reptile is transformed into a warm-blooded mammal through a change which produced the four-chambered heart and complete separation of the arterial and venous circulation. This change may have been initiated in some of the cynodonts. This new constant and higher temperature favors the nervous evolution of the mammals but has no influence whatever upon the mechanical evolution. As pure mechanisms the cold-blooded reptiles exhibit as great plasticity, as great diversity, and perhaps higher stages of perfection than the mammals. Nor does increasing intelligence, as we shall see, favor mechanical perfection.

Turning our survey to the origin and adaptive radiation of the reptiles as a whole, we find that in Permian time all of the

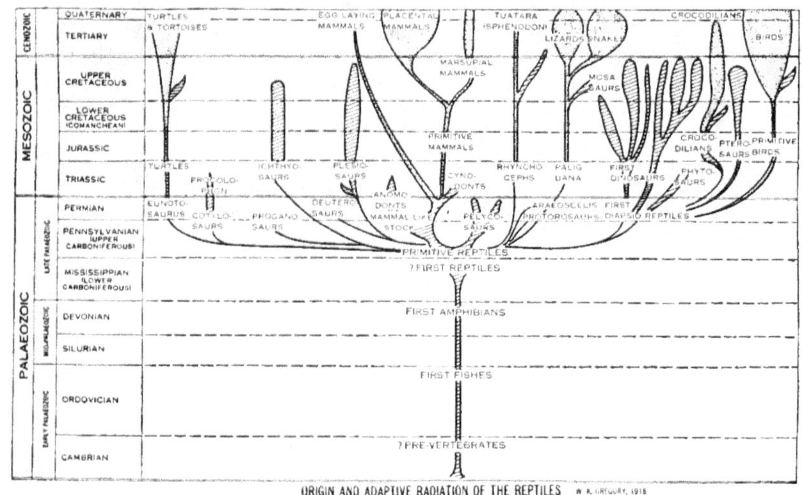

Fig. 72. Adaptive Radiation of the Reptilia.

The reptiles first appear in Upper Carboniferous and Lower Permian time and radiate into eighteen different orders, three of which—the Cotylosaurs, Anomodonts, and Pelycosaurs—attain their full evolution in Permian and Triassic time and later become extinct. Six orders—the Ichthyosaurs, Plesiosaurs, Dinosaurs, Phytosaurs, Pterosaurs, and Turtles—are first discovered in Triassic time, while five of the orders—the Ichthyosaurs, Plesiosaurs, Mosasaurs, Dinosaurs, and Pterosaurs—dominate the Cretaceous Period and become suddenly extinct at its close, leaving the five surviving modern orders—Testudinata (turtles, tortoises), Rhyncocephalia (tuateras), Lacertilia (lizards), Ophidia (snakes), and Crocodilia (crocodiles). These great reptilian dynasties seem to have extended over the estimated ten million years of the Mesozoic Era, namely, the Triassic, Jurassic, and Upper Cretaceous Epochs. Prepared for the author by W. K. Gregory.

ten early adaptive branches of the reptilian stem had radiated and become established as prototypes and ancestors of the great Mesozoic Reptilia. Five divisions, namely, the cotylosaurs, anomodonts, pelycosaurs, proganosaurs, and phytosaurs, were destined to become extinct in Permian or Triassic time, in each instance as the penalty of excessive and premature specialization. Five other great branches, namely, the ichthyosaurs, plesiosaurs, two great branches of the dinosaurs, and the pterosaurs, were destined to dominate the waters, the earth, and the air during the Mesozoic Era, *i. e.*, the Triassic, Jurassic, and Cretaceous Epochs. Thus altogether thirteen great branches of the reptilian stock became extinct either before or near the close of the Age of Reptiles. Out of the total of eighteen reptilian branches only five were destined to survive into Tertiary time, namely, the orders which include the existing turtles, tuateras, lizards, snakes, and crocodiles.

Geologic Blanks and Vistas of Reptilian Evolution

As pointed out in the introduction of this chapter, the reptile ancestor of these eighteen branches of the class Reptilia—a class with an adaptive radiation which represents the mechanical conquest of every one of the great life zones, from the aërial to the deep sea—will some day be discovered as a small, lizard-like, cold-blooded, egg-laying, four-limbed, long-tailed terrestrial form, with a solid skull roof, of carnivorous or more probably insectivorous habit, which lived somewhere on the land surfaces of Carboniferous time. Such undoubtedly was the reptilian prototype from which evolved every one of the marvellous mechanical types which we may now briefly review. By methods first clearly enunciated by Huxley in 1880 several of the ideal vertebrate prototypes have been theoretically reconstructed, and in more than one instance discovery has confirmed these hypothetical reconstructions.

The early geologic vistas of this entire radiation are seen in the reptilian life of the Permian Epoch of North America, Europe, and Africa just described, consisting exclusively of terrestrial and terrestrio-aquatic forms. In the Triassic we obtain succeeding vistas of the terrestrial and fluviatile life of North

America, Europe, and Africa, as well as our first glimpses of the early marine life of North America. In Jurassic time deposits at the bottom of the great interior continental seas give us the

	TERRESTRIAL AND FLUVIATILE				MARINE			
	N AMER	EUROPE	AFRICA	S. AMER.	N AMER	EUROPE	AFRICA	S AMER
QUATERNARY								
TERTIARY								
UPPER CRETACEOUS	FINAL DINOSAUR STAGES (PREDENTATA AND THEROPODA)				FINAL REPTILIAN SEA FAUNA (PLESIOSAURS AND MOSASAURS)			
LOWER CRETACEOUS (COMANCHEAN)	SECOND DINOSAUR STAGES (SAUROPODA)							
JURASSIC					SECOND REPTILIAN SEA FAUNA (PLESIOSAURS AND ICHTHYOSAURS)			
TRIASSIC	FIRST DINOSAUR STAGES (PRIMITIVE DINOSAURS)				FIRST REPTILIAN SEA FAUNA (PRIMITIVE ICHTHYOSAURS)			

FIG. 73. GEOLOGIC RECORDS OF REPTILIAN EVOLUTION, TERRESTRIAL AND MARINE.

Shaded areas represent the geologic vistas of reptilian life which have been discovered from fossils entombed in ancient TERRESTRIAL, FLUVIATILE, and MARINE habitats of different portions of the northern and southern hemispheres.

TRIASSIC. We begin with the deposits of the continental surfaces of North America, Europe, and Africa. During Triassic time the FIRST DINOSAUR STAGES appear, as well as some of the semi-aquatic forms which frequented fluviatile regions, while the PRIMITIVE ICHTHYOSAURS were then fully adapted to marine life.

JURASSIC and LOWER CRETACEOUS. We continue with geologic vistas of the succeeding marine life and the evolution of the SECOND REPTILIAN SEA FAUNA, indicated by the shaded areas of the Jurassic and the Lower Cretaceous of North America and Europe. The remains of these animals are found in the deposits of deep or shallow sea waters. There is one great vista, the SECOND DINOSAUR STAGES, which includes the terrestrial dinosaurs known as SAUROPODA, found in Upper Jurassic and Lower Cretaceous deposits in North America, Europe, Africa, and South America.

UPPER CRETACEOUS. Then there was a long interval, followed by the FINAL DINOSAUR STAGES and a long vista of the terrestrial reptilian life of Upper Cretaceous time, especially in North America. Contemporary with this is the FINAL REPTILIAN SEA FAUNA. Chart by the author.

second reptilian sea fauna of plesiosaurs and ichthyosaurs within the continents of North America and Europe. The story of the marine pelagic evolution of the reptiles is continued with some interruptions through the Lower Cretaceous into the final reptilian sea fauna of plesiosaurs and mosasaurs of Upper Cretaceous time.

In the meanwhile the life of the continents is revealed in the terrestrial and fluviatile deposits of the Triassic Epoch, in the first stages of the terrestrial evolution of the dinosaurs, in the early stages of the fluviatile evolution of the Crocodilia, and in the final stages of the terrestrial phases of the Amphibia and pro-Reptilia. A long interval of time elapses at this period in the earth's history, during which the life of the continents is entirely unknown, until the close of the Jurassic and beginning of Cretaceous time, when there appears a second great stage of dinosaur evolution, revealed especially in the lagoon deposits of North Africa and South America, which have yielded remains of giant Sauropoda. Then another gap occurs in the story as told by continental deposits. Finally, in Upper Cretaceous time we again discover great flood-plain and shore-line deposits, which give a prolonged vista of the terrestrial life of the Reptilia, especially in North America and Europe.

Thus it will be understood that, while the great tree of reptilian descent has been worked out through a century of scientific researches, beginning with those of Cuvier and continued by Owen, Leidy, Cope, Marsh, and our contemporary palæontologists, there are enormous gaps in both the terrestrial and the marine history of several of the reptilian orders which remain to be filled by future exploration. We piece together fossil history on the continents and in the seas from the animals entombed in these deposits, partly by means of the real relationships observed in widely migrating forms, such as the land dinosaurs and the marine ichthyosaurs, plesiosaurs, and mosasaurs. Many of these reptiles ranged over every continent and in every sea. On the whole, the physiographic condition most favorable to the preservation of life in the fossil condition is that known as the flood-plain, in which the rising waters and sediments of the rainy season rapidly entomb animal remains which are deposited on the surface

FIG. 74. CLOSE OF THE AGE OF REPTILES. A RELIC OF ANCIENT FLOOD-PLAIN CONDITIONS.

Iguanodont dinosaur lying upon its back. Integument impressions preserved. The "dinosaur mummy," *Trachodon*, from the Upper Cretaceous flood-plain deposits of Converse County, Wyoming. Due to arid seasonal desiccation, the skin folds and impressions are preserved over the greater part of the body and limbs. Discovered by Sternberg. Mounted specimen in the American Museum of Natural History.

or in small water pools during the drier seasons. Fossils buried in old flood-plain areas of South Africa tell us the story of the life evolution which is continued by the ancient shore and lagoon deposits in other parts of the world as well as by fossils found in the broad, intermittent flood-plain areas of the American Triassic and Cretaceous, which close with the great delta deposits of the Upper Cretaceous lying to the east of the present Rocky Mountain range. The more restricted deposition areas of drying pools and lagoons, such as those observed in the Permian and Triassic shales and sandstones of Texas, entomb many forms of terrestrial life. Vistas of the contemporaneous evolution of fluviatile, aquatic, and marine life are afforded by the animals which perish at the surface and sink to the calcareous bottom oozes of the continental seas of Triassic, Jurassic, and Cretaceous time. It is only in the Tertiary of the Rocky Mountain region of North America that we obtain a nearly continuous and uninterrupted story of the successive forms of continental life, among the mammals entombed in the ancient flood-plains, in the volcanic ash-beds, in the lagoons, and more rarely in the littoral deposits.

Aquatic Adaptation of the Reptilia, Direct and Reversed

From the distinctively terrestrial radiations of Permian time we turn to the development of aquatic habitat phases among the reptiles which lived along the borders of the great interior rivers and continental seas of Permian, Triassic, and Jurassic time.

This reversal of adaptation from terrestrial into aquatic life is, as we might theoretically anticipate, a reversal of function rather than of structure, because, as above stated (p. 159), it is a universal law of form evolution that ancient adaptive characters once lost by the heredity-chromatin are never reacquired. In geologic race evolution there is no process analogous to the wonderful phenomena of individual regeneration or regrowth, such as is seen among amphibians and other primitive vertebrates, whereby the original limb may be completely restored from the mutilated remnant of an amputation.

Such regeneration is attributable to the potentiality of the heredity-chromatin which still resides in the cells of the amputated surfaces. The heredity-chromatin determiners of the bones of the separate digits or separate phalanges if once lost in geologic time are never reacquired; on the contrary, each phase of habitat adaptation is forced to commence with the elements remaining in the organism's heredity-chromatin, which may have been impoverished in previous habitats. When an ancient habitat zone is reentered there must be *readaptation* of the parts which remain. Thus, when the terrestrial reptiles reenter the aquatic zone of their amphibian ancestors they cannot resume the amphibian characters, for these have been lost by the chromatin.

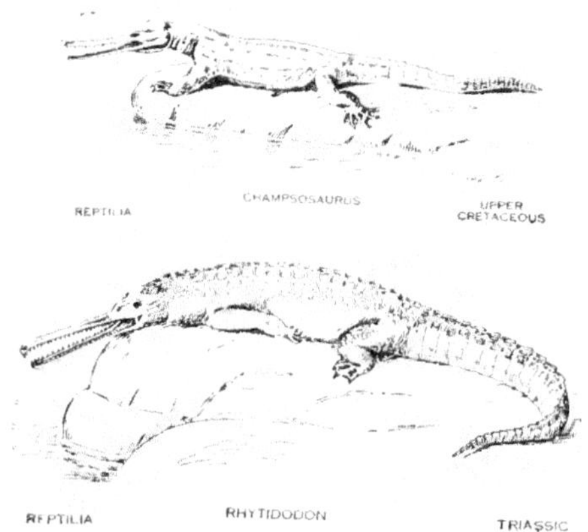

FIG. 75. REPTILES LEAVING A TERRESTRIAL FOR AN AQUATIC HABITAT, THE BEGINNING OF AQUATIC ADAPTATION.

Littoral-fluviatile types independently evolve in the Triassic (*Rhytidodon*, a phytosaur) and in the Upper Cretaceous (*Champsosaurus*). These animals belong to two widely different orders of reptiles, neither of which is closely akin to the modern alligators and crocodiles. The adaptation is convergent to that of the existing gavials and crocodiles. Restorations for the author by W. K. Gregory and Richard Deckert.

This invariable principle underlying reversed evolution is partly illustrated (Fig. 53) in the passage from the reptilian foot into the fin of the aquatic reptile and with equal clearness in the passage of the wing of the flying bird into the fin of the swimming bird (Fig. 110).

In no less than eleven out of the eighteen orders of reptiles reversed adaptation to a renewal of aquatic life, like that of the fishes and amphibians, took place in the long and slow

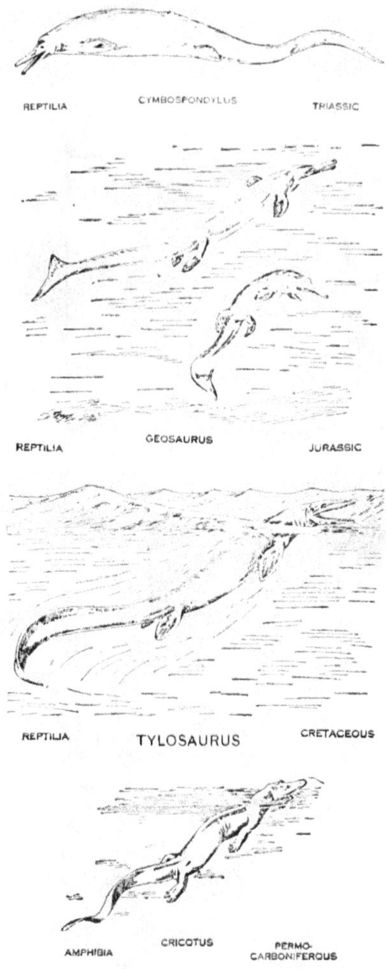

FIG. 76. CONVERGENT AQUATIC ADAPTATION INTO ELONGATE FUSIFORM TYPE IN FOUR DIFFERENT ORDERS OF AMPHIBIANS AND REPTILES.

Independently convergent evolution of four long-bodied, free-swimming, swift-moving, surface-living aquatic types in which the fins and limbs are retained as paddles: *Cricotus*, an amphibian; *Tylosaurus*, an Upper Cretaceous mosasaur; *Geosaurus*, a Jurassic crocodilian; *Cymbospondylus*, a Triassic ichthyosaur. A very similar fusiform type evolves among the mammals in the Eocene cetaceans (*Zeuglodon*), as seen in Fig. 123. Restorations prepared for the author, independent of scale, by W. K. Gregory and Richard Deckert.

passage from a terrestrial phase, through palustral, swamp-living phases into a littoral, fluviatile phase, and from this into littoral and marine salt-water phases; so that finally in no less than six orders of reptiles the pelagic phase of the high seas was independently reached.

The rôle in the economy of oceanic life which is now taken by the whales, dolphins, and porpoises was assumed by families of the plesiosaurs, ichthyosaurs, mosasaurs, snakes, and crocodiles, all flourishing in the high seas, together with families of the turtles, which are the only high-sea reptiles surviving at the present day. Moreover, under the alternating adaptations to terrestrial and marine life, which prevailed during the 10,000,000 years of late Palæozoic and Mesozoic time, several families of the existing orders of reptiles sought a seafaring existence more than once and gave off numerous side branches from the main stem. The adaptations to marine life have been especially studied by Fraas.

Even to-day there are tendencies toward marine invasion observed among several of the surviving families of lizards and crocodiles of seashore frequenting habits.

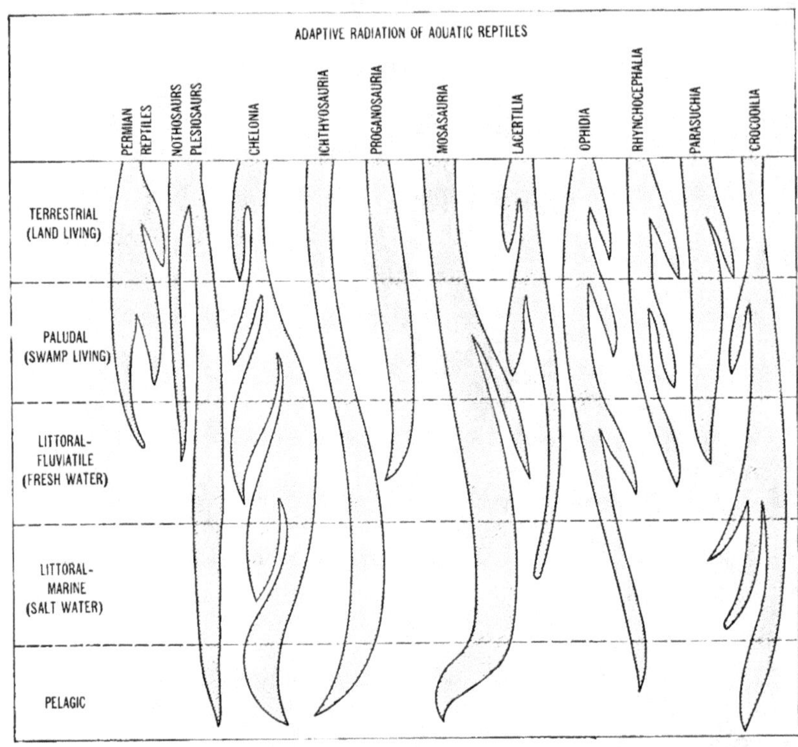

Fig. 77. Independent Reversed Adaptation to the Aquatic Zones in Twelve Orders of Reptiles, Originating on Land and Entering the Seas.

Diagram showing the manner in which twelve of the eighteen orders of reptiles descend from the terrestrial (land-living) zone into the paludal (swamp-frequenting) zone, thence into the littoral-fluviatile (fresh-water and brackish-water) zone, thence into the littoral-marine (salt-water) zone, and finally into the pelagic zones of the high seas. This final marine pelagic phase of evolution is attained in only six orders, namely, the plesiosaurs, Chelonia (sea-tortoises), ichthyosaurs, mosasaurs (marine lizards), crocodiles, and certain ophidians (true sea-snakes found far out at sea in the Indian Ocean). Nine of the reptilian orders give off not only one but from two to five independent branches seeking aquatic life, of which six independently reach the full pelagic high-sea phase.

Still more remarkable than the law of reversed adaptation is that of alternate adaptation, which has been brilliantly developed by Louis Dollo, of Brussels. This is applied hypothetically to the evolution of the existing leatherbacks (Spharidæ), an extremely specialized type of sea turtles. It is believed that after a long period of primary terrestrial evolution

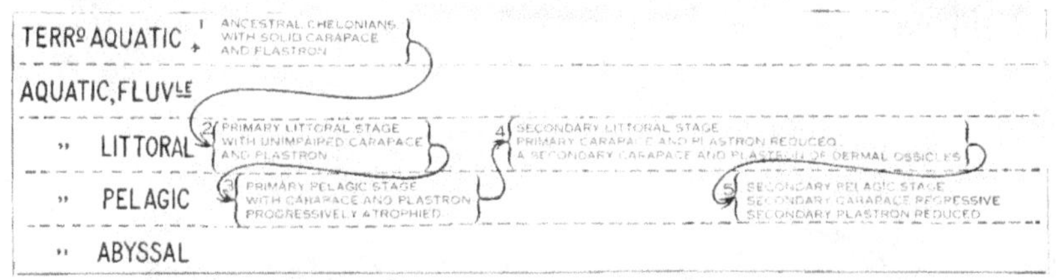

FIG. 78. CHELONIA. DIAGRAM ILLUSTRATING THE ALTERNATE HABITAT MIGRATION OF THE ANCESTRAL "LEATHERBACKS," SPHARGIDÆ.

Dollo's theory is that these animals originate in armored land forms with a solid bony shell, and pass from the terrestrio-aquatic into the littoral and then into the pelagic zone, in which the solid bony shell, being no longer of use, is gradually atrophied. After prolonged marine pelagic existence these animals return secondarily to the littoral zone and acquire a new armature of rounded dermal ossicles which develop on the upper and lower shields of the body. The animals (*Sphargis*) then for a second time take up existence in the pelagic zone, during which the dermal ossicles again tend to disappear.

in which the ancestors of these turtles acquired a firm, bony carapace for land defense, they then passed through various transitions into a primary marine phase during which they gradually lost all their first bony armature. Following this sea phase the animals returned to shore and entered a secondary littoral, shore-living phase, also of long duration, in course of which they developed a second bony armature quite distinct in plan and pattern from the first.

FIG. 79. THE EXISTING "LEATHERBACK" CHELONIAN *Sphargis*.

In this form the solid armature adapted to a former terrestrial existence is being replaced by a leathery shield in which are embedded small polygonal ossicles. After Lydekker.

Descendants of these secondarily armored, shore-living types again sought the sea and entered a secondary marine pelagic phase in course of which they lost the greater part of their

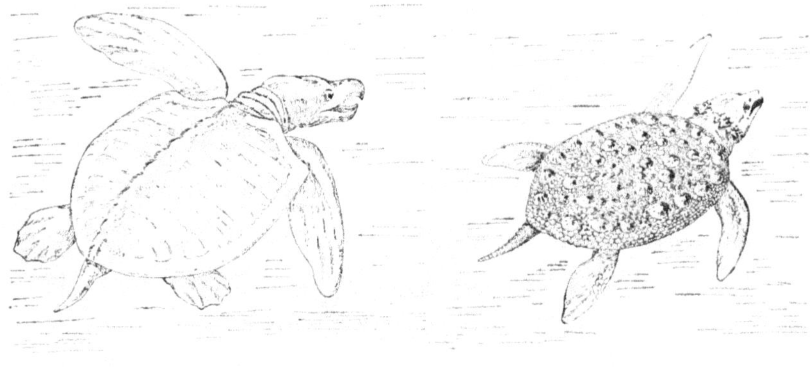

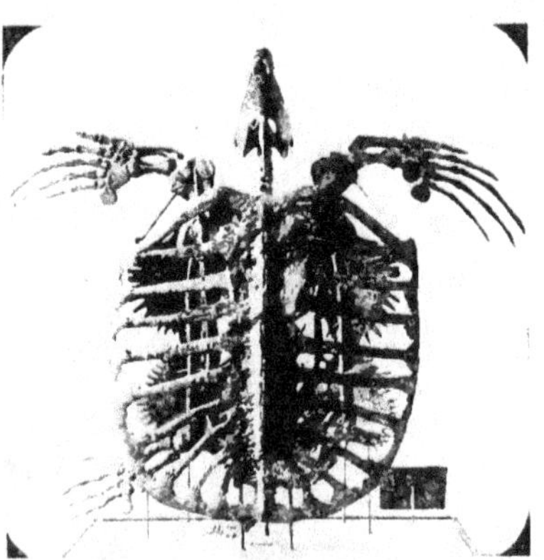

FIG. 80. ARMORED TERRESTRIAL CHELONIA INVADE THE SEAS AND LOSE THEIR ARMATURE.

Convergent or analogous evolution (two upper figures) in the inland seas of the paddle-propelled chelonian *Archelon* (after Williston), the gigantic marine turtle of the Upper Cretaceous continental seas of North America, and of *Placochelys* (after Jaekel in part), a Triassic reptile belonging to the entirely distinct order Placodontia. Skeleton of *Archelon* (lower) in which the bony armature of the carapace has largely disappeared, exposing the ribs. Specimen in the Peabody Museum of Yale University. After Wieland.

second armature and acquired their present leathery covering, to which the popular name "leatherbacks" applies.[1]

In general the law of reversed aquatic adaptation is most brilliantly illustrated in the fossil ichthyosaurs, in the internal

[1] This law of alternate adaptation may be regarded as absolutely established in the case of certain land-living marsupials in which anatomical records remain of an alternation of adaptations from the terrestrial to the arboreal phase, from an arboreal into a secondary terrestrial phase, and from this terrestrial repetition to a secondary arboreal phase. The relics of successive adaptations to alternations of habitat zones and adaptive phases are clearly observed in the so-called tree kangaroos (*Dendrolagus*) of Australia.

anatomy of which land-living ancestry is clearly written, while reversed adaptation for marine pelagic life has resulted in a superficial type of body which presents close analogies to that of the sharks, porpoises, and shark-dolphins (Fig. 41). Integumentary median and tail fins precisely similar to those of the

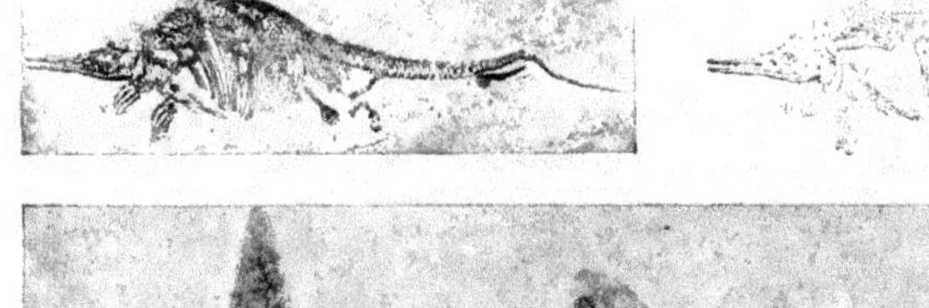

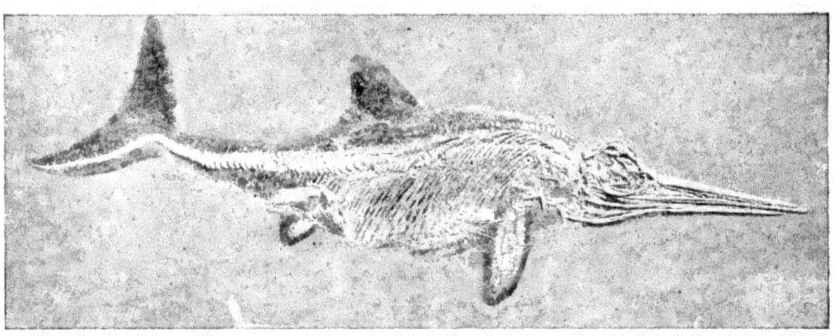

Fig. 81. Extreme Adaptation of the Ichthyosaurs to Marine Pelagic Life.

Although primarily of terrestrial origin the ichthyosaurs become quite independent of the shores through the viviparous birth of the young as evidenced by a fossil female ichthyosaur (upper figures) with the fœtal skeletons of seven young ichthyosaurs within or near the abdominal cavity.

A fossil ichthyosaur (lower figure) with preserved body integument and fin outlines resembling those of the sharks and dolphins (see Fig. 41).

Both specimens in the American Museum of Natural History from Holzmäden, Würtemberg.

sharks evolve, the anterior lateral limbs are secondarily converted into fin-paddles, which are externally similar to those of sharks and dolphins, while the posterior limbs are reduced. As in the shark, the tail fin is vertical, while in the dolphin the tail fin is horizontal. In the early history of their marine pelagic existence the ichthyosaurs undoubtedly returned to shore to deposit their eggs, but a climax of imitation of the dolphins and of certain of the sharks is reached in the development of the power of viviparity, the growth of the young within the body cavity of the mother, resulting in the young ichthyosaurs being born in the water fully formed and able to take care of themselves immediately after birth like the young of modern whales and dolphins. When this viviparous habit finally released the ichthyosaurs from the necessity of returning to land for breeding they developed the extraordinary powers of migration which carried them into the Arctic seas of Spitzbergen, the Cordilleran seas of western North America, and doubtless into the Antarctic. So far as we know this viviparous habit was never developed among the seafaring turtles, which always return to shore to deposit their eggs. While the ichthyosaurs vary greatly in size, they present a reversed evolution from the terrestrial, quadrupedal type into the swift-moving, fusiform body type of the fishes, which is finally reduced in predaceous power through the degeneration of the teeth, as observed in the *Baptanodon*, an ichthyosaur of the Upper Jurassic seas of the ancient Rocky Mountain region.

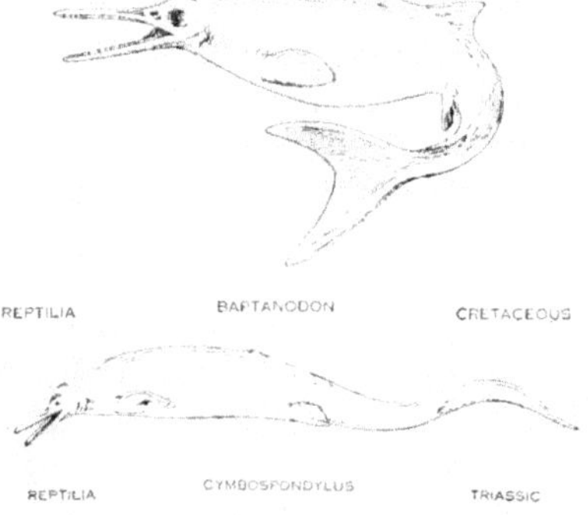

FIG. 82. RESTORATIONS OF TWO ICHTHYOSAURS.

Cymbospondylus, a primitive ichthyosaur from the Triassic seas of Nevada (after Merriam), and the highly specialized *Baptanodon*, a Cretaceous ichthyosaur of the seas of that period in the region of Wyoming, in which the teeth are greatly reduced. Restorations for the author by W. K. Gregory and Richard Deckert.

While the continental seas of Jurassic time were favorable to this remarkable aquatic marine phase of the reptiles, still greater inundations both of North America and of Europe occurred during Upper Cretaceous time. This was the period of the maximum evolution of the sea reptiles, the ultimate food supply of which was the surface life of the oceans, the marine Protozoa, skeletons of which were depositing the great chalk beds of Europe and of western North America.

The Plesiosaurs had begun their invasion of the sea during Upper Triassic time, as shown in the primitive half-lizard

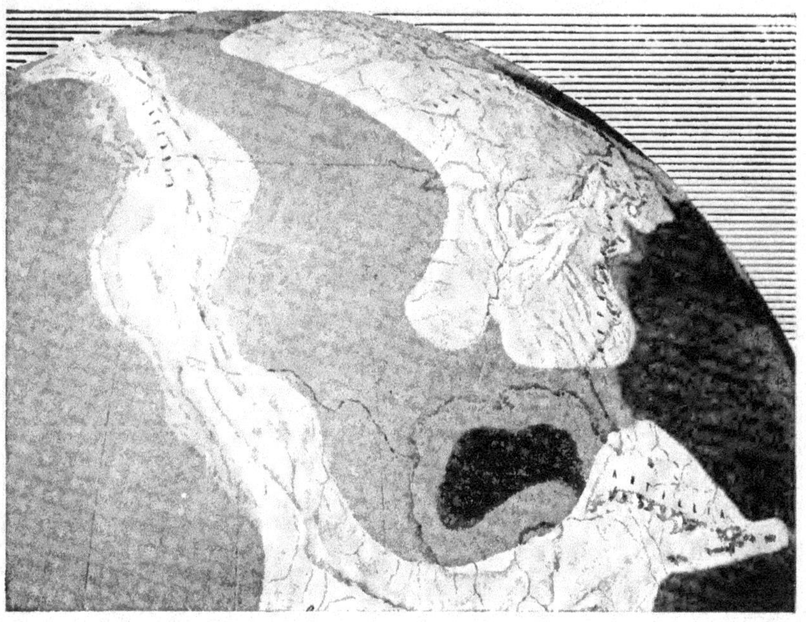

FIG. 83. NORTH AMERICA IN UPPER CRETACEOUS TIME.

The great inland continental sea extending from the Gulf to the Arctic Ocean, was favorable to the evolution of the mosasaurs, plesiosaurs, and giant sea turtles (*Archelon*). This period is marked by the greatest inundation of North America during Mesozoic time, by mountains slowly rising along the Pacific coast from Mexico to Alaska, and by volcanic activity in Antillia. Detail from the globe model in the American Museum by Chester A. Reeds and George Robertson, after Schuchert.

Lariosaurus, discovered in northern Italy, which still retains its original lacertilian appearance, due to the fact that the limbs and feet are not as yet transformed into paddles. In the subsequent evolution of paddles the number of digits remains the same, namely, five, but the number of the phalanges on each digit is greatly increased through the process known as hyperphalangy, an example of the numerical addition of new characters. Propulsion through the water was rather by means of the paddles than by the combined lateral body-and-

FIG. 84. CONVERGENT FORMS OF AQUATIC REPTILES OF DIFFERENT ORIGIN.
Lariosaurus (left), the Triassic ancestor of the plesiosaurs from northern Italy, and *Mesosaurus* (right), from the Permian of Brazil and South Africa, representing another extinct order of the Reptilia, the Proganosauria. Drawn by Deckert after McGregor.

tail motion seen among the ichthyosaurs, because all plesiosaurs exhibit a more or less abbreviated tail and a more or less broadly depressed body. It is also significant that the fore

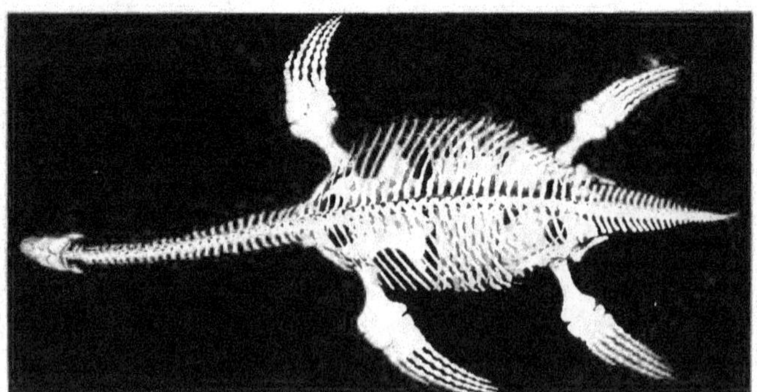

FIG. 85. A PLESIOSAUR FROM THE JURASSIC OF ENGLAND.
Skeleton of *Cryptocleidus oxoniensis* seen from above. Mounted in the American Museum of Natural History.

and hind paddles are homodynamic, *i. e.*, exerting equal power; they are so exactly alike that it is very difficult to distinguish them, whether they are provided with four broad paddles or with four long, narrow, slender paddles. The plesiosaurs afford the first illustration we have noted of another of the great laws of form evolution, namely, adaptation occurs far more frequently through changes of existing proportions than through numerical addition of new characters. It is proportional changes which separate the swift-moving plesiosaurs (*Trinacromerion osborni*), which are invariably provided with long heads, short necks, and broad paddles, from the slow-moving plesiosaurs (*Elasmosaurus*), which are provided with narrow paddles, short bodies, extremely long necks, and small heads.

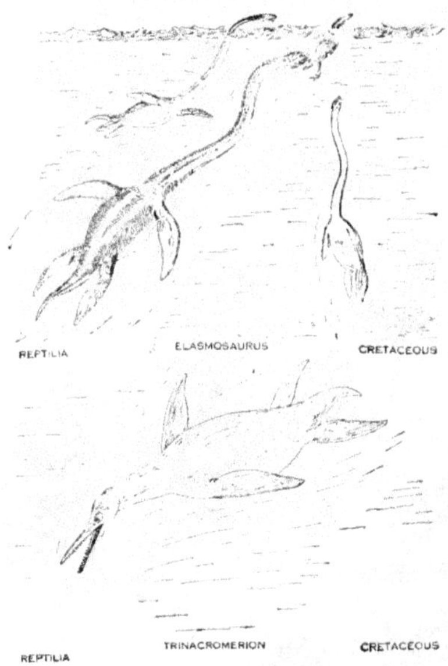

FIG. 86. TYPES OF MARINE PELAGIC PLESIOSAURS OF THE AMERICAN CONTINENTAL CRETACEOUS SEAS.

The slow-moving, long-necked *Elasmosaurus* and the swift-moving, short-necked *Trinacromerion*. The limbs are completely transformed into paddles. The great differences in the proportions of the neck and body represent adaptations to greater or less speed. Restorations for the author by W. K. Gregory and Richard Deckert, chiefly after Williston.

It is believed that the lizard-like ancestors of the mosasaurs left the land early in Cretaceous time; it is certain that throughout the three or four million years of the Cretaceous epoch they spread into all the oceans of the world, from the continental seas of northern Europe and North America to those of New Zealand. In Europe these animals survived to the very close of Mesozoic time since the type genus of the great order Mosasauria (*Mosasaurus*), taking its name from the River Meuse, was found in the uppermost marine Cretaceous.

Detailed knowledge of the structure of these remarkable sea lizards is due chiefly to the researches of Williston and

Fig. 87. A Sea Lizard.

Tylosaurus, a giant mosasaur from the inland Cretaceous seas of Kansas, chasing the giant fish *Portheus*. After a restoration in the American Museum of Natural History, by Charles R. Knight under the author's direction.

Osborn of this country and to those of Dollo in Europe. The head is long and provided with recurved teeth adapted to seizing active fish prey (Fig. 87); the neck is extremely short; as in the plesiosaurs the fore and hind limbs are converted into paddles, symmetrical in proportion; the body is elongate and propulsion is not chiefly by means of the fins but by the sinuous motions of the body, and especially of the very elongate, broad, fin-like tail. These sea lizards of Upper Cretaceous time (Fig. 76) are analogous or convergent to the sea Crocodilia (*Geosaurus*) of Jurassic time and present further analogies with the Triassic ichthyosaur *Cymbospondylus* and the small Permo-Carboniferous amphibian *Cricotus* (Fig. 76). In the American continental seas these animals radiated into the small, relatively slender *Clidastes*, into the somewhat more broadly finned *Platecarpus*, and into the giant *Tylosaurus*, which was capable (Fig. 87) of capturing the great fish of the Cretaceous seas (*Portheus*).

Terrestrial Life. Carnivorous Dinosaurs

Widely contrasting with these extreme adaptations to aquatic marine life, the climax of terrestrial adaptation in the reptilian skeleton is reached among the dinosaurs, a branch which separated in late Permian or early Triassic time from small quadrupedal, swiftly moving, lizard-like reptiles and before the time of their extinction at the close of the Cretaceous had evolved into a marvellous abundance and variety of types. In the Upper Triassic of North America, late Newark time, the main separation of the dinosaurs into two great divisions, (*a*) those with a crocodile-like pelvis, known as Saurischia, and (*b*) those with a bird-like pelvis, known as Ornithischia, had already taken place, and the dinosaurs dominated all other terrestrial forms.

When Hitchcock in 1836 explored the giant footprints in the ancient mud flats of the Connecticut valley he quite naturally attributed many of them to gigantic birds, since at the time the law of parallel mechanical evolution between birds and dinosaurs was not comprehended and the order Dino-

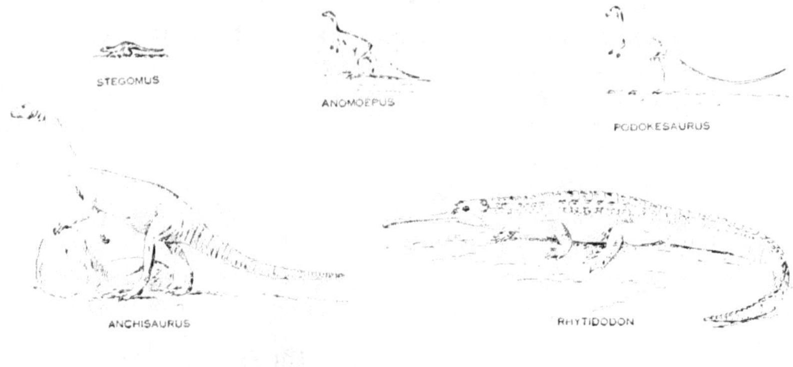

FIG. 88. LIFE OF THE CONNECTICUT RIVER VALLEY IN UPPER TRIASSIC (NEWARK) TIME.

Anchisaurus, a primitive carnivorous bipedal dinosaur. *Rhytidodon*, a phytosaur analogous but not related to the modern gavials. *Stegomus*, a small armored phytosaur related to *Rhytidodon*. *Anomœpus*, a herbivorous bipedal dinosaur related to the "duckbills" or Iguanodonts. *Podokesaurus*, a light, swift-moving, carnivorous dinosaur of the bird-like type. Restorations (except *Rhytidodon*) after R. S. Lull of Yale University. Drawn to uniform scale for the author by Richard Deckert.

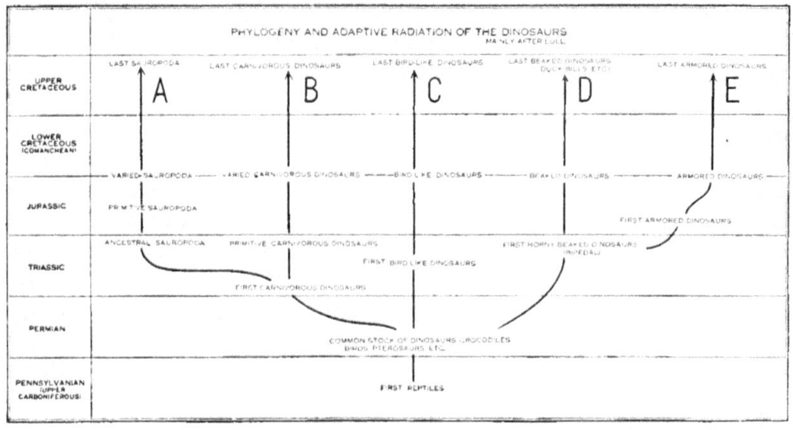

FIG. 89. TERRESTRIAL EVOLUTION OF THE DINOSAURS.

The ancestral tree of the dinosaurs, originating in Lower Permian time, and branching into five great lines during a period estimated at twelve million years. *A*, The giant herbivorous Sauropoda which sprang from Lower Triassic carnivorous ancestors. *B*, Giant carnivorous dinosaurs, which prey upon all the larger herbivorous forms. *C*, Swift-moving, ostrich-like, carnivorous dinosaurs, related to *B*. *D*, Herbivorous Iguanodonts, swift-moving, beaked, or "duck-bill" dinosaurs, related to *E*. *E*, Slow-moving, quadrupedal, heavily armored or horned herbivorous dinosaurs, related to *D*. Prepared for the author by W. K. Gregory, chiefly after Lull.

sauria was not known. It has since been discovered that many of the ancient dinosaurs, especially those of carnivorous habit, were bird-footed and adapted in structure for rapid, cursorial locomotion; the body was completely raised above

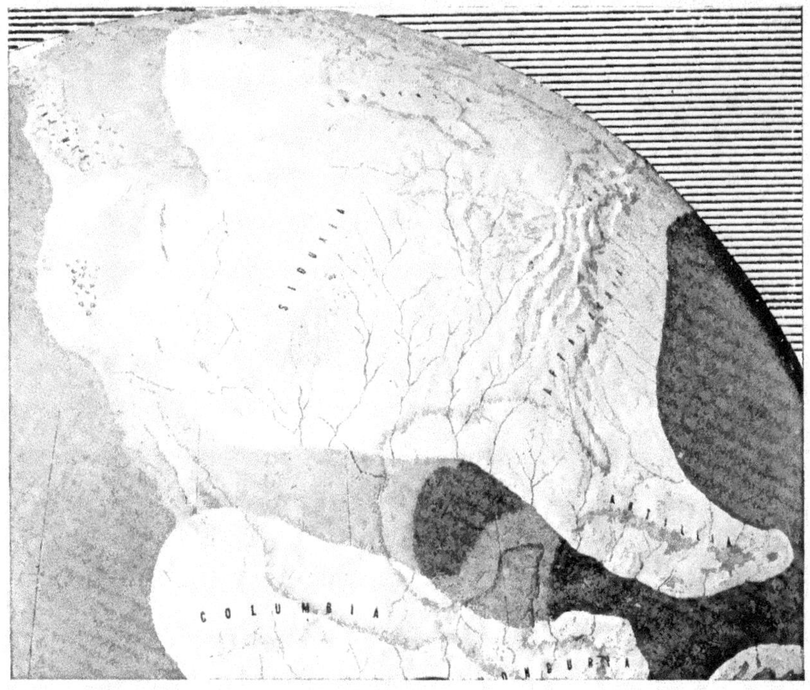

Fig. 90. North America in Upper Triassic (Newark) Time.

The period of the primitive bipedal dinosaurs, with semi-arid, cool to warm climate, and a prevailing flora of cycads and conifers. Remains of amphibians, primitive crocodiles, and dinosaurs are found in the reddish continental deposits. Detail from the globe model in the American Museum by Chester A. Reeds and George Robertson, after Schuchert.

the ground, the forward part being balanced with the aid of the long tail. This primitive type of body structure is common to all the dinosaurs, and is evidence that the group underwent a long period of evolution under semi-arid continental conditions in late Permian and early Triassic time. The reptilian group discovered in the Connecticut valley (Fig.

88) is not inconsistent with the theory of a semi-arid climate advocated by Barrell to explain the reddish continental deposits not only in the region of the Connecticut valley but over the southwestern Great Plains. The flora of ferns, cycads, and conifers indicates moderate conditions of temperature. Along the Pacific coast there was a great overflow of the seas along the western continental border and an archipelago of volcanic islands. In this region there were numerous coral reefs and an abundance of cephalopod ammonites. In the

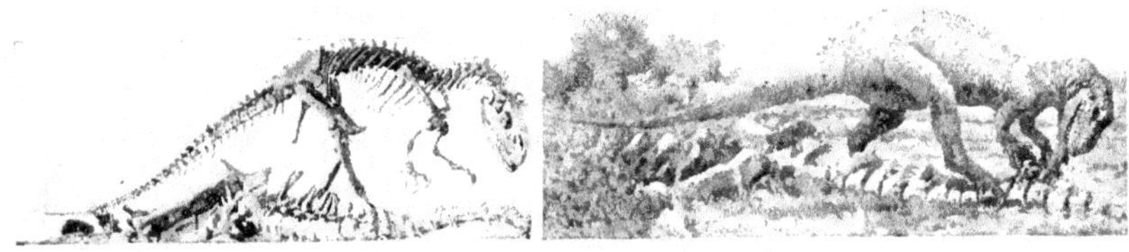

FIG. 91. A CARNIVOROUS DINOSAUR PREYING UPON A SAUROPOD.

Skeletons (left) and restoration (right) of the bipedal dinosaur *Allosaurus* of Upper Jurassic and Lower Cretaceous time in the act of feeding upon the carcass of *Apatosaurus*, one of the giant herbivorous Sauropoda of the same period. Mounted specimens and restoration by Osborn and Knight in the American Museum of Natural History.

interior continental seas great marine reptiles (*Cymbospondylus*, Fig. 82), related to the ichthyosaurs, were abundant.

The primitive light-bodied, long-tailed type of dinosaur of bipedal locomotion originates in this country with Marsh's *Anchisaurus* of the Connecticut valley (Fig. 88) and develops into the more powerful form of the *Allosaurus* of Marsh from the Jurassic flood-plains east of the Rocky Mountains (Fig. 91). Contemporaneous with this powerful animal is the much more delicate *Ornitholestes*, which is departing from the carnivorous habits of its ancestors and seeking some new form of food. It is in turn ancestral to the remarkable "ostrich dinosaur" of the Upper Cretaceous, *Struthiomimus* (*Ornithomimus*), which is bird-like both in the structure of its limbs and feet and in its toothless jaw sheathed in horn. In this animal the carnivorous habit is completely lost; it is secondarily herbivorous. Its limbs are adapted to very rapid motion.

Recently restored skeleton of the light-limbed, bird-like, toothless "ostrich" dinosaur, *Struthiomimus* (*Ornithomimus*), after Osborn.

Lateral view of the "tyrant" dinosaur, *Tyrannosaurus* (left), and the "ostrich" dinosaur, *Struthiomimus* (right), to the same scale.

FIG. 92. EXTREMES OF ADAPTATION IN THE "TYRANT" AND THE "OSTRICH" DINOSAURS.

Skeletons mounted in the American Museum of Natural History.

In the meantime the true carnivorous dinosaur line was evolving over the entire northern hemisphere stage by stage with the evolution of the varied herbivorous group of the dinosaurs. These animals preserved perfect mechanical unity in the evolution of the very swift motions of the hind limb and prehensile powers both of the jaws and of the hind feet, adapted to seizing and rapidly overcoming a struggling powerful prey. This series reaches an astounding climax in the gigantic *Tyrannosaurus rex*, described by Osborn from the Upper Cretaceous of Montana (see frontispiece). This "king of the tyrant saurians" is in respect to speed, size, power, and ferocity the most destructive life engine which has ever evolved. The excessively small size of the brain, probably weighing less than a pound, which is less than 1/4000 of the estimated body weight, indicates that in animals mechanical evolution is quite independent of the evolution of their intelligence; in fact, intelligence compensates for the absence of mechanical perfection. *Tyrannosaurus* is

FIG. 93. FOUR RESTORATIONS OF THE "OSTRICH" DINOSAUR, *Struthiomimus* (*Ornithomimus*).

A. Showing the mode of progression.

B. Illustrating the hypothesis that the animal was an anteater which used the front claws like those of sloths in tearing down anthills.

C. Illustrating the hypothesis that it was a browser which supported the fore part of the body by means of the long, curved claws of the fore limb while browsing on trees.

D. Illustrating the hypothesis that it was a wading type, feeding upon shrimps and smaller crustaceans.

Restorations by Osborn. No satisfactory theory of the habits of this animal has as yet been advanced.

an illustration of the law of compensation, first enunciated by Geoffroy St. Hilaire, first, in the disproportion between the diminutive fore limb and the gigantic hind limb, and second, in the fact that the feeble grasping power and consequent degeneration of the fore limb and hand are more than compensated for by the development of the tail and the hind claws, which enables these animals to feed practically in the same manner as the raptorial birds.

Herbivorous Dinosaurs, Sauropoda

As analyzed by Lull along the lines of modern interpretation, beside the small carnivorous dinosaurs there may be traced in the Connecticut Triassic footprints the beginnings of an herbivorous offshoot of the primitive carnivorous dinosaur stock, leading into the elephantine types of herbivorous dinosaurs known as the Sauropoda, which were first brought to our knowledge in this country through the pioneer studies of Marsh and Cope.

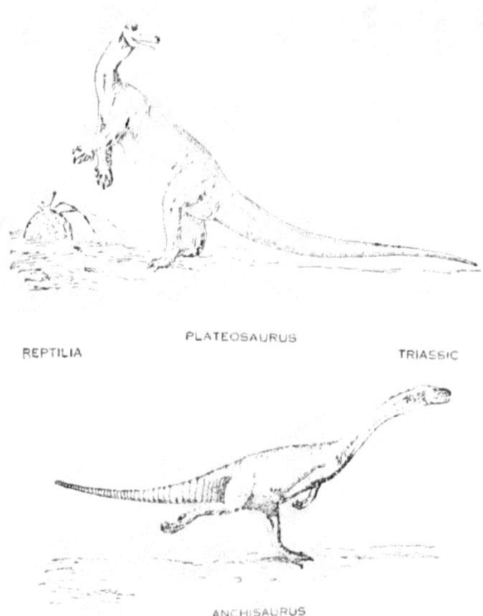

Fig. 94. Analogy Between the Carnivorous *Anchisaurus* Type of the Triassic and the Ancestral Herbivorous Sauropod Type *Plateosaurus*.

The upper restoration (*Plateosaurus*) represents a bipedal stage of sauropod evolution which was discovered in the German Trias, in which the transition from carnivorous to herbivorous habits is observed. Recent discovery renders it probable that the herbivorous Sauropoda descend from carnivorous ancestors like *Anchisaurus*.

Restoration of *Plateosaurus* modified from Jaekel. Restoration of *Anchisaurus* after Lull.

As there is never any need of haste in the capture of plant life these animals underwent a reversed evolution of the limbs from the swift-moving primitive bipedal type into a secondary slow-moving quadrupedal ambulatory type. The original power of occasionally raising the body on the hind limbs was still retained in some of these gigantic forms. The half-way stage between the bipedal and the quadrupedal mode of progression is revealed in the recently described *Plateosaurus* of Jaekel from the Trias of Germany (Fig. 94), an animal which could progress either on two or on four legs.

The Sauropoda reached the climax of their evolution during the close of Jurassic (Morrison formation) and the be-

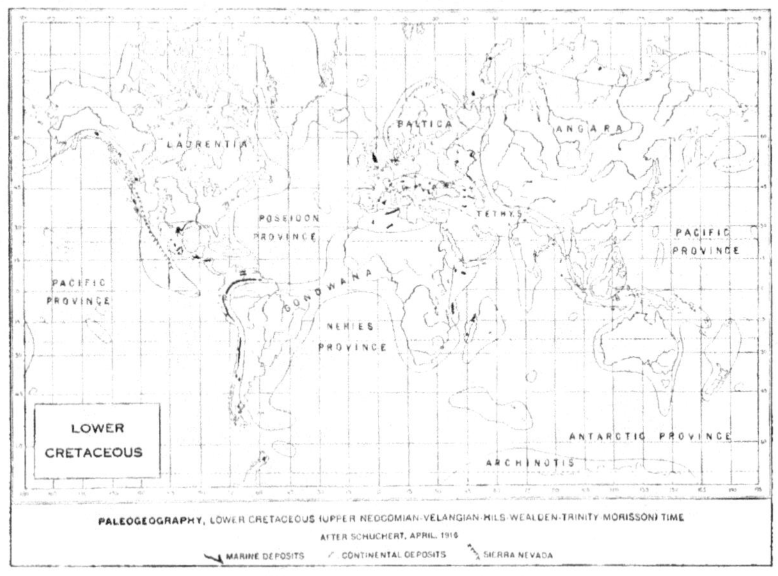

FIG. 95. THEORETIC WORLD ENVIRONMENT IN LOWER CRETACEOUS TIME.

The dominant period of the great sauropod dinosaurs. This shows the theoretic South Atlantic continent *Gondwana* connecting South America and Africa, and the Eurasiatic Mediterranean sea *Tethys*. Shortly afterward comes the rise of the modern flowering plants and the hardwood forests. The shaded patch over the existing region of Wyoming and Colorado is the flood-plain (Morrison) centre of the giant Sauropoda (see Fig. 97). After Schuchert, 1916.

ginning of Cretaceous time (Comanchean Epoch). Meanwhile they attained world-wide distribution, migrating throughout a long stretch of the present Rocky Mountain region of North America, into southern Argentina, into the Upper Jurassic of Great Britain, France, and Germany, and into eastern Africa. The last named region is the one most recently explored, and the widely heralded *Gigantosaurus* (= *Brachiosaurus*), described as the largest land-living vertebrate ever found, is

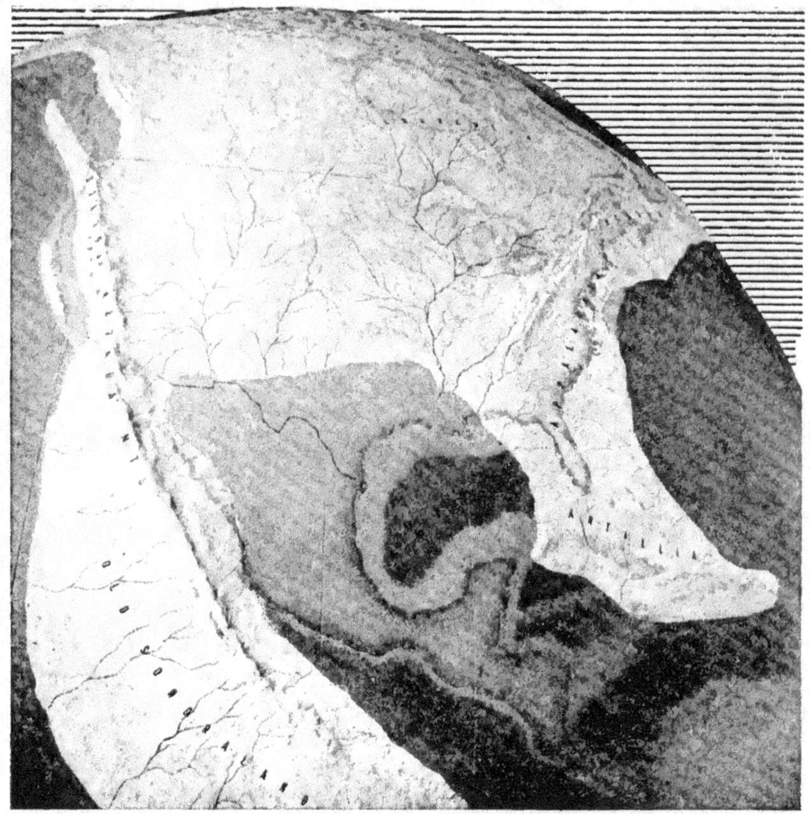

Fig. 96. North America in Lower Cretaceous (Comanchian) Time.

This period, also known as the Trinity-Morrison time, is marked by the maximum development of the giant herbivorous dinosaurs, the Sauropoda. The Sierra Nevada and coast ranges are elevated, also the mountain ranges of the Great Basin which give rise eastward to the flood-plain deposits (Morrison) in which the remains of the Sauropoda are entombed. This epoch is prior to the birth of the Rocky Mountains, which arose between Cretaceous and Eocene time. Detail from the globe model in the American Museum by Chester A. Reeds and George Robertson, after Schuchert.

structurally closely related to and does not exceed in size the sauropods discovered in the Black Hills of South Dakota. Their size is indeed titanic, the length being 100 feet, while the longest whales do not exceed 90 feet. In height these sauropods dwarf the straight-tusked elephant of Pleistocene time, which is the largest land product of mammalian evolution. The Sauropoda for the most part inhabited the swampy meadows and flood-plains of Morrison time. They include, besides the

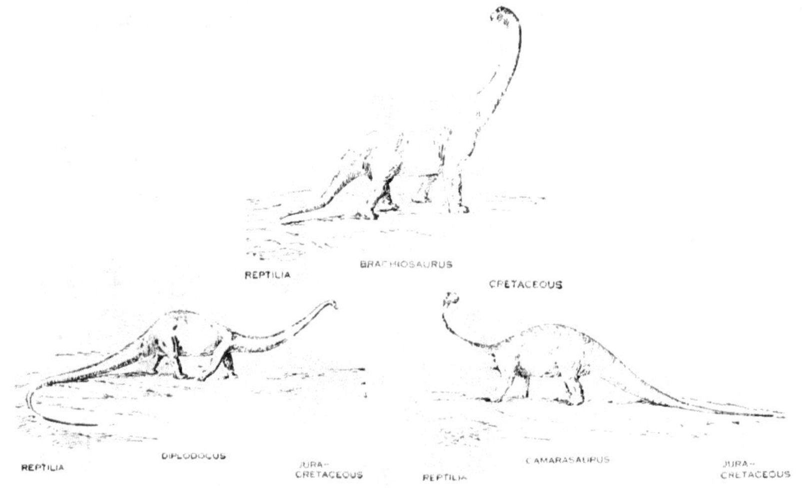

Fig. 97. Three Principal Types of Sauropods.

The body form of the three principal types of giant herbivorous Sauropoda which appear to have been almost world-wide in distribution.

Camarasaurus, a heavy-bodied, short-limbed quadrupedal type. *Diplodocus*, a light-bodied, relatively swift-moving quadrupedal type. *Brachiosaurus*, a short-bodied quadrupedal type in which the fore limbs are more elevated than the hind limbs. *Brachiosaurus* attained gigantic size, being related to the recently discovered *Gigantosaurus* of East Africa. Restorations by Osborn, Matthew, and Deckert.

gigantic type *Brachiosaurus* (*Gigantosaurus*), with its greatly elevated shoulder and forearm, massive quadrupedal types like *Camarasaurus* Cope and *Apatosaurus* (*Brontosaurus*) Marsh, and the relatively long, slender, swiftly moving *Diplodocus*. According to Lull and Depéret the Sauropoda survived until the close of the Cretaceous Epoch in Patagonia and in southern France. In North America they became extinct in Lower Cretaceous time.

In the final extinction of the herbivorous sauropod type we find an example of the selection *law of elimination*, attributable

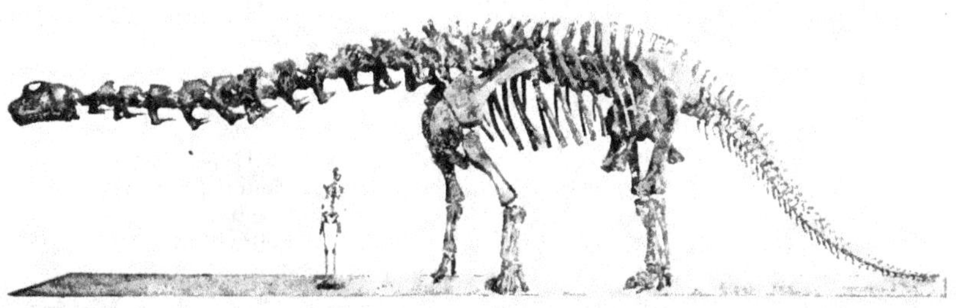

FIG. 98. AMPHIBIOUS OR TERRESTRIO-FLUVIATILE THEORY OF THE HABITS OF APATOSAURUS.

(Upper.) *Apatosaurus* (= *Brontosaurus*), a typical sauropod of Morrison age, quadrupedal, heavy-limbed, herbivorous, inhabiting the flood-plains (Morrison) and lagoons of the region now elevated into the Rocky Mountain chain of Wyoming and Colorado.
(Lower.) Mounted skeleton of *Apatosaurus* (= *Brontosaurus*) in the American Museum of Natural History.

to the fact that these types had reached a *cul-de-sac* of mechanical evolution from which they could not adaptively emerge when they encountered in all parts of the world the new environmental conditions of advancing Cretaceous time.

The Iguanodontia

Contemporaneous with the culminating period of the evolution of the Sauropoda is the world-wide appearance of an

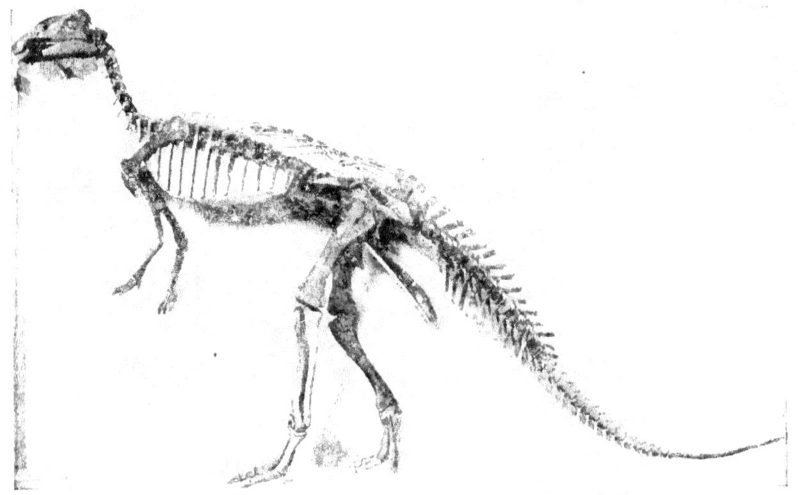

Fig. 90. Primitive Iguanodont *Camptosaurus* from the Upper Jurassic of Wyoming.

This swift bipedal form was contemporary with the giant sauropod *Apatosaurus* and the lighter-bodied *Diplodocus*. These iguanodonts were defenseless and dependent wholly on alertness and speed, or perhaps on resort to the water, for escape from their enemies. They were the prey of *Allosaurus* (see Fig. 91). Mounted specimen in the American Museum of Natural History.

entirely different stock of bipedal herbivorous dinosaurs in which the pelvis is bird-like (Ornithischia, Seeley). These animals may be traced back (von Huene) to the Triassic *Naosaurus*. The front of the jaws at an early stage lost the teeth and developed a horny sheath or beak like that of the birds, within which a new bone (predentary) evolves, giving to this order the name Predentata. Entirely defenseless at this stage (*Camptosaurus*), these relatively small, bipedal types

Fig. 100. A Pair of Upper Cretaceous Iguanodonts from Montana.

After a lapse of 500,000 years of Cretaceous time the *Camptosaurus* (Fig. 99) evolved into the giant "duck-billed" dinosaur *Trachodon*, described by Leidy and Cope from the Upper Cretaceous of New Jersey and Dakota.

Two skeletons of *Trachodon annectens* (upper) discovered in Montana, as mounted in the American Museum of Natural History, and restoration of the same (lower) by Osborn and Knight. (Compare Fig. 74.)

spread all over the northern hemisphere and attained an extraordinary adaptive radiation in the river- and shore-living "duck-bill" dinosaurs, the iguanodonts of the Cretaceous Epoch (Fig. 101). The adaptive radiation of these animals has only recently been fully determined; it led into three great types of body form, all unarmored. First, the less specialized types which retain more or less the body structure of the earlier Jurassic forms and the famous iguanodont of Bernissart, Belgium. Related to these are the kritosaurs of the Cretaceous of Alberta, with a comparatively narrow head, the protection of which was facilitated by a long, backwardly projecting spine. Second, there are the broadly duck-billed, wading dinosaurs (*Trachodon*), with stalking limbs and elevated bodies. Third, there are more fully aquatic, free-swimming forms with crested skulls (*Corythosaurus*). The

Fig. 101. Adaptive Radiation of the Iguanodont Dinosaurs into Three Groups.

(Upper.) Three characteristic types: *A*, Typical "duck-bill" *Trachodon; B*, *Corythosaurus*, the hooded "duck-bill," with a head like a cassowary, probably aquatic; *C*, *Kritosaurus*, the crested "duck-bill" dinosaur. Restorations by Brown and Deckert.

(Lower.) Mounted skeleton of *Corythosaurus* in the American Museum of Natural History, recently discovered in the Upper Cretaceous of Alberta, Canada, with the integument impressions and body lines preserved.

anatomy and habits of all these forms have been made known recently by American Museum explorations in Alberta, Canada, under Barnum Brown (Fig. 101).

The partly armored dinosaurs known as stegosaurs are related to the iguanodonts and belong to the bird-pelvis group

(Ornithischia). The small Triassic ancestors of this great group of herbivorous, ornithischian dinosaurs also gave rise to a number of secondarily quadrupedal, slow-moving forms, in which there developed various forms of defensive and offensive armature. Of these the Jurassic stegosaurs exhibit a reversed evolution in their locomotion since they pass from a bipedal into a quadrupedal type in which the armature takes

FIG. 102. OFFENSIVE AND DEFENSIVE ENERGY COMPLEXES.

The carnivorous "tyrant" dinosaur *Tyrannosaurus* approaching a group of the horned herbivorous dinosaurs known as Ceratopsia. Compare frontispiece.

The Ceratopsia are related to the armored *Stegosaurus* and to the armorless, swift-moving Iguanodontia. Restoration by Osborn in the American Museum of Natural History, painted by Charles R. Knight.

the form of sharp dorsal plates and spiny defenses, the exact arrangement of which has been recently worked out by Gilmore. Doubtless when this animal was attacked it drew its head and limbs under its body, like the armadillo or porcupine, and relied for protection upon its dorsal armature, aided by rapid lateral motions of the great spines of the tail to ward off its enemies. During the progress of Cretaceous time these stegosaurs became extinct, and by the beginning of the Middle Cretaceous two other herbivorous types are given off from the predentate stock.

The first of these are the aggressively and defensively horned Ceratopsia, in which two or three front horns evolved step by step, with a great bony frill protecting the neck. This evolution took place stage by stage with the evolution of the predatory mechanism of the carnivorous dinosaurs, so that the climax of ceratopsian defense (*Triceratops*) was reached simultaneously with the climax of *Tyrannosaurus* offense. This is an example of the *counteracting evolution* of offensive and defensive adaptations, analogous to that which we observe to-day in the evolution of the lions, tigers, and leopards, which counteracts with that of the horned cattle and antelopes of Africa, and again in the evolution of the wolves simultaneously with the horned bison and deer in the northern hemisphere. It is a case where the struggle for existence is very severe at every stage of development and where advantageous or disadvantageous chromatin predispositions in evolution come constantly under the operation of the *law of selection*. Thus in the balance between the reptilian carnivora and herbivora we find a complete protophase of the more recent balance between the mammalian carnivora and herbivora.

The climax of defense was reached, however, in another line of Predentata, in the herbivorous dinosaurs, known as *Ankylosaurus*, in which there developed a close imitation of the armadillo or glyptodon type of mammal, with the head and entire body sheathed in a very dense, bony armature. In these animals not only is motion abandoned as a means of escape, but the teeth become diminutive and feeble, as in most other heavily armored forms of reptiles and mammals. The herbivorous function of the teeth is replaced by the development of horny beaks. Thus these animals reach a ground-dwelling, slow-moving, heavily armored existence.

Pterosaurs

There is no doubt that the pterosaurs, flying reptiles, were adapted to fly far out to sea, for their remains are found mingled with those of the mosasaurs in deposits far from the ancient shore-lines. There is no relation whatever between the feathered birds and these animals, whose analogies in their modes of flight are rather with the bats among the mammals. These flying reptiles are perhaps the most extraordinary of all extinct animals. While some pterosaurs were hardly larger than sparrows, others surpassed all living birds in the spread of the wings, although inferior to many birds in the bulk of the body. It is believed that they depended almost entirely upon soaring for progression. The head in the largest types of the family (*Pteranodon*) is converted into a great vertical fin, used, no doubt, in directing flight, with a long, backwardly projecting bony crest which served in the balancing of the elongate and compressed bill. The feeble development of the muscles of flight in these ancient forms is compensated for by the extreme lightness of the body and the hollowness of the bones.

Fig. 103. Restoration of the Pterodactyl, Showing the Soaring Flight.
After the *Aëronautical Journal*, London.

Origin of Birds

It is believed that in late Permian or early Triassic time a small lizard-like reptile of partly bipedal habit and remotely related to the bipedal ancestors of the dinosaurs passed from a terrestrial into a terrestrio-arboreal mode of life, probably for purposes of safety. This early arboreo-terrestrial phase is indicated in the most ancient known birds (*Archæopteryx*) by the presence of claws at the ends of the bones of the wing, fitting them for clinging to trees, it is argued, through analogy to the tree-clinging habits of existing young hoatzins of South

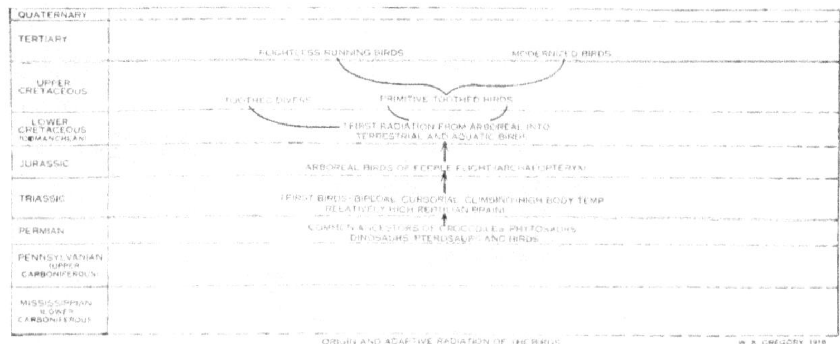

FIG. 104. ANCESTRAL TREE OF THE BIRDS.

The ancestors of the birds branch off in Permian time from the same stock that gives rise to the dinosaurs, adding to swift, bipedal locomotion along the ground the power of tree climbing and, with their very active life, the development of a high and uniform body temperature. Primitive types of birds exhibit a fore limb terminating in claws, probably for grasping tree branches. The power of flight began to develop in Triassic time through the conversion of scales into feathers either on the fore limbs (two-wing theory) or on both fore and hind limbs (four-wing theory). From the Jurassic birds (*Archæopteryx*), capable of only feeble flight, there arises an adaptive radiation into aërial, arboreal, arboreo-terrestrial, terrestrial, and aquatic forms, the last exhibiting a reversal of evolution. Diagram prepared for the author by W. K. Gregory.

America. Ancestral tree existence is rendered still more probable by the fact that the origin of flight was apparently subserved in the parachute function of the fore limb and perhaps of both the fore and hind limbs for descent from the branches of trees to the ground.

Two theories have been advanced as to the origin of flight in the stages succeeding the arboreal phase of bird evolution. First, the *pair-wing theory*, developed from the earlier studies on *Archæopteryx*, in which the transformation of lateral scales

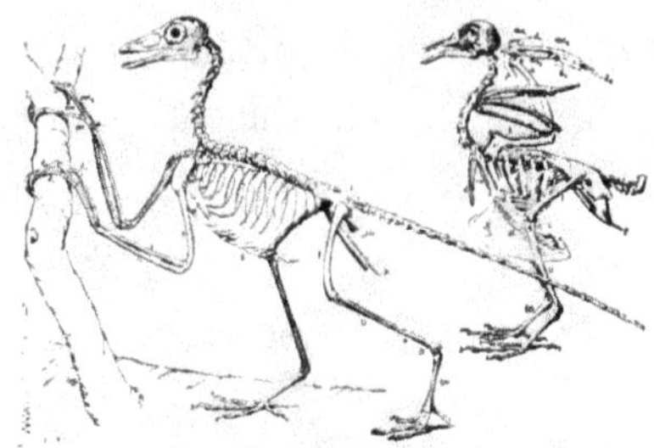

FIG. 105. SKELETON OF *Archæopteryx* (left) COMPARED WITH THAT OF THE PIGEON (right).

Showing the abbreviation of the tail into the pygostyle and the conversion of the grasping fore limb into the bones of the wing. After Heilman.

into long primary feathers on the fore limbs and at the sides of the extended tail would afford a glissant parachute support for short flights from trees to the ground (Fig. 106). Quite recently a *four-wing theory*, the *tetrapteryx theory*, has been proposed by Beebe, based on the observation of the presence of great feathers on the thighs of embryos of modern birds and of supposed traces of similar feathers on the thighs of the oldest known fossil bird, the *Archæopteryx* of Jurassic age. According to this hypothesis after the four-wing stage was reached the two hind-leg wings degenerated as the flight function evolved in the spreading feathers of the forearm-wings and the rudder function was perfected in the spreading feathers of the tail (Fig. 107). Both of these

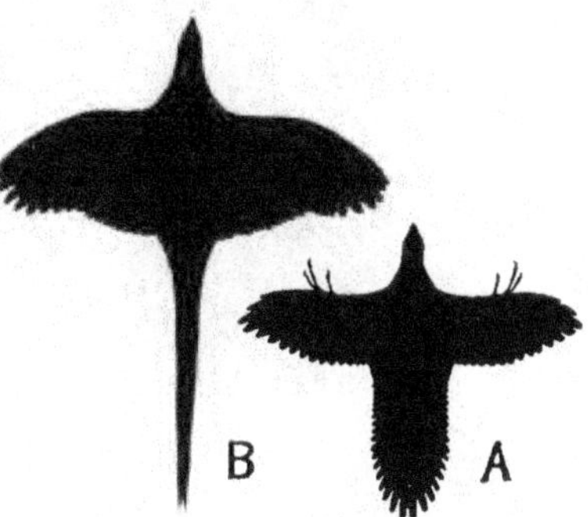

FIG. 106. SILHOUETTES OF *Archæopteryx* (*A*) AND PHEASANT (*B*).

Based on the two-wing theory. After Heilman.

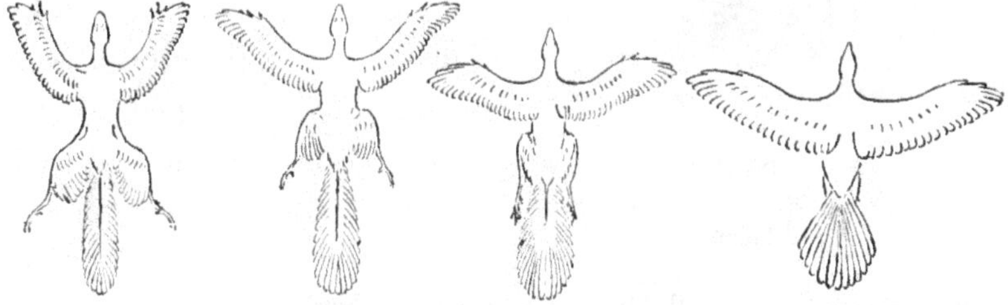

FIG. 107. FOUR EVOLUTIONARY STAGES IN THE HYPOTHETICAL FOUR-WINGED BIRD. After Beebe.

hypotheses assign two phases to the origin of flight in birds: first, a primary terrestrial phase, during which the peculiar characters of the hind limbs and feet were developed with their strong analogies to the bipedal feet of dinosaurs; second, a purely arboreal phase. It is believed by the adherents of both the two-wing and the four-wing theory that following the arboreal phase, in which the powers of flight were fully developed, there occurred among the struthious birds, such as the ostriches, a secondary terrestrial phase in which the powers of flight were secondarily lost and rapid cursorial locomotion on the ground was secondarily developed. This interpretation of the foot and limb structure associated with the loss of teeth, which is characteristic of all the higher birds, will explain the close analogies which exist between the ostrich-like dinosaur *Stru-*

FIG. 108. THEORETIC MODE OF PARACHUTE FLIGHT OF THE PRIMITIVE BIRD.

Based on the four-wing theory. After Beebe.

FIG. 109. RESTORATION OF THE ANCIENT JURASSIC BIRD, *Archæopteryx*.

Capable of relatively feeble flight. After Heilman.

thiomimus and the modern cursorial flightless forms of birds, such as the ostriches, rheas, and cassowaries.

In the opposite extreme to these purely terrestrial forms, the flying arboreal birds also gave off the water-living birds, one phase in the evolution of which is represented in the loon-like *Hesperornis*, the companion of the pterosaurs and mosasaurs in the Upper Cretaceous seas. It was on the jaws of the

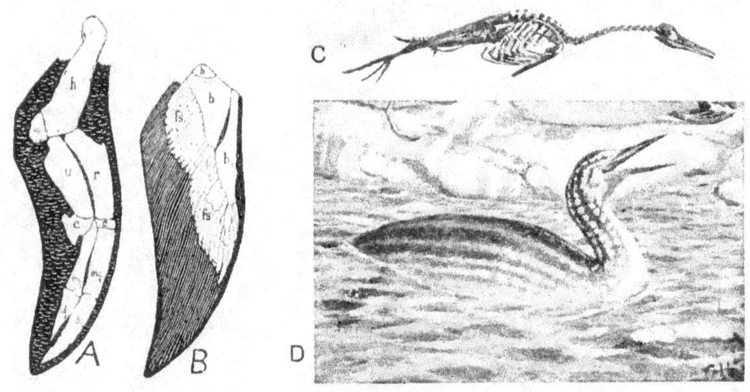

FIG. 110. REVERSED AQUATIC EVOLUTION OF WING AND BODY FORM.

Wing of a penguin (*A*) transformed into a fin externally resembling the fin of a shark (*B*). Skeleton of *Hesperornis* (*C*) in the American Museum of Natural History and restoration of *Hesperornis* (*D*) by Heilman, both showing the transformation of the flying bird into a swimming, aquatic type, and its convergent evolution toward the body shape of the shark, ichthyosaur, and dolphin (compare Fig. 41).

Hesperornis and smaller *Ichthyornis* that Marsh made his sensational announcement of the discovery of birds with teeth, a discovery confirmed by his renewed studies of the classic fossil bird type, the Jurassic *Archæopteryx*. These divers of the Cretaceous seas (*Hesperornis*) are analogous to the modern loons, and represent one of the many instances in which the tempting food of the aquatic habitat has been sought by animals venturing out from the shore-lines. As in the most highly specialized modern swimming birds, the Antarctic penguins, the wing secondarily evolves into a fin or paddle, while the body secondarily develops a fusiform shape in order to diminish resistance to the water in rapid swimming.

Possible Causes of the Arrested Evolution of the Reptiles

Of the eighteen great orders of reptiles which evolved on land, in the sea, and in the air during the long Reptilian Era of 12,000,000 years, only five orders survive to-day, namely, the turtles (Testudinata), tuateras (Rhynchocephalia), lizards (Lacertilia), snakes (Ophidia), and crocodiles (Crocodilia).

The evolution of the members of these five surviving orders has either been extremely slow or entirely arrested during the 3,000,000 years which are generally assigned to Tertiary time; we can distinguish only by relatively minor changes the turtles and crocodiles of the base of the Tertiary from those living to-day. In other words, during this period of 3,000,000 years the entire plant world, the invertebrate world, the fish, the amphibian, and the reptilian worlds have all remained as relatively balanced, static, unchanged or persistent types, while the mammals, radiating 3,000,000 years ago from very small and inconspicuous forms, have undergone a phenomenal evolution, spreading into every geographic region formerly occupied by the Reptilia and passing through multitudinously varied phases not only of direct but of alternating and of reversed evolution. During the same epoch the warm-blooded birds were doubtless evolving, although there are relatively few fossil records of this bird evolution.

This is a most striking instance of the differences in chromatin potentiality or the internal evolutionary impulses underlying all visible changes of function and of form. If we apply our law of the actions, reactions, and interactions of the four physicochemical energies (p. 21), there are four reasons why we may not attribute this relatively arrested development of the reptiles either to an arrested physicochemical environment, to an arrested life environment, or to the relative bodily inertia of reptiles which affects the body-protoplasm and body-chromatin. These four reasons appear to be as follows:

First: We have noted that among the reptiles the velocity of purely mechanical adaptation is quite independent both of brain power and of nervous activity, a fact which seems to strike a blow at the *psychic-direction hypothesis* (p. 143), on which the explanations of evolution by Lamarck, Spencer, and Cope so largely depend. The law that perfection of mechanical adaptation is quite independent of brain power also holds true among the mammals, because the small-brained mammals of early Tertiary time, the first mammals to appear, evolve as mechanisms quite as rapidly or more rapidly than the large-brained mammals.

Second: The law of rapidity of character evolution is independent also of body temperature, for, while the mechanical evolution of the warm-blooded birds and mammals is very rapid and very remarkable it can hardly be said to have exceeded that of the cold-blooded reptiles. Thus the causes of the *velocity of character evolution* in mechanism need not be sought in the psychic influence of the brain, in the nervous system, in the "Lamarckian" influence of the constant exercise of the body, nor in a higher or lower temperature of the circulatory system.

Third: Nor has the relatively arrested evolution of the Reptilia during the period of the Age of Mammals been due to arrested environmental conditions, for during this time the environment underwent a change as great as or greater than that during the preceding Age of Reptiles.

Fourth, and finally, there is no evidence that natural selection has exerted less influence on reptilian evolution during the Age of Mammals than previously. Thus we shut out four out of five factors, namely, physical environment, individual habit and development, life environment, and selection as reasonable causes of the relative arrest of evolution among the reptiles.

Consequently the causes of the arrest of evolution among the Reptilia appear to lie in the internal heredity-chromatin, *i. e.*, to be due to a slowing down of physicochemical interactions, to a reduced activity of the chemical messengers which theoretically are among the causes of rapid evolution.

The inertia witnessed in the entire body form of static or persistent types is also found to occur in certain single characters of the individual. Recurring to the view that evolution is in part the sum of the acceleration, balance, or retardation of the velocity of single characters, the five surviving orders of the reptiles appear to represent organisms in which the greater number of characters lost their velocity at the close of the Age of Reptiles, and consequently the order as a whole remained relatively static.

CHAPTER VIII

EVOLUTION OF THE MAMMALS

First mammals, of insectivorous and tree-living habits. Single character evolution, physicochemical interaction, coordination, and complexity. Problem as to the causes of the origin of new characters and of new bodily proportions. Adaptations of the teeth and of the limbs as observed in direct, reversed, alternate, and counteracting evolution. Physiographic and climatic environment during the period of mammalian evolution, in a measure deduced from adaptive variations in teeth and feet of mammals. Conclusions, present knowledge of biologic evolution among the vertebrate animals. Future lines of inquiry into the causes of evolution.

It required a man of genius like Linnæus to conceive the inclusion within the single class Mammalia of such diverse

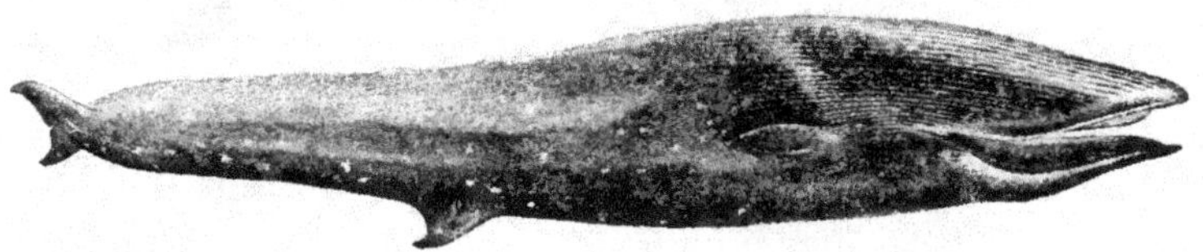

Fig. 111. The Sei Whale, Balænoptera Borealis,
Which attains a total length of forty-nine feet. Restoration (upper) and photograph (lower) after Andrews.

forms as the tiny insect-loving shrew and the gigantic predaceous whale. It has required one hundred and twenty-five years of continuous exploration and research to establish the fact that the whale type (Fig. 111), is not only akin to but is probably a remote descendant of an insectivorous type not very distant from the existing tree shrews (Fig. 112), the transformation of size, of function, and of form between these two extremes having taken place within a period broadly estimated in our geologic time scale at about 10,000,000 years.

Fig. 112. The Tree Shrew *Tupaia*. Insectivore, considered to be near the prototype form of all the higher placental mammals.

Origin of the Mammals, Insectivorous, Arboreal

To the descent of the mammals Huxley was the first, in essaying the reconstruction of the great ancestral tree, to apply Darwin's principles on a large scale and to prophesy that the very remote ancestral form of all the mammals was of an insectivore type. Subsequent research[1] has all tended in the same direction, pointing to insectivorous habits and in many ways to arboreal modes of existence as characteristic

Fig. 113. Primitive Types of Monotreme and Marsupial.
(Below.) Monotreme type—*Echidna*, the spiny ant-eater.
(Above.) Marsupial type—*Didelphys*, the arboreal opossum of South America. After photographs of specimens in the New York Zoological Park.

[1] This insectivorous and tree-inhabiting theory of mammalian origin has recently been advocated by Doctor William Diller Matthew of the American Museum of Natural History, by Doctor William K. Gregory of Columbia University ("The Orders of Mammals"), and Doctor Elliot Smith of the University of Glasgow.

of the earliest mammals. Proofs of arboreal habit are seen in the limb-grasping adaptations of the hind foot in many primitive mammals, and even in the human infant. Thus the

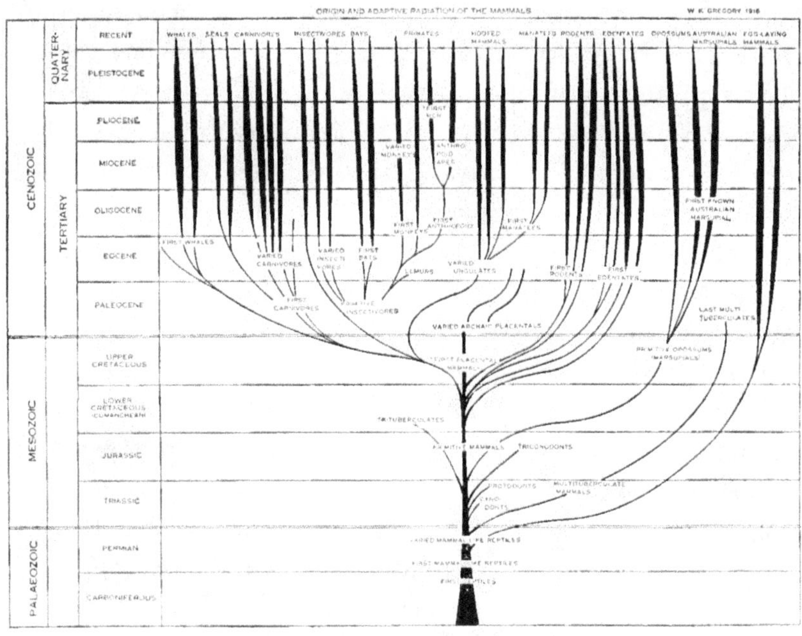

FIG. 114. ANCESTRAL TREE OF THE MAMMALS.

Adaptive radiation of the Mammalia, originating from Triassic cynodont reptiles and dividing into three main branches: (*A*) the primitive, egg-laying, reptile-like mammals (Monotremes); (*B*) the intermediate pouched, viviparous mammals (Marsupials—opossums, etc.); and (*C*) the true Placentals which branch off from small, primitive, arboreo-insectivorous forms (Trituberculata) of late Triassic time into the four grand divisions (1) the clawed mammals, (2) the Primates, (3) the hoofed mammals, and (4) the cetaceans. Dividing into some thirty orders, this grand evolution and adaptive radiation takes place chiefly during the four million years of Upper Cretaceous and Tertiary time. As among the Reptilia, the primary arboreo-terrestrial adaptive phases radiate by *direct evolution* into all the habitat zones, and by *reversed* and *alternate evolution* develop backward and forward in adaptation to one or another habitat zone. Diagram prepared for the author by W. K. Gregory.

existing tree shrews, the tupaias of Africa (Fig. 112), in many characters resemble the hypothetic ancestral forms of Cretaceous time from which the primates (monkeys, apes, and man) may have radiated.

Following Cuvier, Owen, and Huxley in Europe, a period of active research in this country began with Leidy in the middle of the nineteenth century and was continued in the arid regions of the West by Cope, Marsh, and their successors with such energy that America has become the chief centre of vertebrate palæontology. When we connect this research with the older and the more recent explorations by men of all countries in Europe, Asia, Africa, Australia, and South America, we are enabled to reconstruct the great tree of mammalian descent (Fig. 114) with far greater fulness and accuracy than that of the reptiles, amphibians, or fishes (Pisces).

The connection of the ancestral mammals with a reptilian type of Permian time is theoretically established through the survival of a single branch of primitive egg-laying mammals (Monotremata, Fig. 113) in Australia and New Guinea; while the whole intermediate division, consisting of the pouched mammals (Marsupialia) of Australia, which bring forth their young in a very immature condition, represents on the great continent of Australia an adaptive radiation which also sprang from a small, primitive, tree-living type of mammal, typified by the existing opossums of North and South America (Fig. 113). The third great group (Placentalia) includes the mammals in which the unborn young are retained a longer period within the mother and are nourished through the circulation of nutrition in the placenta.

1. Whales.
2. Seals (marine carnivores).
3. Carnivores (terrestrial).
4. Insectivores.
5. Bats.
6. Primates:
   - Lemurs,
   - Monkeys,
   - Apes,
   - Man.
7. Hoofed mammals.
8. Manatees.
9. Rodents.
10. Edentates.

The adaptive radiation of the ten great branches of the placental stock from the primitive insectivorous arboreal ancestors produced a mammalian fauna which inhabited the entire globe until the comparatively recent period of extermination by man, who through the invention of tools in Middle Pleistocene time, about 125,000 years ago, became the destroyer of creation.

Single Character Evolution and Physicochemical Correlation

The principal modes of evolution as we observe them among the mammals are threefold, namely:

I. The modes in which new characters first appear, whether suddenly or gradually and continuously, whether accidentally or according to some law.

II. The modes in which characters change in proportion, quantitatively or intensively, both as to form and color.

III. The modes in which all the characters of an organism respond to a change of environment and of individual habit.

The key to the understanding of these three modes is to be sought first in changes of food and in changes of the medium in which the mammals move, whether on the earth, in the water, or in the air. The complexity of the environmental influence becomes like that of a lock with an unlimited number of combinations, because the adaptations of the teeth to varied forms of insectivorous, carnivorous, and herbivorous diet may be similar among mammals living in widely different habitat zones, while the adaptations of the locomotor apparatus, the limbs and feet, to the primary arboreal zone may radiate into structures suited to any one of the remaining ten life zones. Thus there is invariably a double adaptive and independent radiation of the teeth to food and of the limbs to progression, and therefore two series of organs are evolving. For example, there always arises a more or less close analogy between the teeth of all insect-eating mammals, irrespective of the habitat in which they find their food. Similarly there arises a more or less close analogy between the motor organs of all the mammals living in any particular habitat; thus the glissant or volplaning limbs of all aëro-arboreal types are externally similar, irrespective of the ancestral orders from which

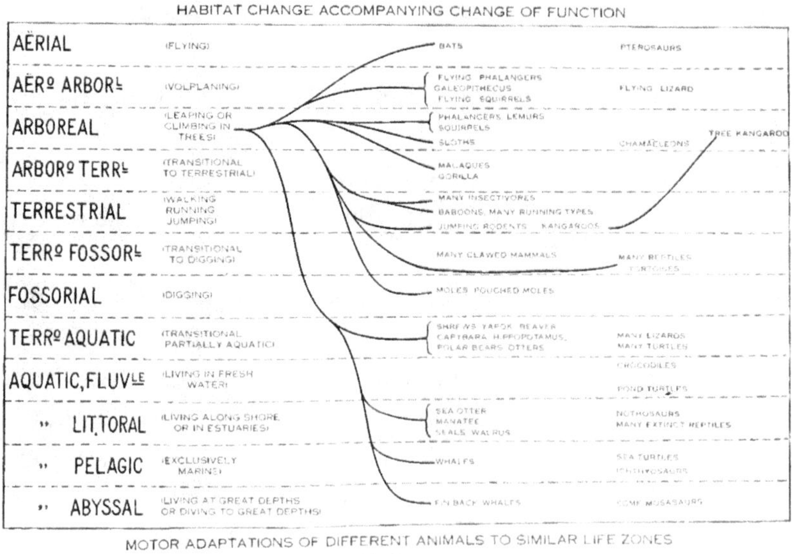

HABITAT CHANGE ACCOMPANYING CHANGE OF FUNCTION

AËRIAL	(FLYING)	BATS	PTEROSAURS
AËRº ARBORL	(VOLPLANING)	FLYING PHALANGERS GALEOPITHECUS FLYING SQUIRRELS	FLYING LIZARD
ARBOREAL	(LEAPING OR CLIMBING IN TREES)	PHALANGERS, LEMURS SQUIRRELS SLOTHS	CHAMÆLEONS TREE KANGAROO
ARBORº TERRL	(TRANSITIONAL TO TERRESTRIAL)	MACAQUES GORILLA	
TERRESTRIAL	(WALKING RUNNING JUMPING)	MANY INSECTIVORES BABOONS, MANY RUNNING TYPES JUMPING RODENTS KANGAROOS	
TERRº FOSSORL	(TRANSITIONAL TO DIGGING)	MANY CLAWED MAMMALS	MANY REPTILES TORTOISES
FOSSORIAL	(DIGGING)	MOLES, POUCHED MOLES	
TERRº AQUATIC	(TRANSITIONAL, PARTIALLY AQUATIC)	SHREWS, YAPOK, BEAVER CAPYBARA, HIPPOPOTAMUS, POLAR BEARS, OTTERS	MANY LIZARDS MANY TURTLES
AQUATIC, FLUVLE	(LIVING IN FRESH WATER)		CROCODILES POND TURTLES
" LITTORAL	(LIVING ALONG SHORE OR IN ESTUARIES)	SEA OTTER MANATEE SEALS, WALRUS	NOTHOSAURS MANY EXTINCT REPTILES
" PELAGIC	(EXCLUSIVELY MARINE)	WHALES	SEA TURTLES ICHTHYOSAURS
" ABYSSAL	(LIVING AT GREAT DEPTHS OR DIVING TO GREAT DEPTHS)	FIN BACK WHALES	SOME MOSASAURS

MOTOR ADAPTATIONS OF DIFFERENT ANIMALS TO SIMILAR LIFE ZONES

FIG. 115. ADAPTIVE RADIATION OF THE MAMMALS.

The mammals, probably originating in arboreal leaping or climbing phases, radiate adaptively into all the other habitat zones and thus acquire many types of body form and of locomotion more or less convergent and analogous to those previously evolved among the reptiles (shown in the right-hand column), the amphibians, and the fishes. Diagram by Osborn and Gregory.

they are derived. A mammal may seek any one of twelve different habitat zones in search of the same general kind of food; conversely, a mammal living in a single habitat zone may seek within it six entirely different kinds of food.

This principle of the independent adaptation of each organ of the body to its own particular function is in keeping with the heredity law of individual and separate evolution of "characters" and "character complexes" (p. 147), and is fatal to some of the hypotheses regarding animal structure and evolution which have been entertained since the first analyses of animal form were made by Cuvier at the beginning of the last century. The independent adaptation of each character group to its own particular function proves that there is no such essential correlation between the structure of the teeth and the structure of the feet as Cuvier claimed in what was perhaps his most famous generalization, namely, his "Law of Correlation."[1]

Again this principle, of twofold, threefold, or manifold adaptation, is fatal to any form of belief in an internal perfecting tendency which may drive animal evolution in any particular direction or directions. Finally, it is fatal to Darwin's original natural-selection hypothesis, which would imply that the teeth, limbs, and feet are varying fortuitously rather than evolving under certain definite although still unknown laws.

The adaptations which arise in the search of many varieties of food and in overcoming the mechanical problems of locomotion, offense, and defense in the twelve different habitat zones are not fortuitous. On the contrary, observations on successive members of families of mammals in process either of direct, of reversed, or of alternate adaptation admit of but one interpretation, namely, that the evolution of characters is in definite directions toward adaptive ends; nor is this definite direction limited by the ancestral constitution of the heredity-chromatin as conceived in the logical mind of Huxley. The passage in which Huxley expressed this conception is as follows:

"The importance of natural selection will not be impaired even if further inquiries should prove *that variability is definite, and is determined in certain directions rather than in others*, by

[1] Cuvier's law of correlation has been restated by Osborn. There is a fundamental correlation, coordination, and cooperation of all parts of the organism, but not of the kind conceived by Cuvier, who was at heart a special creationist. Contrary to Cuvier's claim, it is impossible to predict from the structure of the teeth what the structure of the feet may prove to be.

conditions inherent in that which varies. It is quite conceivable that every species tends to produce varieties of a limited number and kind, and that the effect of natural selection is to favor the development of some of these, while it opposes the development of others along their predetermined lines of modification."[1] It is true that the variations of the organism are in some respects limited in the heredity-chromatin, as Huxley imagined; on the contrary, every part of a mammal may exhibit such plasticity in course of geologic time as enables it to pass from one habitat zone into another, and from that into still others until finally traces of the adaptations to previous habitats and anatomical phases may be almost if not entirely lost. The heredity-chromatin never determines beforehand into what new environment the lot of a mammal family may be cast; this is determined by cosmic and planetary changes as well as by the appetites and initiative of the organism (p. 114). For example, one of the most remarkable instances which have been discovered is that of the reversed aquatic adaptation of *Zeuglodon*,[2] first terrestrial, then aquatic, in succession a dog-like, a fish-like, and finally an eel-like mammal. These peculiar whales (Archæoceti) appear to have originated in the littoral and pelagic waters of Africa in Eocene time from a purely terrestrial ancestral form of mammal (allied to *Hyænodon*), in which the body is proportioned like that of the wolf or dog, and this terrestrial mammal in turn was descended from a very remote arboreal ancestor. Thus in its long history the Zeuglodon passed through at least three habitat zones and as many life phases.

Yet in another sense Huxley was right, for palæontolo-

[1] Huxley, Thomas, 1893, p. 223 (first published in 1878).

[2] *Zeuglodon* itself is a highly specialized side branch of the primitive toothed whales. The true whales may have arisen from the genera *Protocetus*, probably ancestral to the toothed whales, and *Patriocetus* which combines characters of the zeuglodonts and whalebone whales.

gists actually observe in the characters springing from the heredity-chromatin a *predetermination* of another kind, namely, the origin through causes we do not understand of a tendency toward the independent appearance or birth at different periods of geologic time of *similar new and useful characters.* In fact, a very large number of characters spring not from the visible ancestral body forms but from invisible predispositions and tendencies in the ancestral heredity-chromatin. For example, all the radiating descendants of a group of hornless mammals may at different periods of geologic time give rise to similar horny outgrowths upon the forehead. This heredity principle partly underlies what Osborn has termed the *law of rectigradation.* Moreover, once a new character or group of characters makes its visible appearance in the body its invisible chromatin evolution may assume certain definite directions and become cumulative in successive generations in accordance with the principle of *Mutationsrichtung*, first perceived by Neumayr (p. 138); in other words, the tendency of a character to evolve in one direction often accumulates in successive generations until it reaches an extreme.

The application of our law of quadruple causes, namely, of the incessant action, reaction, and interaction of the four physicochemical complexes under the influence of natural selection, to the definite and orderly origin of myriads of characters such as are involved in the transformation of a shrew type of mammal into the quadrupedal wolf type and of the wolf type into the *Zeuglodon* eel type, has not yet even approached the dignity of a working hypothesis, much less of an explanation. The truth is that the *causes* of the orderly coadaptation of separable and independent characters still remain a mystery which we are only beginning to dimly penetrate.

As another illustration of the complexity of the evolution

process in mammals, let us observe the operation of Dollo's law of alternate adaptation (p. 202) in the evolution of the tree kangaroo (*Dendrolagus*), belonging to the marsupial or pouched division of the Mammalia. This is a case where many of the intermediate stages are known to survive in existing types. These tree kangaroos theoretically have passed through four phases, as follows: (1) An arboreo-terrestrial phase, including primitive marsupials like the opossum, with no special adap-

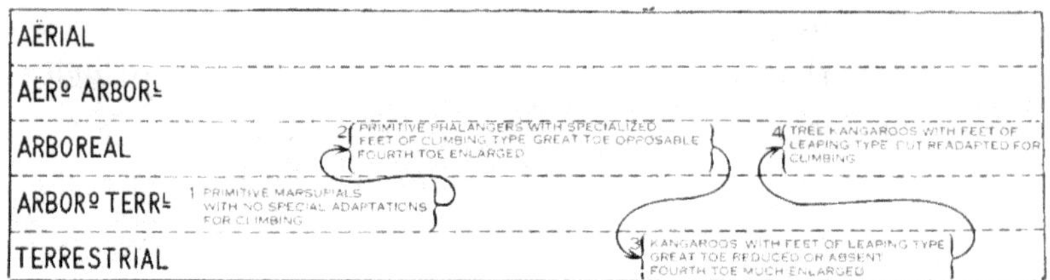

FIG. 116. FOUR PHASES OF ALTERNATING ADAPTATION IN THE KANGAROO MARSUPIALS, ACCORDING TO DOLLO'S LAW.

1. Primitive arboreo-terrestrial phase—tree and ground living forms.
2. Primitive arboreal phalanger phase—tree-living forms.
3. Kangaroos—terrestrial, saltatorial phase—ground-living, jumping forms.
4. Tree kangaroos—secondarily arboreal, climbing phase.

tations for climbing; (2) a true arboreal phase of primitive tree phalangers with the feet specialized for climbing purposes through the opposability of the great toe (hallux), the fourth toe enlarged; (3) a cursorial terrestrial phase, typified by the kangaroos, with feet of the leaping type, the big toe (hallux) reduced or absent, the fourth toe greatly enlarged; (4) a second arboreal phase, typified by the tree kangaroos (*Dendrolagus*), with limbs fundamentally of the cursorial terrestrial leaping type but superficially readapted for climbing purposes. It is clear that there can be no internal perfecting tendency or predetermination of the heredity-chromatin to anticipate such a tortuous course of evolution from terrestrial into arboreal life, from arboreal back to a highly specialized terrestrial life, and finally from the leaping over the ground of the kangaroo into the incipiently specialized arboreal phase of the tree kangaroo. In the evolution of the tree kangaroos adaptation is certainly not limited by the inherent tendencies of the heredity-chromatin to evolve in certain directions. The physicochemical theory of these remarkable alternate adaptations is that an animal leaving the terrestrial habitat and taking on arboreal habits initiates an entirely new series of actions, reactions, and interactions with its physical environment, with its life environment, in its body cell and individual development, and, in some manner entirely unknown to us, in its heredity-chromatin, which begins to show new or modified determiners of bodily character. That natural selection is continuously operating at every stage of the transformation there can be no doubt.

One interpretation which has been offered up to the present time of the mode of transformation of a terrestrial into an arboreal mammal is through a form of Darwinism known as the "organic selection" or "coincident selection" hypothesis, which was independently proposed by Osborn,[1] Baldwin, and Lloyd Morgan, namely: that the individual bodily modifications and adaptations caused by growth and habit (while not themselves heritable) would tend to preserve the organism during the long transition into arboreal life; they would tend to nurse the family over the critical period and allow time to favor all predispositions and tendencies in the heredity-chromatin toward arboreal function and structure, and would tend also to eliminate all structural and functional predispositions in the heredity-chromatin which would naturally adapt a mammal to life in any one of the other habitat zones. This interpretation is consistent with our law that selection is constantly operating

[1] Osborn, H. F., 1897.

on all the actions, reactions, and interactions of the body, but it does not help to explain the definite origin of new characters which cannot enter into "organic selection" before they exist. Nor is there any evidence that while adapting itself to one mode of life fortuitous variations in the heredity-chromatin for every other mode of life are occurring.

Theoretic Causes of Evolution in Mammals

We have thus far described only the *modes of evolution* and said nothing of the *causes*. In speculating on the *causes of character evolution* in the mammals, in comparison with similar body forms and characters in the lower vertebrates and even in the invertebrates, it is very important to keep in mind the preceding evidence that mammalian heredity-chromatin may preserve all the useful functional and structural properties of action, reaction, and interaction which have accumulated in the long series of ancestral life forms from the protozoan and even the bacterial stage.

Since structurally the mammalian embryo passes through primitive protozoan (single-celled) and metazoan (many-celled) phases, it is probable that chemically it passes through the same. The heredity-chromatin even in the development of the highest mammals still recalls primitive stages in the development of the fishes, for example, the gill-arch structure at the side of the throat, which through change of function serves to form the primary cartilaginous jaws (Meckelian cartilages) of mammals as well as the bony ossicles which are connected with the auditory function of the middle ear (Reichert's theory). Similarly profound structural ancestral phases in protozoan, fish, and reptile structure pervade every part of the mammalian body. In race evolution there may be changes of adaptation as in the *law of change of function* (*Prinzip des Funk-*

tionswechsels), first clearly enunciated by Anton Dohrn in 1875. But no function is lost without good cause, and the heredity-chromatin retains every character which through change of function and adaptation can be made useful.

The same law which we observe in the conservation of all adaptive characters and functions will probably be discovered also in the conservation of ancestral physicochemical actions, reactions, and interactions of the organism from the protozoan stages onward. The primordial chemical messengers—enzymes or organic catalyzers, hormones and chalones, and other accelerators, retarders, and balancers of organ formation (see p. 72)—are certainly not lost; if useful, they are retained, built up, and unceasingly complicated to control the marvellous coordinations and correlations of the various organs of the mammalian body. The principal endocrine (internal secretory) as well as duct secretory glands established in the fish stage of evolution (p. 160), through which they can be partly traced back even to the lancelet stage (chordate), doubtless had their beginnings among the ancestors (protochordates) of the vertebrated animals, which extend back into Cambrian and pre-Cambrian time. Since these chemical messenger functions among the mammals are enormously ancient, we may attribute an equal antiquity to the powers of chemical storage and entertain the idea that the chromatin potentiality of storing phosphate and carbonate of lime for skeletal and defensive armature in the protozoan stage of 50,000,000 years' antiquity is the same chromatin potentiality which builds up the superb internal skeletal structures of the Mammalia and the highly varied forms of offensive and defensive armature either of the calcium compound or the chitinous type.

It is, moreover, through the fundamental similarity of the physicochemical constitution of the fishes, amphibians, reptiles, birds, and mammals that we may interpret the similarities of form evolution and understand why, the other three causes being similar, mammals repeat so many of the habitat form phases in adaptation to the environments previously passed through by the lower orders of life. Thus advancing structural complexity is the reflection or the mirror of the invisible physicochemical complexity; the visible structural complexity of a great animal like the whale (Fig. 234), for example, is something we can grasp through its anatomy; the physicochemical complexity of the whale is quite inconceivable.

In research relating to the physicochemical complexity of the mammals, so notably stimulated by the work of Ehrlich and further advanced by later investigators, there are perhaps few studies more illuminating than those of Reichert and Brown[1] on the crystals of oxyhemoglobin, the red coloring matter of the mammalian blood. Their research proves that every species of mammal has its highly distinctive specific and generic form of hemoglobin crystals, that various degrees of kinship and specific affinity are indicated in the crystallography of the hemoglobin. For example, varieties of the dog family, such as the domestic dog, the wolf, the Australian dingo, the red, Arctic, and gray fox, are all distinguished by only slightly differing crystalline forms of oxyhemoglobin. The authors' philosophic conclusions arising from this research are as follows:[1]

"The possibilities of an inconceivable number of constitutional differences in any given protein are instanced in the fact that the serum-albumin molecule may, as has been estimated, have as many as 1,000,000,000 stereoisomers. If we assume that serum-globulin, myoalbumin, and other of the highest pro-

[1] Reichert, E. T., and Brown, A. P., 1909, pp. iii–iv.

[1] Certain insertions in brackets being made for purposes of comparison with other portions of this series of lectures.

teins may have a similar number, and that the simpler proteins and the fats and carbohydrates and perhaps other complex organic substances, may each have only a fraction of this number, it can readily be conceived how, primarily by differences in chemical constitution of vital substances, and secon-

FIG. 117. EVOLUTION OF PROPORTION. ADAPTATION IN LENGTH OF NECK.

Short-necked okapi (left), the forest-living giraffe of the Congo, which browses upon the lower branches of trees.

Long-necked giraffe (right), the plains-living type of the African savannas, which browses on the higher branches of trees. After Lang.

darily by differences in chemical composition, there might be brought about all of those differences which serve to characterize genera, species, and individuals. Furthermore, since the factors which give rise to constitutional changes in one vital substance would probably operate at the same time to cause related changes in certain others, the alterations in one may logically be assumed to serve as a common index to all.

"In accordance with the foregoing statement it can readily be understood how environment, for instance, might so affect the individual's metabolic processes as to give rise to modifications of the constitutions of certain corresponding proteins and other vital molecules which, even though they be of too subtle a character for the chemist to detect by his present methods, may nevertheless be sufficient to cause not only physiological and morphological differentiations in the individual, but also

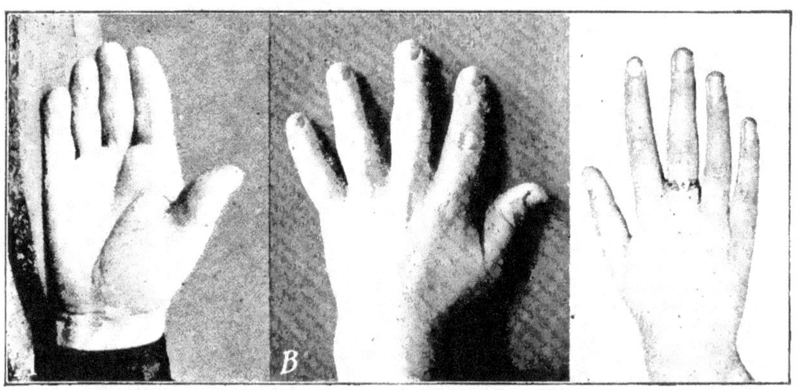

FIG. 118. SHORT-FINGEREDNESS (BRACHYDACTYLY) AND LONG-FINGEREDNESS (DOLICHODACTYLY). CONGENITAL, AND DUE TO INTERNAL SECRETION.

(Left.) Congenital brachydactyly, theoretically due either to a sudden alteration in the chromatin or to a congenital defect in the pituitary gland. After Drinkwater.

(Centre.) Brachydactyly, after birth, due to abnormally excessive secretions of the pituitary gland. After Cushing.

(Right.) Dolichodactyly, after birth, due to abnormally insufficient secretions of the pituitary gland. After Cushing.

become manifested physiologically [functionally] and morphologically [structurally] in the offspring."

The above summary adumbrates the lines along which some of the chemical interactions, if not causes, of mammalian evolution may be investigated during the present century.

The *cause* of different bodily proportions, such as the very long neck of the tree-top browsing giraffe, is one of the classic problems of adaptation. In the early part of the nineteenth century Lamarck (p. 143) attributed the lengthening of the neck to the inheritance of bodily modifications caused by the neck-stretching habit. Darwin attributed the lengthening of the neck to the constant selection of individuals and races which were born with the longest necks. Darwin was probably right. This is an instance where length or shortness of neck is obviously a selective survival character in the struggle for existence, because it directly affects the food supply.

FIG. 110. RESULT OF REMOVING THE THYROID AND PARATHYROID GLANDS.

(Right.) Normal sheep fourteen months old.

(Left.) A sheep of the same age from which the thyroids and parathyroids were removed twelve months previously.

After Sutherland Simpson.

But there are many other changes of proportion in mammals, which are not known to have a selective survival value. We may instance in man, for example, the long head-form (dolichocephaly) and the broad head-form (brachycephaly), or the long-fingered form (dolichodactyly) and the short-fingered form (brachydactyly), which have been interpreted as congenital characters appearing at birth and tending to be transmitted to offspring. Brachydactyly may be transmitted through several generations, but until recently no one has suggested what may be its possible cause.

It has now been found[1] that both the short-fingered condition (brachydactyly) and the slender-fingered condition may be induced during the lifetime of the individual in a previously healthy and normal pair of hands by a diseased or injured condition of the pituitary body at the base of the brain. If the

[1] Cushing, Harvey, 1911, pp. 253, 256.

secretions of the pituitary are abnormally active (hyperpituitarism) the hand becomes broad and the fingers stumpy (Fig. 118, *B*). If the secretions of the pituitary are abnormally reduced (hypopituitarism) the fingers become tapering and slender (Fig. 118, *C*). Thus in a most remarkable manner the internal secretions of a very ancient ductless gland, attached to the brain and originating in the roof of the mouth in our most remote fish-like ancestors, affect the proportions both of flesh and bones in the fingers, as well as the proportions of many other parts of the body.

Fig. 120. Result of Removing the Pituitary Body.

(Right.) Normal dog twelve months old.

(Left.) A dog of the same age and litter from which the pituitary body was removed at the age of two months. After Aschner.

Whether this is a mere coincidence of a heredity-chromatin congenital character with a mere bodily chemical messenger character it would be premature to say. It certainly appears that chemical interactions from the pituitary body control the normal and abnormal development of proportions in distant parts of the body.

Chief Modes of Evolution of Mammalian Characters

What we have gained during the past century is positive knowledge of the *chief modes of evolution;* we know almost the entire history of the transformation of many different kinds of mammals.

These *modes* as distinguished from the unknown *causes* are expressed in the following general laws: first, the *law of continuity; Natura non facit saltum,* there is prevailing continuity in the changes of form and proportion in evolution as in growth. Second, the *law of rectigradation,* under which many important new characters appear definitely and take an adaptive direction from the start; third, the *law of acceleration and retardation,* witnessed both in racial and individual development, whereby each character has its own velocity, or rate of development, which displays itself both in the time of its origin, in its rate of evolution, and its rate of individual development. This last law underlies the profound changes of proportion in the head and different parts of the body and limbs which are among the dominant features of mammalian evolution. In the skeleton of mammals very few new characters originate; most of the changes are in the loss of characters and in the profound changes of proportion. For example, by the addition of many teeth and by stretching or pulling, swelling or contracting, the skeleton of a tree shrew may almost be transformed into that of a whale.

The above laws are the controlling ones and make up four-fifths of mammalian evolution in the hard parts of the body. So far as has been observed the remaining fifth or even a much smaller fraction of mammalian evolution is attributable to the *law of saltation, or discontinuity,* namely, to the *sudden* appearance of new characters and new functions in the heredity-chromatin. For example, the sudden addition of a new vertebra or vertebræ to the backbone, which gives rise to the varied vertebral formulæ in different orders and even the different genera of mammals, or the sudden addition of a new tooth are instances of saltatory evolution in the hard parts of the body. There are also many instances of the sudden appearance of new functional, physiological, or physicochemical characters, such as immunity or non-immunity to certain diseases.

Responses of Mammal Characters to Changing Environment

Buffon was the first to observe the direct responses of mammals to their environment and naturally supposed that environment was the *cause of animal modification*, chiefly in adaptation to changes of climate. It did not occur to him to inquire whether these modifications were heritable or not, any more than it did to Lamarck.

It is now generally believed that these reactions are for the most part modifications of the body cells and body chromatin only, which give rise to what may be known as *environmental species*, as distinguished from true *chromatin species* which are founded upon new or altered hereditary characters. Of the former order are many geographic varieties and doubtless many geographic species. These visible species of body cell characters are quite distinct from the invisible species of heredity-chromatin characters. Both occur in nature.

Geologic and secular changes of environment have preceded many of the most profound changes in the evolution of the mammals, which interlock and counteract with their physical and life environments quite as closely as do the reptiles, amphibians, and fishes; yet a very large part of mammalian evolution has proceeded and is proceeding quite independently of change of environment. Thus environment holds its rank as *one* of the four complexes of the causes of evolution instead of being *the* cause *par excellence* as it was regarded in the brilliant speculations of Buffon.

The interlocking of mammals with their life environment is extremely close, namely, with Bacteria, Protozoa, Insecta, and many other kinds of Invertebrata, with other Vertebrata, as well as with the constantly evolving food supply of the plant world; consequently the vicissitudes of the physical environment as causes of the vicissitudes of the life environment of mammals afford the most complex examples of interlocking which we know of in the whole animal world. In other words, the mammals interlock in relation to all the surviving forms of the life which evolved on the earth before them. Although suggested nearly a century ago by Lyell, the demonstration is comparatively recent that one of the principal causes of the extinction of certain highly adaptive groups of mammals is their non-immunity to the infections spread by Bacteria and Protozoa.[1] Thus a change of environment and of climate may not affect a mammal directly but may profoundly affect it indirectly through insect life.

These closely interlocking relations of the mammals with their physicochemical environment and their life environment have been subject to constant disturbances through the geologic and geographic shifting of the twelve or more habitat zones which they occupy. Yet the earth changes during the Tertiary, the era during which mammalian evolution mainly took place, were less extreme than those during Mesozoic and Palæozoic time. This is because the trend of development of the earth's surface and of its climate during the past 3,000,000 years has been toward continental stability and lowering of general temperature in both the northern and southern hemispheres, terminating in the geologically sudden advent of the Glacial Epoch, with its alternating periods of moisture and aridity, cold and heat, which exerted the most profound influence upon the food supply, insect barriers, and other causes affecting the migrations of the Mammalia. These causes completely change the general aspect of the mammalian world in

[1] For the history and discussion of this entire subject see Osborn, H. F.: "The Causes of Extinction of Mammalia," *Amer. Naturalist*, vol. XL, November and December, 1906, pp. 769–795, 829–859.

the whole northern hemisphere, South America, and Australia, and leave only the world of African mammalian life untouched. The water content of the atmosphere during the 3,000,000 years of the Age of Mammals has tended toward a repetition of the environmental conditions of Permian and Triassic times in the development of areas of extreme humidity as well as areas of extreme aridity, interrupted, however, by widespread humid conditions in the Pleistocene Epoch. Marine invasion of the continents of Europe and North America, while far less extreme than during Cretaceous time, has served to give us the complete history of the littoral and marine Mollusca, both in the eastern and western hemispheres, which is the chief basis of the geologic time scale as discovered in the Paris basin by Brogniart at the beginning of the eighteenth century.

The clearest conception of the length of Tertiary time is afforded (Fig. 121) by the completion in Eocene time of the Rocky Mountain uplift of America and the eastern Alps of Europe, by the elevation of the Pyrenees in Oligocene time, by the rise of the wondrous Swiss Alps between the Oligocene and Miocene Epochs, and finally by the creation of the titanic Himalaya chain in the latter part of Miocene time.

Through the phenomena of the migration of various kinds of mammals from continent to continent, we are able to date with some precision the rise and fall of the land bridges and the alternating periods of connection and separation of the two northern continental masses, Eurasia and America, as well as of the northern and southern continents. Few writers maintain seriously for Tertiary time the "equatorial theory" of connection between the eastern and western hemispheres such as figures largely in the speculations of Suess, Schuchert, and others in relation to plant and animal migrations of Palæozoic and Mesozoic time. The less radical "bipolar theory" that the eastern and western hemispheres were connected both at the north pole and at the south pole, or through Arctic and Antarctic land areas, still has many adherents, especially in

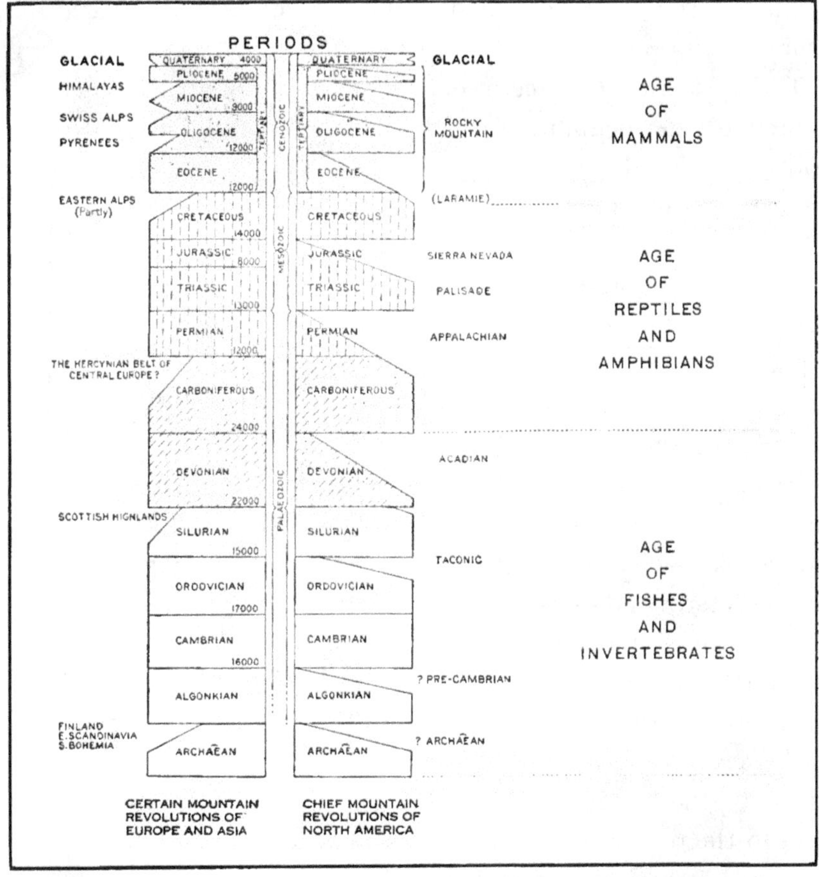

FIG. 121. MAIN SUBDIVISIONS OF GEOLOGIC TIME.

The subdivisions are not to the same scale. The notches at the sides of the scale (which is simplified from that on p. 153) represent chiefly the periods of mountain uplift in the northern hemisphere of the Old World (left) and of the New World (right).

regard to the former relations of the Australian continent and South America through the now partly sunken continent of Antarctica. The still more conservative "north polar theory" of Wallace, of an exclusively northern land connection of the eastern and western hemispheres during Tertiary time, has recently been maintained by Matthew[1] as adequate to explain all the chief facts of mammalian migration and geographic evolution.

The feet and the teeth of mammals become so closely adapted to the medium in which they move and the kind of food consumed that through the interpretation of their structure we shall in time write a fairly complete physiographic and climatic history of the Tertiary Epoch along the lines of the investigations initiated by Gaudry and Kowalevsky. Through the successive adaptations of the limbs and sole of the foot and the adaptations of the teeth, which are most delicately adjusted—the former to impact with varying soils and the latter to the requirements of the consumption of various forms of nourishment—we may definitely trace the influences or rather the adaptive responses to the habitat subzones, such as the forest, forest-border, meadow, meadow-border, river-border, the lowland, the upland, the meadow-fertile, the meadow-arid, the plains, and the desert-arid. This mirror of past geography, climate, evolution of plant life in the anatomy of the limbs

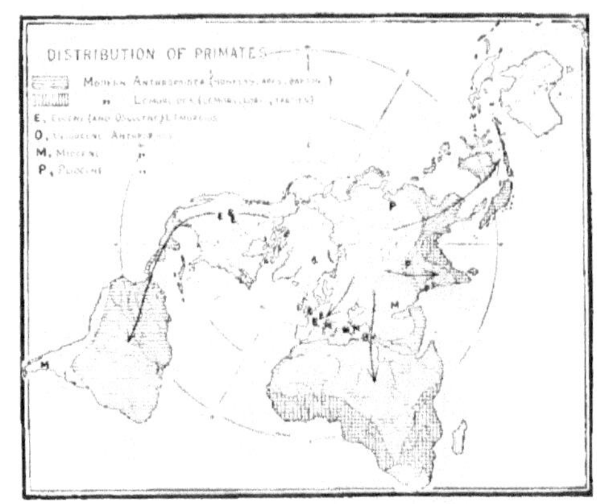

Fig. 122. The North Polar Theory of the Distribution of Mammals.

A zenith view of the earth from the north pole, showing (arrows) the North Polar theory of the geographic migrations and distribution of the mammals, especially of the Primates (monkeys, lemurs, and apes). After W. D. Matthew, 1915.

[1] Matthew, W. D., 1915.

and feet, is one of the most fascinating fields of philosophic study.

In the more humid, semi-forested regions, which preserve the physiographic conditions of early Eocene times (Fig. 123), we discover most of the examples of the survival of primitive mammalian forms and functions. The borderland between the extremes of aridity and humidity has afforded the most

FIG. 123. SCENE IN WESTERN WYOMING IN MIDDLE EOCENE TIME.

The period of the four-toed mountain horse, *Orohippus* (right), of the Uintathere (left), and of the Titanothere (left lower). From study for a mural decoration in the American Museum of Natural History by Charles R. Knight under the author's direction.

favorable habitats for the rapid evolution of all the forms of terrestrial life. From these favored regions the mammals have entered the semi-arid and arid deserts, in which also evolution has been relatively rapid. Since Tertiary geologic succession is nearly unbroken we can now trace the evolution of many families of the carnivores, the greater number of the hoofed mammals, and the rodents, with few interruptions through the entire 3,000,000 years of Tertiary time. It is through our very close observation of the origin and history of numerous single characters as exhibited in palæontologic lines of evolution that the three chief modes (p. 251) of mammalian evolution and the continued definite direction and differences of velocity in the development of characters have been discovered.

General Succession of Mammalian Life in North America

In Upper Cretaceous and Palæocene time we find that the northern hemisphere is covered with an archaic adaptive radiation of mammals distinguished by the extremely small size of the brain and clumsy mechanics of the skeleton. Of these the carnivorous forms radiate into a number of families adapted to a great variety of feeding and locomotor habits which are analogous to the families of existing Carnivora. Similarly the hoofed mammals (Condylarthra, Amblypoda) divide into swift-footed (cursorial) and heavy-footed (graviportal) forms, the latter including the Amblypoda (*Coryphodon* and *Dinoceras*). From surviving members of this archaic adaptive radiation of small-brained mammals there arise all the stem forms of the orders existing to-day, which almost without exception have now been traced back to the close of Eocene time, namely, the ancestors of the whales, of the modern families of carnivores, insectivores, bats, lemurs, rodents, and the edentates (armadillos and ant-eaters). Especially remarkable is the discovery in the Lower Eocene of the ancestors of

Fig. 124. Two Stages in the Early Evolution of the Ungulates.

Pantolambda (*A*), an archaic Palæocene form which transforms into *Coryphodon* (*B*), a Lower Eocene form of increased size, with greatly enlarged head, abbreviated tail, and defensive tusks. This transformation occupied a period estimated at 500,000 years, nearly one-sixth of Tertiary time. Restorations in the American Museum of Natural History, by Osborn and Knight.

the modern horses, tapirs, rhinoceroses, and various types of cloven-footed animals.

A very general principle of mammalian evolution is illustrated in Fig. 124 (*A*, *B*), namely, the increase of size characteristic of all the herbivorous mammals, which almost without exception are in the beginning extremely small forms that evolve into massive forms possessing for defense either power-

FIG. 125. A PRIMITIVE WHALE FROM THE EOCENE OF ALABAMA.

Zeuglodon cetoides exhibits a secondary elongate, eel-shaped body form analogous to that of many of the aquatic, free-swimming, surface-dwelling reptiles, aquatic amphibians, and fusiform fishes. Restoration by Gidley and Knight in the American Museum of Natural History.

ful tusks or horns. The most conspicuous example of very rapid evolution which has taken place prior to the close of Eocene time is that of the great primitive whale *Zeuglodon cetoides*, discovered in the Upper Eocene of Alabama, and now known to have been distributed eastward to the region of the Mediterranean. As described above (p. 241), as an example of reversed adaptation and evolution, this animal had already passed through a prior terrestrial phase and had reached a stage of extreme specialization for marine life. These zeuglodonts parallel several of the marine groups of reptiles (Figs. 76, 87), also certain of the amphibians and fishes (Figs. 60, 44), in the extreme elongation and eel-like mode of propulsion of the body.

A zoogeographic feature of Eocene life is the strong and increasing evidence of migration between South America and North America by means of land connection in late Cretaceous or basal Eocene time, between the northern and southern hemispheres, which was then interrupted for 1,000,000 or perhaps 1,500,000 years until the middle of the Pliocene Epoch, when the South American types again appear in North America. Another relation which has been established by recent discoveries is seen in the resemblance between certain Rocky Mountain primates (lemurs) and those existing at the present time in the Malayan Peninsula.

North America and western Europe pass alike through three great phases of mammalian life in Eocene time: first, the archaic phase of the Palæocene; second, a long phase in which the archaic and modern mammals of the Lower Eocene intermingle; third, a very prolonged period from the Lower to the Upper Eocene, in which Europe and North America are widely separated and each of the ancestral types of mammals undergoes an independent evolution. This is followed in Oligocene time by a phase in which the animal life of western Europe and North America was reunited. Again in Miocene time a further wave of European mammalian life sweeps over North America, including the advance wave of the great order Proboscidea embracing both mastodons and elephants which appear to have originated in Africa or in southern Asia. During the entire Miocene and Pliocene Epochs there is more or less unity of evolution between North America, Europe, and Asia, but it is a very striking fact that in Middle Pliocene time, when a wave of South American life enters North America, certain very highly characteristic forms of North American mammals (camels) enter Europe. In late Pliocene and early Pleistocene time the grandest epoch of mammalian life is reached; certain great orders like the proboscidians and the horses, with very high powers of adaptation as well as of migration, spread over every continent except Australia.

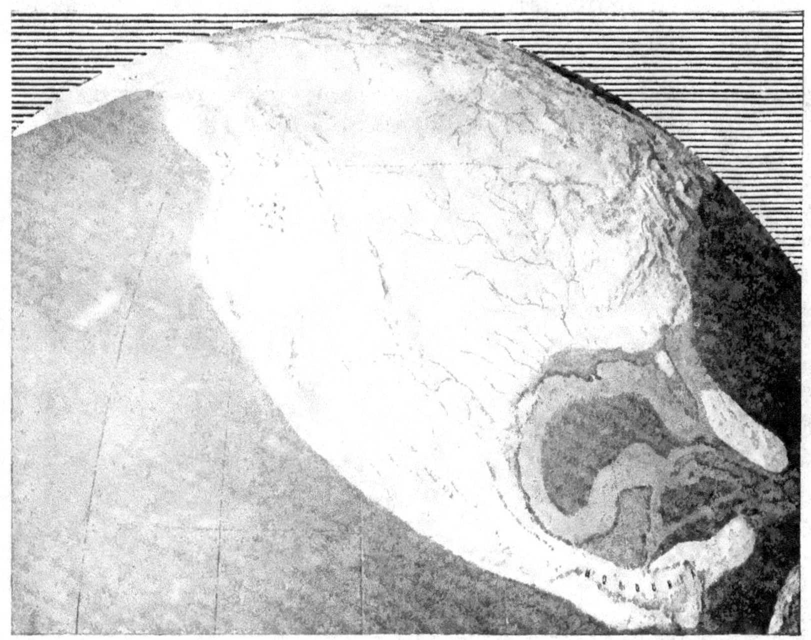

FIG. 126. NORTH AMERICA IN UPPER OLIGOCENE TIME.

East of the recently born Rocky Mountains the region of the Great Plains was made up of broad fluviatile flood-plains, fan-deltas, and lagoons, accumulating the detritus of the Rocky Mountains on the west and with a general eastern drainage. It was the scene of a continuous evolution of a plains fauna of mammals for a period of 1,500,000 years. Detail from the globe model in the American Museum by Chester A. Reeds and George Robertson, after Schuchert.

This great epoch of mammalian distribution is followed by the Pleistocene phases in the northern and southern hemispheres, at the close of which the world wears a greatly impoverished aspect; the northern hemisphere banishes all the forms of mammalian life evolving in the southern hemisphere and in the tropics, and the high table-lands of Africa alone retain the grandeur of the Pliocene Epoch.

The Definite Course of Chromatin Evolution in the Origin of New Characters Partly Predetermined by Ancestry

Some of the most universal laws as to the modes (p. 251) of evolution emerge from the comparative study of the horses,

B

Fig. 127. Two Stages in the Evolution of the Titanotheres.

Transformation of the small hoofed quadruped *Eotitanops* (A) of the Eocene—a relatively light-limbed, swift-moving, cursorial herbivore—into the gigantic *Brontotherium* (B) of the Lower Oligocene—a ponderous, slow-moving, graviportal type, horned for offense and defense. These titanotheres were remotely related to the existing rhinoceroses, horses, and tapirs, but they became suddenly extinct on attaining this impressive stage of evolution. They exemplify the increase of size characteristic of the evolution of the greater number of the hoofed Herbivora. The time during which this transformation occurred is estimated at 1,200,000 years—about one-third of the whole Tertiary Epoch.

the proboscidians, and the rhinoceroses, from areas so widely separated geographically that there was no possibility of hybridizing or of a mingling of strains. For example, during a period estimated at not less than 500,000 years the horses of France, Switzerland, and North America evolve in these widely separated regions in a closely similar manner and develop closely similar characteristics in approximately a similar length of time. The same is true of the widely separated lines of descendants from the mastodons, elephants, and rhinoceroses. This law of uniform evolution and of the development independently in descendants from the same ancestors of closely similar characters is confirmed in Osborn's study of the evolution of the titanotheres (Fig. 127). In these animals, which have been traced through discoveries of their fossil remains over a period of time extending from the beginning of the Lower Eocene to the beginning of the Middle Oligocene, inclusive, is exhibited a nearly continuous,[1] unbroken transformation from the diminutive *Eotitanops* of the Lower Eocene to the massive *Brontotherium* of the Lower Oligocene, the latter form being so far as known the most imposing product of mammalian evolution,

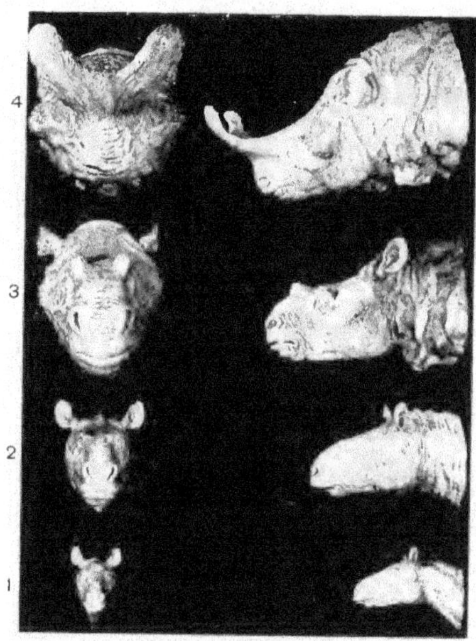

FIG. 128. STAGES IN THE EVOLUTION OF THE HORN IN THE TITANOTHERES.

This shows that these important weapons arise as rectigradations, *i. e.*, orthogenetically and not as the result of the selection of chance or fortuitous variations. Horns, large, 4, *Brontotherium platyceras*, Lower Oligocene; horns, small, 3, *Protitanotherium emarginatum*, Upper Eocene; horns, rudimentary, 2, *Manteoceras manteoceras*, Middle Eocene; hornless stage, 1, *Eotitanops borealis*, Lower Eocene.

Models in the American Museum of Natural History, prepared for the author by Erwin S. Christman.

[1] The continuity is broken by the extinction of one branch and the survival of another. It is a continuity of *character* rather than of lines of descent. In some cases there is a continuity both of characters and of branches.

with the exception of the Proboscidea. Every known step in this transformation is determinate and definite, every additional character which has been observed arises according to a fixed law and not according to any principle of chance. In the eleven principal branches which radiate from the earliest known forms (*Eotitanops gregoryi*) of this family exactly similar new characters arise quite independently at different periods of geologic time which are separated by the lapse of tens of thousands of years.

The titanotheres exhibit an absolutely independent but definite origin and development in each branch; so far as observed, every new character has its own rate of evolution and its own peculiar kind of form change; for example, in certain branches of the family the horns will appear many thousands of years later in the evolution history than in other branches, and after their appearance in many instances they may exhibit a singular inertia, or lack of momentum, over a long period of time, which is exactly in accord with our general principle (p. 149) that every character has its own rate of velocity both in individual development and in racial development.

The Origin of New Proportional Characters Not Predetermined by Ancestry

The titanotheres exhibit another very important principle, namely, that the linear proportions of the bones of the limbs are exactly adapted to the weight they are destined to carry and to the speed which they are destined to develop; in other words, the speed and the weight of all these great herbivora may be very precisely estimated by ratios and indices of the proportionate lengths of the different segments of the limbs, upper, middle, and lower. These proportionate lengths are not predetermined by the heredity-chromatin, because the same law of limb proportion prevails in all heavy, slow-moving mammals, whatever their descent; for example, this law holds among the heavy, slow-moving reptiles, the Sauropoda (Fig. 97), as well as among the heavy, slow-moving mammals.

The most beautiful adjustment of the proportions of the limb segments to speed is observed in the evolution of the horses (Fig. 130). Here we see that the upper segments (humerus, femur) are abbreviated, while the lower segments (forearm, lower leg, manus, and pes) are elongated. This is precisely the reverse of the conditions obtaining among the slow-moving titanotheres and proboscidians (Fig. 131). Among the horses, too, the same law prevails and governs the very precise adjustment of the ratios of each of the limb segments, quite irrespective of ancestry. In the swift *Hipparion* of America, for example, the highest phase of equine adaptation to speed, the indices and ratios of the limb segments are very similar to those in the existing prong-horn antelopes (*Antilocapra*) of our western plains. Contemporary with the *Hipparion* of Pliocene time, adapted to racing over hard, stony ground, is the relatively slow-moving, forest-living horse (*Hypohippus*) of the river borders of western North America (Fig. 130), in which the limb proportions are quite different. There is reason

FIG. 120. HORSES OF OLIGOCENE TIME. The horses frequenting the semi-arid plains of Oligocene times present an intermediate stage in the evolution of of cursorial motion—*Mesohippus*, with a narrow, three-toed type of foot, elongate, graceful limbs, and teeth with crowns beginning to be adapted to the comminution of silicious grasses in accommodation to the contemporaneous world-wide evolution of grassy plains. This law of the contemporaneous evolution of an environment of grassy plains and of swift-moving Herbivora was first clearly enunciated by Kowalevsky in 1873.
Restorations by Osborn, painted by Charles R. Knight, in the American Museum of Natural History.

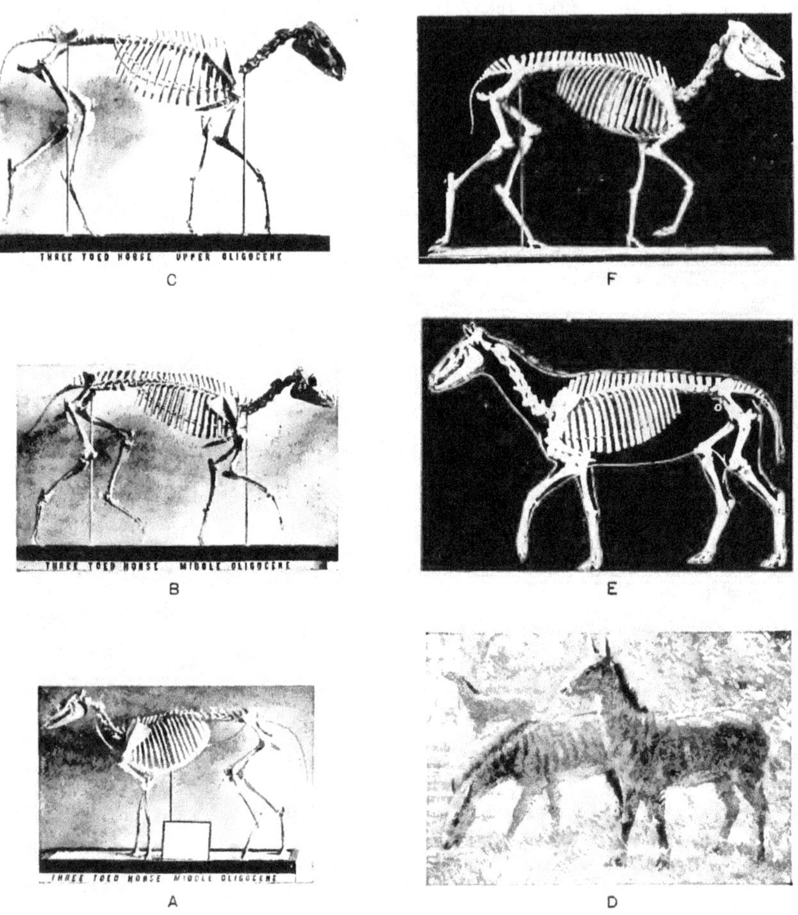

FIG. 130. STAGES IN THE EVOLUTION OF THE HORSE.

(Left.) An ascending series of Oligocene three-toed horses (*A*, *B*, *C*), showing their evolution in size, form, and dental structure, which involved continuous change in thousands of distinct characters and occupied a period of time estimated at 100,000 to 200,000 years.

(Right.) Two Upper Miocene American types of horses, *Hipparion* (*F*), with limbs proportioned like those of the deer, representing the climax of the swift-moving, grassy plains type, in contrast with *Hypohippus* (*D*, *E*), a conservative forest and browsing type. This is an instance of the survival of an ancient browsing type in an ancient forested environment (*D*, *E*), while in the adjacent grassy plains there exists contemporaneously the fleet *Hipparion* (*F*).

Skeletons mounted in the American Museum of Natural History. Restoration under the direction of the author, painted by Charles R. Knight.

to believe that this animal, like the existing okapi, was protected by coloration and by its swamp-living habits.

The above examples illustrate the general fact that *changes of proportion* make up the larger part of mammalian evolution and adaptation. The gain and loss of parts, the presence and absence of parts, which is so conspicuous a phenomenon in heredity as studied from the Mendelian standpoint, is a comparatively rare phenomenon. These changes of proportion are brought about through the greater or less velocity of single characters and of groups of characters; for example, the transformation of the four-toed horse of the base of the Lower Eocene[1] into the three-toed embryo of the modern horse is brought about by the acceleration of the central digit and the retardation of the side digits. This process is so gradual that it required 1,000,000 years to accomplish the reduction of the fifth digit, which left the originally tetradactyl horse in the tridactyl stage (Fig. 130); and it has required 2,000,000 years more to complete the retardation of the second and fourth digits, which are still retained in the chromatin and develop side by side with the third digit for many months during the early intrauterine life of the horse.

No form of sudden change of character (saltation, mutation of de Vries) or of the chance theory of evolution (pp. 7, 8) accounts for such precise steps in mechanical adjustment; because for all proportional changes, which make up ninety-five per cent of mammalian evolution, we must seek a similar cause, namely, the cause of acceleration, balance or persistence, and retardation. This cause may prove to be in the nature of physicochemical interactions (p. 71) regulated by selection. The great importance of selection in the evolution of proportion is

[1] The earliest-known fossil horses are four-toed, having lost the first digit (thumb). No five-toed fossil horse has yet been found.

demonstrated by the universal law that the limb proportions of mammals are closely adjusted to provide for escape from enemies at each stage of development.

Africa as a Great Theatre of Radiation

The part which Africa has played in the early stages of mammalian evolution is a matter of comparatively recent discovery, and we are not yet positive whether the great life centre of North Africa was not closely related to that of southern Asia in Eocene and early Oligocene time, as the most recent discoveries appear to indicate. At all stages of geologic history Africa was, as it is today, a great theatre of evolution of terrestrial life. According to present knowledge, North Africa developed a highly varied fauna, including three chief elements: first, types which are closely ancestral to the higher monkeys and apes, and which may thus be related to man himself; second, a series of forms which attained gigantic size and never migrated from the continent of Africa, but became extinct; and, thirdly, a series of forms, such as the zeuglodons, ancestral whales, sirenians, manatees, and dugongs, which emerged from this African home and enjoyed a very wide dis-

Fig. 131. Epitome of Proportion Evolution in the Proboscidea.

These animals originated in the *Palæomastodon* (lower), frequenting the ancient borders of the Nile in Egypt during Oligocene time, which developed during a period of 1,500,000 years into the existing types of the Indian and African elephants and into the ancient type of the *Elephas* (upper).

Restoration in the American Museum of Natural History under the direction of the author, painted by Charles R. Knight.

tribution in the northern hemisphere and in the equatorial regions.

Among the giant tribes which issued from this ancient continent the evolution of the proboscidians gives us an instance of the most extreme divergence of a terrestrial type from a related family, the sirenians, which evolve into the aquatic, fluviatile, and littoral type of the existing sea-cows and manatees.

FIG. 132. THE ICE-FIELDS OF THE FOURTH GLACIATION.
Southward extension of the ice-fields over the northeastern United States during the period of the fourth glaciation. After studies of Chamberlain. Modelled by Howell.

In the transformation of *Palæomastodon* (Fig. 131) into *Elephas* there are notable changes of proportion as well as the loss of many characters, as seen in the disappearance of the lower tusks, the enlargement and curvature of the upper tusks, the elongation of the proboscis, the abbreviation of the skull, the elongation of the limbs, the relative abbreviation of the vertebræ of the neck and of the backbone, the reduction of the tail. The limbs become of the weight-bearing type, the hind limbs attaining proportions which converge toward those of the titanothere *Brontotherium* (Fig. 127). The final numerical loss of characters as witnessed in the very gradual reduction of the lower tusks affords an instance of the leisurely methods of nature, for the process requires 2,000,000 years in the elephant line while in the mastodon line the lower tusks were still present at the time of the comparatively recent extinction of this animal, which occurred since the final glaciation of North America. The loss of parts through retardation is also seen in the reduction of the number of the pairs of grinding teeth, from seven to six and finally in the adult modern elephant stage to one. The addition of new characters is principally observed in the remarkable evolution of the plates of the grinding teeth and of the elaborate muscular system of the proboscis. It is very important to note that, as in the evolution of the horses (p. 263), this evolution independently follows similar lines among the Proboscidea throughout all parts of the world. In other words, the unity of the evolution of the proboscidians in various parts of the world was not main-

FIG. 133. GROUPS OF REINDEER (*Rangifer tarandus*) AND WOOLLY MAMMOTH (*Elephas primigenius*).

Conditions of the reindeer-mammoth period of Europe during the maximum cold of the fourth glaciation of the Glacial Epoch. Mural painting in the American Museum of Natural History, painted by Charles R. Knight, under the direction of the author.

tained by *interbreeding*, but by the unity of ancestral heredity and the unity of the actions, reactions, and interactions of the animals with their environment. Widely separated descendants of similar ancestors may evolve in a closely but not entirely similar manner. The resemblances are due to the independent gain of similar new characters and loss of old characters. The differences are chiefly due to the unequal velocity of characters; in some lines certain characters appear or disappear more rapidly than others.

The general fact that the slow-breeding elephants evolved very much more rapidly than the frequently breeding rodents, such as the mice and rats (Muridæ), is one of the many evidences that the rate of evolution may not be governed by the frequency of natural selection and elimination. For example, in the murine family of rodents, the annual progeny is very numerous and reproduction is very frequent, while among the elephants there is only a single offspring and reproduction is comparatively infrequent, yet the grinding teeth of the Proboscidea evolve far more rapidly and into much more highly complicated structures than the grinding teeth of any of the

FIG. 134. PLEISTOCENE OR GLACIAL ENVIRONMENT OF THE WOOLLY RHINOCEROS. *Rhinoceros tichorhinus*, of northern Europe, a contemporary of the woolly mammoth. Restoration in the American Museum of Natural History, painted by Charles R. Knight, under the direction of the author.

rapidly breeding rodents. If evolution were due to the natural selection of chance variations this would not be the case.

The elephants, like the horses, afford an example of superb mechanical perfection in a single organ, the teeth, evolved in relatively slow-breeding forms, within a relatively short period of geologic time. In their grinding-tooth structure the Proboscidea closely interlock with their environment, that is, there are complete transitions of dental structure between partly grazing, partly browsing, and exclusively browsing forms, such as the mastodon. The psychic and bodily adaptability and plasticity of the Proboscidea to extreme ranges of habitat is paralleled only by the human adaptation to extremes of climate which is achieved through the intelligence of man. The woolly

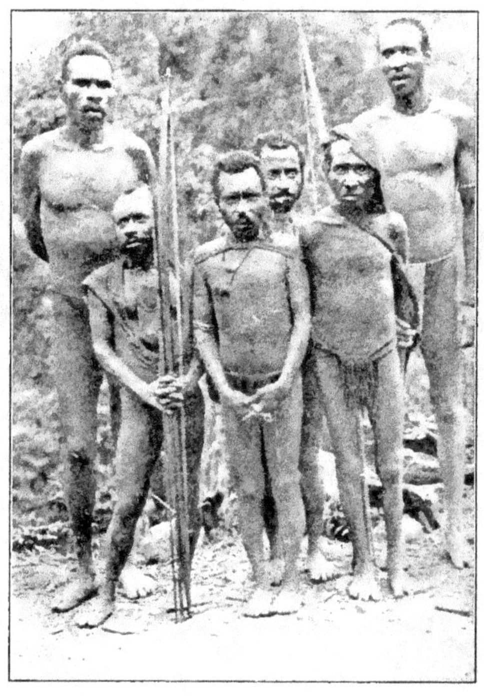

FIG. 135. PYGMIES OF THE HILLS COMPARED WITH THE PLAINSMEN OF WEST CENTRAL NEW GUINEA.

From Rawling's *Land of the New Guinea Pigmies*, by permission of Seeley, Service & Co.—The question arises whether the dwarfing is due to natural selection, to prolonged unfavorable environment, or to abnormal internal secretions of certain glands like the thyroid. It will be observed that the dwarfing is disproportional, the heads being relatively large. Compare the dwarfed sheep and dog in Figs. 119 and 120.

mammoth (Fig. 131) presents one extreme of proboscidian adaptation, comparable to the Eskimo among human races as superbly adapted to the rigors of the arctic climate, while the hairless African and Indian elephants are comparable to the hairless human races living under the equator.

Undoubtedly the most promising field for future palæontological research and discovery is in Asia. The links in the series of mammals—especially in the line known as the Primates leading into the ancestors of man, namely, the Lemurs, Monkeys, and Apes—are probably destined to be found in this still very imperfectly explored continent, for it is indicated by much evidence that the still unexplored region of northern Asia was a great centre of animal population and of adaptive radiation into Europe on the west and into North America on the northeast. Ancient vertebrate fossils from this vast region are as yet absolutely unknown, but will doubtless be discovered, and it is here that the Eocene, and perhaps the Oligocene ancestors of man are likely to be unearthed, that is, in deposits of the first half of the Tertiary Period. Fossil records of the descent of man during the second half of the Tertiary also, namely, from the Oligocene Epoch to the close of the Pliocene time, we believe may be discovered in Asia, most probably in the region lying south of the Himalayas.

This subject of prehuman ancestry and evolution is reserved for the concluding series of Hale Lectures, but in our search for suggestions as to the causes of evolution, especially along the lines of internal physicochemical factors and the doctrine of energy, man himself is proving to be one of the most helpful of all mammals because chemically, physically, and experimentally man is the best known of all organisms at the present time.

Retrospect and Prospect

The initial question raised in this volume arises as soon as we undertake a summary of evolution as we see it in the retrospect of the ages.

Does the energy conception of evolution bring us nearer to the *causes* either of the *origin* or of the *transformation* of characters? Before answering these crucial questions let us see what our brief survey has taught us as to the kind of causes to look for.

The foregoing comparison in the second part of this volume of the evolutionary development that has taken place in many series of animals belonging to the five great classes of vertebrates—fishes, reptiles, amphibians, birds, and mammals—in response to twelve different kinds of environment, gives repeated evidence of their continuous powers of ever-plastic adaptation, not only to one kind of physical and life environment, but to any direct, reversed, or alternating change of environment which a group of animals may encounter either on its own initiative or by force of circumstances.

In the large vertebrates we are enabled to observe and often to follow in minute details this continuous adaptation not merely in one, but in hundreds and sometimes in thousands of characters. In this respect a vertebrate differs from a relatively simple plant organism like the pea or the bean on which some of the prevailing conceptions of evolution have been grounded. In the well-ordered evolution of these single characters we have a picture like that of a vast army of soldiers; the organism as a whole is like the army; the "characters" are like the individual soldiers; and the evolution of each character is coordinated with that of every other character. Sometimes a character lags behind and through failure to keep pace produces the *dysteleogy* or imperfect fitness of certain parts of the organism observed by Metchnikoff in the human body.

Sometimes there are serial regiments of such well-ordered characters which are exactly or closely alike—for example, the 1092 teeth in the upper jaw of the iguanodont dinosaur, *Trachodon*, all very similar in appearance, all evolving and all perfectly coordinated in form and function with the 910 teeth in the lower jaw of the same animal. There are other serial regiments of characters, however, like the vertebræ in the backbone of a large dinosaur, for example, in which every single character, large and small, is different in form from every other. These are among the many miracles of adaptation referred to in the Preface.

The evidence for this continuous and more or less adaptive direction in the simultaneous evolution of numberless characters which can be observed only by means of an ancestral fossil series was unknown to the master mind of Darwin during the preparation of his "Origin of Species" through his observations on the variations of domestic animals and plants between 1845 and 1858; for it was not until the discovery by Waagen, in 1869, of a continuous series of fossil ammonites, in which minute changes originate and can be followed continuously, that the rudiments of a true conception of the orderly and continuous modes of evolution which prevail in nature were reached. Among invertebrates and vertebrates, this conception has been abundantly confirmed by modern palæontology in all its branches, namely, that of a well-ordered continuity as the prevailing mode of evolution. This is the greatest contribution which palæontology has made to biology and to natural philosophy.

Discontinuity is found chiefly in those characters in which a continuous mode of change is impossible. As to the physicochemical constitution of animals and plants it has been well said that there can be no continuity between two distinct chemical formulæ, or in many physicochemical functions and reactions. There are also certain form and proportion characters in which continuity is impossible—for example, the sudden addition of a new tooth to the jaw, or of a new vertebra to the backbone.

From these well-ascertained facts of the sudden or saltatory appearance of characters, some have rashly inferred that there can be no continuity between species, whereas it is now known in mammalogy, in palæontology, and to a less extent in ornithology that a large number of so-called species in nature show a complete continuity. Although the part which sudden changes or "saltations" from character to character play in experimental evolution and artificial selection is very prominent, it remains to be seen how large a part they play under *natural* conditions.

We realize that it is far more difficult to ascertain the causes of such continuous independent and more or less orderly and adaptive evolution of single characters than to comprehend evolution as Darwin's adherents of the present day imagine it to be, namely fortuitous and saltatory, for it is incumbent upon us to discover the *cause* of the orderly origin of every single character. The nature of such a law we cannot even dream of at present, for the *causes* of the majority of vertebrate adaptations remain wholly unknown.

Negatively we may say from palæontology that there is positive disproof of the existence of an internal perfecting principle or entelechy of any kind which would impel animals to evolve in a given direction regardless of the direct, reversed, or alternating directions taken by the organism in seeking its life environment or physical environment.

It is true, we have found (p. 264) among the descendants of similar, though remote, ancestors something determinate or definite—a similarity which reminds us of the *potential* of the physicist—as to the origin of certain characters rather than others in the heredity-chromatin. It is as if certain latent power or potency of character-origin in the chromatin were there waiting to be called forth. It is partly due to this, as well as to inheritance of a similar ancestral form, that the mammals, as studied by the comparative anatomist, are so much alike, despite their superficial differences as seen by the student of adaptation. This definite or determinate origin of certain new characters appears to be partly a matter of hereditary predisposition. That is, animals from a common stock independently give rise at different times to similar new characters, as seen, for example, in the origin of similar horn defenses and similar bony and dental structures.

The conclusive evidence against an *élan vital* or internal perfecting tendency, however, is that these characters do not spring up autonomously at any time; they may lie dormant or remain rudimentary for great periods of time, and here we find a correspondence which may be only an analogy with the principle of *latent* energy in physics. They require something to call them forth, to make them *active*, so to speak.

It is in this function of arousing such character predispositions that the chemical messenger phenomena of *interaction* in the organism present some analogy to latent energy, although future experiment may prove that this does not constitute a real cause or likeness. If the transformation of energy is accelerated in certain organs or parts of existing organs by the arrival of interacting chemical messengers and these parts thereby change their form and proportions, it is not inconceivable that chemical messengers may arouse a latent new character by stimulating the transformation of energy at a specific point.

Then character-velocity must be considered. Although we may find that in the course of evolution in one group of animals a character moves extremely slowly, it lags along, it is *retarded*, as if partly suffering from inertia, or perhaps, for a while it stops altogether; yet in another group we may find that the very same character is full of life and velocity, it is accelerated like the alert soldier in the regiment. Here again is a point where the energy conception of evolution may throw a gleam of light. Some of the phenomena of interaction in the organism give us the first insight into the possible causes of the slow or rapid movement of character evolution—of its acceleration and retardation. Such individual character movements may govern the proportions of certain parts as well as of all parts of the organism.

Combined, these character velocities and movements create all the extraordinary differences of proportion which distinguish the mammals—for example, the extraordinarily long neck of the giraffe, the short neck of the elephant, the elongated skull of the ant-eater, the abbreviated head of the tree sloth. Wherever such changes of proportion weigh in the struggle for existence they may be hastened or retarded by natural selection.

We discover that the chief principles of comparative anatomy formulated by Aristotle, Cuvier, Lamarck, Goethe, St. Hilaire, Dohrn, and other philosophic anatomists[1] may all be expressed anew in terms treating the organism as a

[1] Russell, E. S., 1916.

complex of energies. This is shown in a final scheme of action, reaction, and interaction[1] which is an elaboration of the simplified scheme expressed on page 16 of the Introduction, as follows:

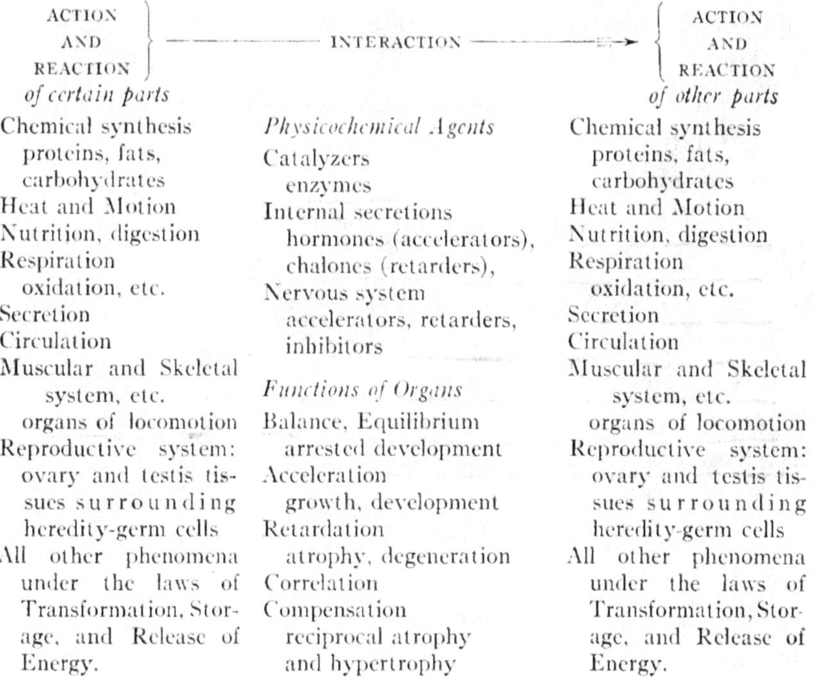

COORDINATED ACTIVITY OF THE ORGANISM WITHIN ITSELF

ACTION AND REACTION *of certain parts*	——— INTERACTION ———→	ACTION AND REACTION *of other parts*
Chemical synthesis	*Physicochemical Agents*	Chemical synthesis
proteins, fats,	Catalyzers	proteins, fats,
carbohydrates	enzymes	carbohydrates
Heat and Motion	Internal secretions	Heat and Motion
Nutrition, digestion	hormones (accelerators),	Nutrition, digestion
Respiration	chalones (retarders),	Respiration
oxidation, etc.	Nervous system	oxidation, etc.
Secretion	accelerators, retarders,	Secretion
Circulation	inhibitors	Circulation
Muscular and Skeletal		Muscular and Skeletal
system, etc.	*Functions of Organs*	system, etc.
organs of locomotion	Balance, Equilibrium	organs of locomotion
Reproductive system:	arrested development	Reproductive system:
ovary and testis tis-	Acceleration	ovary and testis tis-
sues surrounding	growth, development	sues surrounding
heredity-germ cells	Retardation	heredity-germ cells
All other phenomena	atrophy, degeneration	All other phenomena
under the laws of	Correlation	under the laws of
Transformation, Stor-	Compensation	Transformation, Stor-
age, and Release of	reciprocal atrophy	age, and Release of
Energy.	and hypertrophy	Energy.

The eternal question remains, How do these energy phenomena which govern the life, form, and function of the organism interact with the supposed latent and potential energy phenomena of the heredity-germ cells? As stated in the Preface and Introduction, this question can only be answered by experiment. There is no proof at present.

[1] This notion of coordinated activity is particularly well expressed in Mathews's *Physiological Chemistry* (1916), a volume which came to the author after this work was written (see Appendix, Notes V and VI).

Conclusion

In the foregoing pages we have attempted to sketch in broad outlines the course of the origin and evolution of life upon the earth in the light of our present imperfect knowledge, which offers few certainties to guide us and probabilities and possibilities innumerable among which to choose.

The difference between the non-living world and the living world seems like a vast chasm when we think of a very high organism like man, the result of perhaps a hundred million years of evolution. But the difference between primordial earth, water, and atmosphere and the lowliest known organisms which secure their energy directly from simple chemical compounds is not so vast a chasm that we need despair of bridging it some day by solving at least one problem as to the actual nature of life—namely, whether it is solely physicochemical in its energies, or whether it includes a *plus* energy or element which may have distinguished Life from the beginning.

The energy conception of the origin and evolution of life, on which are based our fresh stimulus to experiment and renewed hope of progress in solving the riddle of Heredity, is as yet in its infancy. Our vision will doubtless be amplified by experiment. In seeking the causes of the complex adaptations even of the simplest organisms described in Chapters III and IV we soon face the boundaries of the unknown, boundaries which human imagination entirely fails to penetrate, for Nature never operates as man expects her to, and we believe that imagination itself is strictly limited to recombinations of ideas which have come through observation.

It may be said that the bulk of experimental work hitherto has been in the domain of action and reaction—here lie all the simple energy processes of growth, of waste and repair, of use and disuse, of circulatory, muscular, digestive, and nervous action. Lamarckism has sought in vain for evidences of the inheritance of the effects of such action and reaction processes.

Experiment and observation in the mysterious field of interaction are relatively new, yet they are now being pressed with intensity by many workers. There is an encouraging likeness—pointed out in many parts of this volume—between some of the effects visibly produced in the body by internal secretions and other chemical messengers, and certain of the familiar processes of germ evolution, especially in adaptation through changes of proportion (see p. 268) of various parts of the body—a kind of adaptation which is of great importance in all animals. And while this likeness between interaction and germ evolution may be mere coincidence and have no deeper significance, it is also possible that it may betoken some real similarity of cause.

For our theory of action, reaction, and interaction—which is fully set forth and illustrated in the second and third chapters of this work, dealing with biochemical evolution and the evolution of bacteria and algæ, as well as in certain sections of the chapters describing the evolution of the vertebrates—it may be claimed that it brings us somewhat nearer a consistent physicochemical conception of the original processes of life. If our theory is still far from offering any conception of the nature of Heredity and the causes of elaborate Adaptation in the higher organisms, it may yet serve the desired purpose of directing our imagination, our experiment, and our observation along lines whereby we may attain small but real advances into the unknown. As pointed out in our Preface and Introduction the only processes in inorganic Nature and in living organisms themselves which are in the least suggestive of the processes of Heredity are some of the processes of interaction.

We know, for example, that certain cells of the reproductive glands[1] have a profound and commanding influence on all the body cells, including even the brain-cell centres of thought and intelligence—all this is, in a sense, an outflowing from the heredity-germ region, a *centrifugal* interaction. Is there any reversal of this process, any inflowing or *centripetal* interaction whereby chemical messengers from any part of the body specifically affect the heredity-germ, and thus the new organism to which it will give rise? This is one of the first things to be ascertained by future experiment.

Being still at the very beginning of the problem of the causes of germ evolution—a problem which has aroused curiosity and baffled inquiry throughout the ages—it were idle to entertain or present any settled conviction in regard to it, yet we cannot avoid expressing as our present opinion that these causes are internal-external rather than purely internal—in other words, that some kind of relation exists between the actions, reactions, and interactions of the germ, of the organism, and of the environment. Moreover, this opinion is probably capable of experimental proof or disproof.

We may well conclude with the dictum of Francis Bacon,[2] one of the first natural philosophers to counsel experiment, who in his *Novum Organum* (1620) shows that living objects are well adapted to experimental work, and points out that it is possible for man to produce variations experimentally:

> "*They* [*i. e.*, the deviations or mutations of Nature] *differ again from singular instances, by being much more apt for practice and the operative branch. For it would be very difficult to generate new species, but less so to vary known species, and thus produce*

[1] Goodale, H. D., 1916; Lillie, Frank R., 1917.
[2] Bacon, Francis, 1620, book II, sec. 29, p. 180.

many rare and unusual results. The passage from the miracles of nature to those of art is easy; for if nature be once seized in her variations, and the cause be manifest, it will be easy to lead her by art to such deviation as she was at first led to by chance; and not only to that but others, since deviations on the one side lead and open the way to others in every direction."

APPENDIX

In the following citations from the recent works of friends all but one of which have come into the author's hands since the present volume was written, the reader will find not only an amplification by Gies (Note I) and Loeb (Notes III and IV) of certain passages in the text, but in Notes V and VI original views previously and independently expressed by Mathews, which are somewhat similar to those the author has developed under the law of interaction.

NOTE I

DIFFERENT MODES OF STORAGE AND RELEASE OF ENERGY IN LIVING ORGANISMS[1]

"The elements referred to" ("This energy is distributed among the eighty or more chemical elements of the sun and other stars," p. 18) "are available to plants, in the first place, in the form of compound substances only, simple though those substances are, such as water, carbon dioxid, nitrate, phosphate, etc. When these substances are taken from the air and soil into plants they are reduced in the main, that is, the elements are combined there into new groupings with a storage of energy, the effective radiant kinetic energy from the sun becoming potential energy in the constituents of plants. Plant substances are eaten by herbivorous animals, that is to say, these substances are hydrolyzed and oxidized in such animals; the elements are, in the main, 'burst asunder' into new groupings, with the release of energy, the stored potential energy becoming kinetic. Carnivorous and omnivorous animals obtain plant substances, either directly or in the form of animal matter from herbivorous animals, thus, in effect, doing what herbivorous animals do, namely, using plant substances by disintegrating them with the release of energy."

NOTE II

BLUE-GREEN ALGÆ POSSIBLY AMONG THE FIRST SETTLERS OF OUR PLANET[2]

"In 1883 the small island of Krakatau was destroyed by the most violent volcanic eruption on record. A visit to the islands two months after the eruption showed that 'the three islands were covered with pumice

[1] W. J. Gies, letter of May 16, 1917.

[2] Loeb, Jacques, 1916, *The Organism as a Whole*, p. 21.

and layers of ash reaching on an average a thickness of thirty metres, and frequently sixty metres.'[1] Of course all life on the islands was extinct. When Treub in 1886 first visited the island, he found that blue-green algæ were the first colonists on the pumice and on the exposed blocks of rock in the ravines on the mountain-slopes. Investigations made during subsequent expeditions demonstrated the association of diatoms and bacteria" [with the algæ]. "All of these were probably carried by the wind. The algæ referred to were according to Euler of the nostoc type. Nostoc does not require sugar, since it can produce that compound from the CO_2 of the air by the activity of its chlorophyll. This organism possesses also the power of assimilating the free nitrogen of the air. From these observations and because the *Nostocaceæ* generally appear as the first settlers on sand the conclusion has been drawn that they or the group of *Schizophyceæ* to which they belong formed the first settlers of our planet."[2]

NOTE III

ONE SECRET OF LIFE—SYNTHETIC TRANSFORMATION OF INDIFFERENT MATERIAL[3]

"The essential difference between living and non-living matter consists then in this: the living cell synthetizes its own complicated specific material from indifferent or non-specific simple compounds of the surrounding medium, while the crystal simply adds the molecules found in its supersaturated solution. This synthetic power of transforming small 'building stones' into the complicated compounds specific for each organism is the 'secret of life' or rather one of the secrets of life."

NOTE IV

INTERACTION THROUGH CATALYSIS—THE ACCELERATION OF CHEMICAL REACTIONS THROUGH THE PRESENCE OF ANOTHER SUBSTANCE WHICH IS NOT CONSUMED BY THE REACTION[4]

"The discovery of Lavoisier and La Place left a doubt in the minds of scientists as to whether after all the dynamics of oxidations and of chemical reactions in general is the same in living matter and in inanimate matter. . . . The way out of the difficulty was shown in a remarkable article by Berzelius.[5] He pointed out that in addition to the forces of

[1] Ernst, A., *The New Flora of the Volcanic Island of Krakatau*, Cambridge, 1908.

[2] Euler, H., *Pflanzenchemie*, 1909, ii and iii, 140.

[3] Loeb, Jacques, 1916. *The Organism as a Whole*, p. 23.

[4] Loeb, Jacques, 1906. *The Dynamics of Living Matter*, pp. 7, 8.

[5] Berzelius, *Einige Ideen über eine bei der Bildung organischer Verbindungen in der lebenden Natur wirksame aber bisher nicht bemerkte Kraft.* Berzelius u. Woehler, *Jahresbericht*, 1836.

affinity, another force is active in chemical reactions: this he called catalytic force. As an example he used Kirchhoff's discovery of the action of dilute acids in the hydrolysis of starch to dextrose. In this process the acid is not consumed, hence Berzelius concluded that it did not act through its affinity, but merely by its presence or its contact. . . . He then suggests that the specific and somewhat mysterious reactions in living organisms might be due to such catalytic bodies as act only by their presence, without being consumed in the process. He quotes as an example the action of diastase in the potato. 'In animals and plants there occur thousands of catalytic processes between the tissues and the liquids.' The idea of Berzelius has proved fruitful. . . . We now know that we have no right to assume that the catalytic bodies do not participate in the chemical reaction because their quantity is found unaltered at the end of the reaction. On the contrary, we shall see that it is probable that they can exercise their influence only by participating in the reaction, and by forming intermediary compounds, which are not stable. The catalyzers may be unaltered at the end of the reaction, and yet participate in it.

"In addition we owe to Wilhelm Ostwald[1] the conception that the catalyzer does not as a rule initiate a reaction which otherwise would not occur, but only accelerates a reaction which otherwise would indeed occur, but too slowly to give noticeable results in a short time."

NOTE V

THE CAUSES OR AGENTS OF SPEED AND ORDER IN THE REACTIONS OF LIVING BODIES—ENZYMES, COLLOIDS, ETC.[2]

"There is still another feature of cell chemistry which must strike even the most superficial observer, and that is the *speed* with which growth and the chemical reactions occur in it. . . . Starch boiled with water does not easily take on water and split into sweet glucose, but in the plant cell it changes into sugar under appropriate conditions very rapidly. How does it happen then that the chemical changes of the foods go on so rapidly in living matter and so slowly outside? This is owing to the fact, as we now know, that living matter always contains a large number of substances, or compounds, called enzymes (Gr. *en*, in; *zyme*, yeast; in yeast) because they occur in a striking way in yeast. These enzymes, which are probably organic bodies, but of which the exact composition is as yet unknown, have the property of greatly hastening, or as is generally said, catalyzing, various chemical reactions. The word catalytic (*kata*, down; *lysis*, separation) means literally a down separation or decomposition, but

[1] Ostwald, W., *Lehrbuch der allgemeinen Chemie*, vol. II, 2d part, p. 248, 1902.
[2] Mathews, Albert P., *Physiological Chemistry*, pp. 10–12.

it is used to designate any reaction which is hastened by a third substance, this third substance not appearing much, if at all, changed in amount at the end of the reaction. Living matter is hence peculiar in the *speed* with which these hydrolytic, oxidative, reduction, or condensation reactions occur in it; and it owes this property to various substances, catalytic agents, or enzymes, found in it everywhere. Were it not for these substances reactions would go on so slowly that the phenomena of life would be quite different from what they are. Since these catalytic substances are themselves produced by a chemical change preceding that which they catalyze, we might, perhaps, call them the memories of those former chemical reactions, and it is by means of these memories, or enzymes, that cells become teachable in a chemical sense and capable of transacting their chemical affairs with greater efficiency. Whether all our memories have some such basis as this we cannot at present say, since we do not yet know anything of the physical basis of memory.

"Living reactions have one other important peculiarity besides speed, and that is their '*orderliness*.' The cell is not a homogeneous mixture in which reactions take place haphazard, but it is a well-ordered chemical factory with specialized reactions occurring in various parts. If protoplasm be ground up, thus causing a thorough intermixing of its parts, it can no longer live, but there results a mutual destruction of its various structures and substances. The orderliness of the chemical reactions is due to the cell structure; and for the phenomena of life to persist in their entirety that structure must be preserved. It is true that in such a ground-up mass many of the chemical reactions are presumably the same as those which went on while structure persisted, but they no longer occur in a well-regulated manner; some have been checked, others greatly increased by the intermixing. This orderliness of reactions in living protoplasm is produced by the specialization of the cell in different parts. . . . Thus the nuclear wall, or membrane, marks off one very important cell region and keeps the nuclear sap from interacting with the protoplasm. Profound, and often fatal, changes sometimes occur in cells when an admixture of nuclear and cytoplasmic elements is artificially produced by rupture of this membrane. Other localizations and organizations are due to the colloidal nature of the cell-protoplasm and possibly to its lipoid character. By a colloid is meant, literally, a glue-like body; a substance which will not diffuse through membranes and which forms with water a kind of tissue, or gel. It is by means of the colloids of a protein, lipoid, or carbohydrate nature which make up the substratum of the cell that this localization of chemical reactions is produced; the colloids furnish the basis for the organization or machinery of the cell; and in their absence there could be nothing more than a homogeneous conglomeration of reactions. The properties of colloids become, therefore, of the greatest importance in interpreting cell life, and it is for this reason that they have been studied so keenly in the past ten years. The colloids localize the cell reactions and furnish the physical basis of its physiology; they form the cell machinery."

NOTE VI

INTERACTIONS OF THE ORGANS OF INTERNAL SECRETION AND HEREDITY[1]

The following table expresses the action of some of the organs of internal secretion:

On Protein Metabolism

Stimulating (accelerating)	*Inhibiting* (retarding)
Thyroid	Pancreas
Pituitary body	Parathyroids
Suprarenal glands and other adrenalin-secreting tissue	
Reproductive glands	

On Calcium Retention

Favorable to	*Inhibiting*
Pituitary body	Reproductive glands
Thyroids	
Parathyroids	

The facts that are here presented show that the action of the anterior lobe of the pituitary body upon the chemical changes or transformations taking place in the vertebrate organism or in any of its cells strongly resembles the action of the thyroid, although less pronounced. It is clear from its relation to the reproductive organs, to the adrenalin-secreting tissues of the suprarenal glands and other similar tissues, and to the formation of an abnormal amount of glucose in the urine, that the pituitary body, thyroids, reproductive glands, suprarenals, and thymus are a closely related series of organs which mutually influence each other's growth.

Important as these organs are, it must be remembered that the coordination of all the chemical changes and transformations within the body—all processes of renewal, change, or disorganization such as respiration, nutrition, excretion, etc.—embraces every organ in it. The body is an organic whole, and the so-called organs of internal secretion are not unique, but the bones, muscles, skin, brain, and every part of the body are furnishing internal secretions necessary to the development and proper

[1] Mathews, Albert P., 1916. *Physiological Chemistry*, pp. 649, 650 (modified).

functioning of all the other organs of the body. A scheme of the organs of internal secretion, to be complete, must embrace every organ, and so far only the barest beginning has been made in this study so important, so necessary for the understanding of development and inheritance. Problems of development and inheritance cannot be solved until these physiological questions are answered.

As for the bearing of these processes upon Heredity, the internal secretions of the body appear to Mathews to constitute strong evidence against the existence of such things as inheritance by means of structural units in the germ which represent definite characters in the body. We see in the internal secretions, he observes, that *every character in the body involves a large number of factors* (*i. e.*, determiners). The shape and size of the body, the coarseness of the hair, the persistence of the milk-teeth, a tendency toward fatness—all these may easily depend on the pituitary body, on the thyroid, and on the reproductive organs, and these—in their turn—are but the expression of other influences played upon them by their surroundings and their own constitution. An accurate examination shows the untrustworthiness of any such simple or naïve view as that of unit characters.

NOTE VII

TABLE—RELATIONS OF THE PRINCIPAL GROUPS OF ANIMALS REFERRED TO IN THE TEXT

Phylum	*Class*		PAGES
PROTOZOA (the simplest animals)	[1] Rhizopoda	Lobosa—*Amœba*, etc	93, 112, 114, 116
		Foraminifera (porous-shelled protozoa)	32, 103, 115
		Radiolaria (siliceous-shelled protozoa)	115
	Mastigophora		112, 115
	Infusoria—ciliates, etc		112, 115
	Sporozoa		
PORIFERA (sponges)	[1] Calcarea	Calcareous sponges	
	[1] Non-Calcarea	Siliceous "	130
		Fibrous "	
CŒLENTERATA	[1] Hydrozoa	Hydroids—millepores	113
		Siphonophores	
		Graptolithida	
	[1] Scyphozoa	Jellyfishes	120, 129, 130
	[1] Actinozoa	Sea-anemones, corals, sea-fans, etc	103
	Ctenophora		

[1] Fossil and recent forms.
All other classes listed are as yet unknown in the fossil state.

Phylum	Class		PAGES
PLATYHELMINTHES	Turbellaria	Flat worms	
	Trematoda	Flukes	
	Cestoda	Tape-worms	
NEMATHELMINTHES	Nematoda	Round worms	
	Acanthocephala	Hook-headed worms	
	[1] Chætognatha	Arrow-worms	120, 129
TROCHELMINTHES	Rotifera	Wheel-animalcules	
MOLLUSCOIDA	[1] Polyzoa	Bryozoa (moss animals)	
	Phoronida		
	[1] Brachiopoda	Lamp-shells	120, 123, 130, 138, 140
ECHINODERMATA	[1] Asteroidea	Sea-stars, starfishes	136, 172
	[1] Ophiuroidea	Brittle stars	
	[1] Echinoidea	Sea-urchins	94
	[1] Holothuroidea	Sea-cucumbers	125, 127
	[1] Crinoidea	Sea-lilies (stone-lilies)	66
	[2] Cystoidea	primitive echinoderms	
	[2] Blastoidea		
ANNULATA (true worms)	[1] Chætopoda	Sea-worms, earthworms	128
	Gephyrea	Sipunculids	
	Hirudinea	Leeches	
ARTHROPODA	*Branchiata*		
	[1] Crustacea	Crabs, lobsters, shrimp, barnacles, ostracods	120, 124, 134
	[2] Trilobita	Trilobites, eurypterids	121, 125, 132, 133
	[1] Xiphosura	Horseshoe crabs	124, 125, 132
	Tracheata		
	Onychophora	Peripatus	
	[1] Myriapoda	Centipedes, millepedes	
	[1] Arachnoidea	Spiders, scorpions, mites, ticks	130, 132, 136
	[1] Insecta	Insects	105, 130, 136, 254
MOLLUSCA	[1] Pelycypoda	Clams, oysters, mussels	130
	[1] Amphineura	Chitons	
	[1] Gastropoda	Limpets, snails, slugs, sea-hares, etc.	120, 130
	[1] Scaphopoda	Tusk-shells	
	[1] Cephalopoda	Nautilus, cuttle-fish, ammonites	130, 137–139

[1] Fossil and recent forms.
[2] Extinct fossil forms.
All other classes listed are as yet unknown in the fossil state.

Phylum	*Class*		PAGES
CHORDATA			
Sub-phylum			
Adelochorda		*Balanoglossus*, etc.—worm-like chordates	
Urochorda		Ascidians, salps, etc.—sessile and secondarily free-swimming marine chordates,	162, 168
Vertebrata	Acrania	*Amphioxus* (lancelets)	162
	Cyclostomata	Lampreys, hags	168
	[1] Pisces (fishes)	Ostracodermata (Palæozoic shelly-skinned fishes)	161, 165–168
		Arthrodira (Palæozoic joint-necked fishes)	166–168
		Elasmobranchii—sharks, rays, chimæroids	161, 167–169
		Dipnoi (lung-fishes)	168, 170, 172
		Teleostomi	173
		lobe-finned ganoids (Crossopterygii)	168, 172, 174
		true ganoids—sturgeons, garpike, bowfins, etc.	168, 170
		teleosts (bony fishes)	168, 170, 175
	[1] Amphibia	Frogs, toads, newts, mud-puppies, Stegocephalia, etc.	177–183
	[1] Reptilia	Turtles, tortoises, tuateras, lizards, mosasaurs, snakes, crocodilians, dinosaurs, mammal-like reptiles, ichthyosaurs, plesiosaurs, pterosaurs (flying reptiles), etc.	184–226
	[1] Aves (birds)	Reptile-like birds (*Archæopteryx*)	226–229
		Modernized birds	227–231
		"Ratite" birds—ostriches, moas, etc.	228, 229
		"Carinate" birds—toothed birds and all other birds	230, 231
	[1] Mammalia	Monotremes (egg-laying mammals)—duck-bills, etc.	235, 273
		Marsupials (pouched mammals)—opossums, kangaroos, etc.	235, 237, 243, 244
		Placentals	
		insectivores, carnivores, primates, rodents, bats, whales, artiodactyls (cattle, deer, pigs, antelopes, giraffes, camels, hippopotami, etc.), ungulates including proboscidea (mastodons and elephants) and perissodactyls (horses, tapirs, rhinoceroses, titanotheres, etc.), and many other orders	259–274

[1] Fossil and recent forms.
All other classes listed are as yet unknown in the fossil state.

BIBLIOGRAPHY

INTRODUCTION

Campbell, William Wallace.

1915 (1914) The Evolution of the Stars and the Formation of the Earth. Second series of lectures on the William Ellery Hale foundation, delivered December 7 and 8, 1914. *Pop. Sci. Mon.*, September, 1915, pp. 209–235; *Scientific Monthly*, October, 1915, pp. 1–17; November, 1915, pp. 177–194; December, 1915, pp. 238–255.

Chamberlin, Thomas Chrowder.

1916 (1915) The Evolution of the Earth. Third series of lectures on the William Ellery Hale foundation, delivered April 19–21, 1915. *Scientific Monthly*, May, 1916, pp. 417–437; June, 1916, pp. 536–556.

Clarke, Frank Wigglesworth.

1873 Evolution and the Spectroscope. *Pop. Sci. Mon.*, January, 1873, pp. 320–326.

Crile, George W.

1916 Man—An Adaptive Mechanism. Macmillan Co., New York, 1916.

Cushing, Harvey.

1912 The Pituitary Body and its Disorders, Clinical States Produced by Disorders of the Hypophysis Cerebri. Harvey Lecture, delivered in 1910, amplified. J. B. Lippincott Co., Philadelphia and London, 1912.

Davies, G. R.

1916 Plato's Philosophy of Education. *School and Society*, April 22, 1916, pp. 582–585.

Eucken, Rudolf.

1912 Main Currents of Modern Thought. Transl. by Meyrick Booth. Charles Scribner's Sons, New York, 1912.

Goodale, H. D.

1916 Gonadectomy in Relation to the Secondary Sexual Characters of Some Domestic Birds. Carnegie Institution of Washington, Publ. no. 243, Washington, 1916.

Henderson, Lawrence J.

1913 The Fitness of the Environment. Macmillan Co., New York, 1913.

James, William.

1902 The Varieties of Religious Experience, a Study in Human Nature. Fourth impression. Longmans, Green & Co., London and Bombay, 1902.

Morgan, Thomas Hunt.

1915 The Constitution of the Hereditary Material. *Proc. Amer. Phil. Soc.*, May–July, 1915, pp. 143–153.

1916 A Critique of the Theory of Evolution. The Louis Clark Vanuxem foundation lectures for 1915–1916. Princeton University Press, Princeton; Humphrey Milford, London; Oxford University Press, 1916.

Osborn, Henry Fairfield.

1894 From the Greeks to Darwin. Macmillan Co., New York, 1894.

1912 Tetraplasy, the Law of the Four Inseparable Factors of Evolution. *Jour. Acad. Nat. Sci. Phila.*, Special volume published in commemoration of the One Hundredth Anniversary of the Founding of the Academy, March 21, 1912. Issued September 14, 1912, pp. 275–300.

1917 Application of the Laws of Action, Reaction, and Interaction in Life Evolution. *Proc. National Acad. Sci.*, January, 1917, pp. 7–9.

Rutherford, Sir Ernest.

1915 (1914) The Constitution of Matter and the Evolution of the Elements. First series of lectures on the William Ellery Hale foundation, delivered April, 1914. *Pop. Sci. Mon.*, August, 1915, pp. 105–142.

CHAPTER I

Becker, George F.

1910 The Age of the Earth. *Smithsonian Misc. Colls.*, vol. 56, no. 6, Publ. no. 1936, Washington, 1910.

1915 Isostasy and Radioactivity. *Bull. Geol. Soc. Amer.*, March, 1915, pp. 171–204.

Chamberlin, Thomas Chrowder.

1916 (1915) The Evolution of the Earth. Third series of lectures on the William Ellery Hale foundation, delivered April 19–21, 1915. *Scientific Monthly*, May, 1916, pp. 417–437; June, 1916, pp. 536–556.

Clarke, Frank Wigglesworth.

1916 The Data of Geochemistry. Third edition. *U. S. Geol. Survey*, Bull. 491. Gov't Printing Office, Washington, 1916.

Cuvier, Baron Georges L. C. F. D.

1825 Discours sur les révolutions de la surface du globe et sur les changemens qu'elles ont produit dans le règne animal. See Recherches sur les Ossemens fossiles. Third edition, vol. I, G. Dufour et E. d'Ocagne, Paris, 1825, pp. 1–172.

Henderson, Lawrence J.

1913 The Fitness of the Environment. Macmillan Co., New York, 1913.

Hutton, James.

1795 Theory of the Earth with Proofs and Illustrations. Edinburgh, 1795.

Jordan, Edwin O.

1908 A Text-Book of General Bacteriology. W. B. Saunders, Philadelphia and London, 1908.

Judd, John W.

1910 The Coming of Evolution. The Story of a Great Revolution in Science. Cambridge Manuals of Science and Literature, Cambridge University Press, Cambridge, 1910.

Loeb, Jacques.

1906 The Dynamics of Living Matter. Columbia University Press, New York, 1906.

Lyell, Charles.

1830 Principles of Geology. Murray, London, 1830.

Moulton, F. R.

1912 Descriptive Astronomy. Amer. School of Correspondence, Chicago, 1912.

Pirsson, Louis V., and Schuchert, Charles.

1915 A Text-Book of Geology. Part I, Physical Geology, by Louis V. Pirsson. Part II, Historical Geology, by Charles Schuchert. John Wiley & Sons, New York; Chapman & Hall, London, 1915.

Poulton, Edward B.

1896 A Naturalist's Contribution to the Discussion upon the Age of the Earth. Pres. Addr. Zool. Sec. Brit. Ass., delivered September 17, 1896. *Rept. Brit. Ass.*, Liverpool, 1896, pp. 808–828.

Rutherford, Sir Ernest.

1906 Radioactive Transformations. Charles Scribner's Sons, New York, 1906.

Schuchert, Charles.

1915 A Text-Book of Geology (with Pirsson, Louis V.). See Pirsson.

Walcott, Charles D.

1893 Geologic Time, as indicated by the sedimentary rocks of North America. *Jour. Geol.*, October–November, 1893, pp. 639–676.

CHAPTER II

Abel, John J.

1915 Experimental and Chemical Studies of the Blood with an Appeal for More Extended Chemical Training for the Biological and Medical Investigator. First Mellon Lecture, Soc. Biol. Res., Univ. Pittsburgh. *Science*, August 6, 1915, pp. 165–178.

Bechhold, Heinrich.

1912 Die Kolloide in Biologie und Medizin. Theodor Steinkopf, Dresden, 1912.

Biedl, Artur.

1913 The Internal Secretory Organs: Their Physiology and Pathology. Transl. by Linda Forster. William Wood & Co., New York, 1913.

Calkins, Gary N.

1916 General Biology of the Protozoan Life Cycle. *Amer. Naturalist*, May, 1916, pp. 257–270.

Cunningham, J. T.

1908 The Heredity of Secondary Sexual Characters in Relation to Hormones, a Theory of the Heredity of Somatogenic Characters. *Archiv für Entwicklungsmechanik*, November 24, 1908, pp. 372–428.

Cushing, Harvey.

1912 The Pituitary Body and its Disorders, Clinical States Produced by Disorders of the Hypophysis Cerebri. Harvey Lecture, 1910, amplified. J. B. Lippincott Co., Philadelphia and London, 1912.

Cuvier, Baron Georges L. C. F. D.

1817 Le Règne animal distribué d'après son Organisation. Tome I, contenant l'introduction, les mammifères et les oiseaux. Deterville, Paris, 1817.

Hedin, Sven G.

1915 (1914) Colloidal Reactions and Their Relations to Biology. Harvey Lecture, delivered January 24, 1914. See The Harvey Lectures, 1913–1914, J. B. Lippincott Co., Philadelphia, 1915, pp. 162–173.

Henderson, Lawrence J.

1913 The Fitness of the Environment. Macmillan Co., New York, 1913.

Jordan, Edwin O.

1908 A Text-Book of General Bacteriology. W. B. Saunders, Philadelphia and London, 1908.

Loeb, Jacques.

1906 The Dynamics of Living Matter. Columbia University Press, New York, 1906.

Loeb, Leo.

1916 The Scientific Investigation of Cancer. *Scientific Monthly*, September, 1916, pp. 209–226.

Moore, F. J.

1915 Outlines of Organic Chemistry. John Wiley & Sons, New York and London, 1915.

Osborn, Henry Fairfield.

1895 The Hereditary Mechanism and the Search for the Unknown Factors of Evolution. *Amer. Naturalist*, May, 1895, pp. 418–439.

Pirsson, Louis V., and Schuchert, Charles.

1915 A Text-Book of Geology. Part I, Physical Geology, by Louis V. Pirsson. Part II, Historical Geology, by Charles Schuchert. John Wiley & Sons, New York; Chapman & Hall, London, 1915.

Poulton, Edward B.

1896 A Naturalist's Contribution to the Discussion upon the Age of the Earth. Pres. Addr. Zool. Sec. Brit. Ass., delivered September 17, 1896. *Rept. Brit. Ass.*, Liverpool, 1896, pp. 808–828.

Richards, Herbert M.

1915 Acidity and Gas Interchange in Cacti. Carnegie Institution of Washington, Publ. no. 209, Washington, 1915.

Russell, H. N.

1916 On the Albedo of the Planets and their Satellites. *Proc. National Acad. Sci.*, February 15, 1916, pp. 74–77.

Rutherford, Sir Ernest.

1915 The Constitution of Matter and the Evolution of the Elements.
(1914) First series of lectures on the William Ellery Hale foundation, delivered April, 1914. *Pop. Sci. Mon.*, August, 1915, pp. 105–142.

Sachs, Julius.

1882 A Text-Book of Botany, Morphological and Physiological. Clarendon Press, Oxford, 1882.

de Saussure, N. T.

1804 Recherches chimiques sur la Végétation. Paris, 1804.

Schäfer, Sir Edward A.

1916 The Endocrine Organs, an Introduction to the Study of Internal Secretion. Longmans, Green & Co., London, New York, Bombay, Calcutta, Madras, 1916.

Schuchert, Charles.

1915 A Text-Book of Geology (with Pirsson, Louis V.). See Pirsson.

Smith, Alexander.

1914 A Text-Book of Elementary Chemistry. The Century Co., New York, 1914.

Wilson, Edmund B.

1906 The Cell in Development and Inheritance. Second edition. Macmillan Co., New York, 1906.

Zinsser, Hans.

1915 (1914) The More Recent Developments in the Study of Anaphylactic Phenomena. Harvey Lecture, delivered January 30, 1914. *Archives of Internal Medicine*, August, 1915, pp. 223-256.

1916 Infection and Resistance. Macmillan Co., New York, 1916.

CHAPTER III

Barnes, Charles Reid.

1910 A Text-Book of Botany for Colleges and Universities (with Coulter, John Merle, and Cowles, Henry Chandler). See Coulter.

Berry, Edward Wilber.

1914 The Upper Cretaceous and Eocene Floras of South Carolina and Georgia. *U. S. Geol. Survey.* Professional Paper no. 84. Gov't Printing Office, Washington, 1914.

Clarke, Frank Wigglesworth.

1916 The Data of Geochemistry. Third edition. *U. S. Geol. Survey*, Bull. 491. Gov't Printing Office, Washington, 1916.

Coulter, John Merle; Barnes, Charles Reid; and Cowles, Henry Chandler.

1910 A Text-Book of Botany for Colleges and Universities. American Book Co., New York, Cincinnati, Chicago, 1910.

Cowles, Henry Chandler.

1910 A Text-Book of Botany for Colleges and Universities (with Coulter, John Merle, and Barnes, Charles Reid). See Coulter.

Czapek, Friedrich.

1913 Biochemie der Pflanzen. Second edition, revised. Gustav Fischer, Jena, 1913.

Drew, George H.

1914 On the Precipitation of Calcium Carbonate in the Sea by Marine Bacteria. Papers from the Tortugas Laboratory, Carnegie Institution of Washington, vol. V, 1914, pp. 7-45.

Driesch, Hans.

1908 The Science and Philosophy of the Organism. The Gifford Lectures delivered before the University of Aberdeen in the years 1907 and 1908. Vols. I (1907) and II (1908). Adam and Charles Black, London, 1908.

Fischer, Alfred.

1900 The Structure and Functions of Bacteria. Transl. by A. Coppen Jones. Clarendon Press, Oxford, 1900.

Harder, E. C.

1915 Iron Bacteria. *Science*, September 3, 1915, pp. 310, 311.

Harvey, E. Newton.

1915 Studies on Light Production by Luminous Bacteria. *Amer. Jour. Physiol.*, May, 1915, pp. 230–239.

Henderson, Lawrence J.

1913 The Fitness of the Environment. Macmillan Co., New York, 1913.

Jepson, Willis Linn.

1911 A Flora of Western Middle California. Second edition. Cunningham, Curtiss & Welch, San Francisco, 1911.

Jordan, Edwin O.

1908 A Text-Book of General Bacteriology. W. B. Saunders, Philadelphia and London, 1908.

Kendall, A. I.

1915 The Bacteria of the Intestinal Tract of Man. *Science*, August 13, 1915, pp. 209–212.

Kohl, F. G.

1903 Ueber die Organisation und Physiologie der Cyanophyceenzelle und die mitotische Teilung ihres Kernes. Gustav Fischer, Jena, 1903.

Lipman, Charles B.

1912 The Distribution and Activities of Bacteria in Soils of the Arid Region. *Univ. Cal. Publ. Agric. Sciences*, October 15, 1912, pp. 1–20.

Minchin, E. A.

1916 The Evolution of the Cell. *Amer. Naturalist*, January, 1916, pp. 5–38; February, 1916, pp. 106–118; May, 1916, pp. 271–283.

Moore, F. J.

1915 Outlines of Organic Chemistry. John Wiley & Sons, New York and London, 1915.

Olive, E. W.

1904 Mitotic Division of the Nuclei of the Cyanophyceæ. *Beih. Bot. Centralbl.*, Bd. XVIII, Abt. I, Heft 1, 1904.

Osborn, Henry Fairfield.

1912 The Continuous Origin of Certain Unit Characters as Observed by a Palæontologist. *Harvey Soc. Volume*, November, 1912, pp. 153–204.

Phillips, O. F.

1904 A Comparative Study of the Cytology and Movements of the Cyanophyceæ. *Contrib. Bot. Lab. Univ. Penn.*, vol. II, no. 3, 1904.

Pirsson, Louis V., and Schuchert, Charles.

1915 A Text-Book of Geology. Part I, Physical Geology, by Louis V. Pirsson. Part II, Historical Geology, by Charles Schuchert. John Wiley & Sons, New York; Chapman & Hall, London, 1915.

Richards, A.

1915 Recent Studies on the Biological Effects of Radioactivity. *Science*, September 3, 1915, pp. 287–300.

Rutherford, Sir Ernest.

1915 (1914) The Constitution of Matter and the Evolution of the Elements. First series of lectures on the William Ellery Hale foundation, delivered April, 1914. *Pop. Sci. Mon.*, August, 1915, pp. 105–142.

Schuchert, Charles.

1915 A Text-Book of Geology (with Pirsson, Louis V.). See Pirsson.

de Vries, Hugo

1901 Die Mutationstheorie. Vol. I. Veit & Co., Leipsic, 1901.

1903 Die Mutationstheorie. Vol. II. Veit & Co., Leipsic, 1903.

1905 Species and Varieties, Their Origin by Mutation. Open Court Publ. Co., Chicago; Kegan Paul, Trench, Trübner & Co., London, 1905.

Wager, Harold.

1915 Behaviour of Plants in Response to the Light. *Nature*, December 23, 1915, pp. 468–472.

Walcott, Charles D.

1914 Cambrian Geology and Palæontology, vol. III, no. 2, Pre-Cambrian Algal Flora. *Smithsonian Misc. Colls.*, vol. 64, no. 2, pp. 77–156, Washington, 1914.

1915 Discovery of Algonkian Bacteria. *Proc. National Acad. Sci.*, April, 1915, pp. 256, 257.

Wilson, Edmund B.

1906 The Cell in Development and Inheritance. Second edition. Macmillan Co., New York, 1906.

CHAPTER IV

Calkins, Gary N.

1916 General Biology of the Protozoan Life Cycle. *Amer. Naturalist*, May, 1916, pp. 257-270.

Darwin, Charles.

1859 On the Origin of Species, by Means of Natural Selection; or the Preservation of Favored Races in the Struggle for Life. Murray, London, 1859.

Douglass, Andrew E.

1914 The Climatic Factor as Illustrated in Arid America (with Huntington, Schuchert, and Kullmer). See Huntington.

Heron-Allen, Edward.

1915 Contributions to the Study of the Bionomics and Reproductive Processes of the Foraminifera. *Phil. Trans.*, vol. CCVI, B 320, June 23, 1915, pp. 227-279.

Huntington, Ellsworth; Schuchert, Charles; Douglass, Andrew E., and Kullmer, Charles J.

1914 The Climatic Factor as Illustrated in Arid America. Carnegie Institution of Washington, Publ. no. 192, Washington, 1914.

Hutchinson, Henry Brougham.

1909 The Effect of Partial Sterilization of Soil on the Production of Plant Food (with Russell, Edward John). Introd. and part I. See Russell.

1913 *Ibid.*, part II. See Russell.

Jennings, H. S.

1906 Behavior of the Lower Organisms. Columbia University Press, New York, 1906.

1916 Heredity, Variation and the Results of Selection in the Uniparental Reproduction of *Difflugia corona*. *Genetics*, September, 1916, pp. 407-534.

Kullmer, Charles J.

1914 The Climatic Factor as Illustrated in Arid America (with Huntington, Schuchert, and Douglass). See Huntington.

Loeb, Jacques, and Wasteneys, Hardolph.

1915 On the Identity of Heliotropism in Animals and Plants. *Proc. National Acad. Sci.*, January, 1915, pp. 44-47.

1915 The Identity of Heliotropism in Animals and Plants. Second note. *Science*, February 26, 1915, pp. 328-330.

Minchin, E. A.

1916 The Evolution of the Cell. *Amer. Naturalist*, January, 1916, pp. 5-38; February, 1916, pp. 106-118; May, 1916, pp. 271-283.

Neumayr, M.

1889 Die Stämme des Thierreiches. Bd. I, Wirbellose Thiere. F. Tempsky, Vienna and Prague, 1889.

Osborn, Henry Fairfield.

1912 The Continuous Origin of Certain Unit Characters as Observed by a Palæontologist. *Harvey Soc. Volume*, November, 1912, pp. 153–204.

Pirsson, Louis V., and Schuchert, Charles.

1915 A Text-Book of Geology. Part I, Physical Geology, by Louis V. Pirsson. Part II, Historical Geology, by Charles Schuchert. John Wiley & Sons, New York; Chapman & Hall, London, 1915.

Russell, Henry John, and Hutchinson, Henry Brougham.

1909 The Effect of Partial Sterilization of Soil on the Production of Plant Food. Introd. and part I. *Jour. Agric. Sci.*, October, 1909, pp. 111–144.

1913 *Ibid.* Part II. *Jour. Agric. Sci.*, March, 1913, pp. 152–221.

Schuchert, Charles.

1914 The Climatic Factor as Illustrated in Arid America (with Huntington, Douglass, and Kullmer). See Huntington.

1915 A Text-Book of Geology (with Pirsson, Louis V.). See Pirsson.

Waagen, W.

1869 Die Formenreihe des *Ammonites subradiatus*, Versuch einer paläontologischen Monographie. Geognostisch-paläontologische Beiträge, herausgegeben . . . von Dr. E. W. Benecke, Bd. II, pp. 179–257 (Heft II, S. 78). R. Oldenbourg, Munich, 1869.

Walcott, Charles D.

1899 Pre-Cambrian Fossiliferous Formations. *Bull. Geol. Soc. Amer.*, April 6, 1899, pp. 199–244.

1911 Cambrian Geology and Palæontology, vol. II, no. 5. Middle Cambrian Annelids. *Smithsonian Misc. Colls.*, vol. 57, no. 5, September 4, 1911, pp. 109–144.

1912 Cambrian Geology and Palæontology, vol. II, no. 6. Middle Cambrian Branchiopoda, Malacostraca, Trilobita and Merostomata. *Smithsonian Misc. Colls.*, vol. 57, no. 6, March 13, 1912, pp. 145–228.

Wasteneys, Hardolph.

1915 On the Identity of Heliotropism in Animals and Plants (with Loeb, Jacques). See Loeb.

1915 The Identity of Heliotropism in Animals and Plants (with Loeb, Jacques). Second note. See Loeb.

CHAPTER V

Abel, O.

1912 Grundzüge der Paläobiologie der Wirbeltiere. E. Schweizerbart'sche Verlagsbuchhandlung Nägele und Dr. Sproesser, Stuttgart, 1912.

Dollo, Louis.

1895 Sur la Phylogénie des Dipneustes. *Bull. Soc. Belge de Géol., de Paléontologie et d'Hydrologie*, tome IX, 1895, Mémoires, pp. 79–128.

1909 La Paléontologie ethnologique. *Bull. Soc. Belge de Géol., de Paléontologie et d'Hydrologie*, tome XXIII, 1909, Mémoires, pp. 377–421.

Huxley, T. H.

1880 On the Application of the Laws of Evolution to the Arrangement of the Vertebrata, and More Particularly of the Mammalia. *Proc. Zool. Soc. of London*, 1880, pp. 649–662.

Newcomb, Simon.

1902 Astronomy for Everybody. McClure, Phillips & Co., New York, 1902.

Patten, Wm.

1912 The Evolution of the Vertebrates and Their Kin. P. Blakiston's Sons & Co., Philadelphia, 1912.

CHAPTER VI

Case, E. C.

1915 The Permo-Carboniferous Red Beds of North America and Their Vertebrate Fauna. Carnegie Institution of Washington, Publ. no. 207, June 25, 1915.

Dahlgren, Ulric, and Silvester, C. F.

1906 The Electric Organ of the Stargazer, *Astroscopus* (Brevoort). *Anatomischer Anzeiger*, Bd. XXIX, no. 15, 1906, pp. 387–403.

Dahlgren, Ulric.

1910 The Origin of the Electricity Tissues in Fishes. *Amer. Naturalist*, April, 1910, pp. 193–202.

1915 Structure and Polarity of the Electric Motor Nerve-Cell in Torpedoes. Carnegie Institution of Washington, Publ. no. 212, 1915, pp. 213–256.

Dean, Bashford.

1895 Fishes, Living and Fossil. Columbia Univ. Biol. Ser. III, Macmillan & Co., New York, 1895.

Dohrn, Felix Anton.

1875 Der Ursprung der Wirbelthiere und das Prinzip des Funktionswechsels. Leipsic, 1875.

Klaatsch, Hermann.

1896 Die Brustflosse der Crossopterygier. Ein Beitrag zur Anwendung der Archipterygium-Theorie auf die Gliedmaassen der Landwirbelthiere. *Festschrift zum siebenzigsten Geburtstage von Carl Gegenbaur*, Bd. I, 1896, pp. 259–392.

Moody, Roy Lee.

1916 The Coal Measures Amphibia of North America. Carnegie Institution of Washington, Publ. no. 238, September 28, 1916.

Silvester, C. F.

1906 The Electric Organ of the Stargazer, *Astroscopus* (with Dahlgren, Ulric). See Dahlgren.

Willey, Arthur.

1894 *Amphioxus* and the Ancestry of the Vertebrates. Columbia Univ. Biol. Ser. II, Macmillan & Co., New York, 1894.

Williston, Samuel W.

1911 American Permian Vertebrates. University of Chicago Press, Chicago, 1911.

Woodward, A. Smith.

1915 The Use of Fossil Fishes in Stratigraphical Geology. *Proc. Geol. Soc. of London*, vol. LXXI, part 1, 1915, pp. lxii-lxxv.

CHAPTER VII

Beebe, C. William.

1915 A Tetrapteryx Stage in the Ancestry of Birds. *Zoologica*, November, 1915, pp. 39–52.

Dollo, Louis.

1901 Sur l'origine de la Tortue Luth (*Dermochelys coriacea*). Extrait du *Bull. Soc. roy. des sciences méd. et nat. de Bruxelles*, February, 1901, pp. 1–26.

1903 *Eochelone brabantica*, Tortue marine nouvelle du Bruxellien (Éocène moyen) de la Belgique. *Bull. de l'Acad. roy. de Belgique* (Classe des sciences), no. 8, August, 1903, pp. 792–801.

1903 Sur l'Évolution des Chéloniens marins. (Considérations bionomiques et phylogéniques.) *Ibid.*, pp. 801–850.

1905 Les dinosauriens adaptés à la vie quadrupède secondaire. *Bull. Soc. Belge de Géol., de Paléontologie et d'Hydrologie*, tome XIX, 1905, Mémoires, pp. 441–448.

Heilmann, Gerhard.

1913 Vor Nuværende Viden om Fuglenes Afstamming. *Dansk Ornithologisk Forenings Tidsskrift*, January, 1915, Aarg. 7, H. I, II, pp. 1–71.

Lull, Richard Swann.

1915 Triassic Life of the Connecticut Valley. *State of Connecticut State Geol. and Nat. Hist. Survey*, Bull. 24, 1915.

Williston, Samuel W.

1914 Water Reptiles of the Past and Present. University of Chicago Press, Chicago, 1914.

CHAPTER VIII

Bacon, Francis, Lord Bacon, Baron Verulam and Viscount St. Albans.

1620 Novum Organum. English version, edited by Joseph Devey, M. A. P. F. Collier & Son, New York, 1911.

Brown, Amos Peaslee.

1909 The Differentiation and Specificity of Corresponding Proteins and Other Vital Substances in Relation to Biological Classification and Organic Evolution: The Crystallography of Hemoglobins (with Reichert, Edward Tyson). See Reichert.

Cushing, Harvey.

1912 The Pituitary Body and its Disorders, Clinical States Produced by Disorders of the Hypophysis Cerebri. Harvey Lecture, 1910, amplified. J. B. Lippincott Co., Philadelphia and London, 1912.

Dollo, Louis.

1906 Le pied de l'*Amphiproviverra* et l'origine arboricole des marsupiaux. *Bull. Soc. Belge de Géol., de Paléontologie et d'Hydrologie*, tome XX, 1906. Procès verbaux, pp. 166–168.

Gregory, Wm. K.

1910 The Orders of Mammals. *Bull. Amer. Mus. Nat. Hist.*, vol. XXVII, February, 1910.

Goodale, H. D.

1916 Gonadectomy in Relation to the Secondary Sexual Characters of some Domestic Birds. Carnegie Institution of Washington, Publ. no. 243, Washington, 1916.

Huxley, Thomas H.

1893 Darwiniana (vol. II of Essays). D. Appleton & Co., New York and London, 1893.

Lillie, Frank R.

1917 The Free-Martin; a Study of the Action of Sex Hormones in the Fœtal Life of Cattle. *Jour. Experimental Zoology*, July 5, 1917, pp. 371–452.

Mathews, Albert P.

1916 Physiological Chemistry, A Text-Book and Manual for Students. William Wood & Co., New York, 1916.

Matthew, W. D.

1915 Climate and Evolution. *Ann. N. Y. Acad. Sciences*, vol. XXIV, February 18, 1915, pp. 171–318.

Osborn, Henry Fairfield.

1897 Organic Selection. *Science*, October 15, 1897, pp. 583–587.

1910 The Age of Mammals in Europe, Asia, and North America. Macmillan Co., New York, 1910.

Reichert, Edward Tyson, and Brown, Amos Peaslee.

1909 The Differentiation and Specificity of Corresponding Proteins and Other Vital Substances in Relation to Biological Classification and Organic Evolution: The Crystallography of Hemoglobins. Carnegie Institution of Washington, Publ. no. 116, Washington, 1909.

Russell, E. S.

1916 Form and Function, A Contribution to the History of Animal Morphology. John Murray, London, 1916.

Scott, William B.

1913 A History of Land Mammals in the Western Hemisphere. Macmillan Co., New York, 1913.

APPENDIX

Loeb, Jacques.

1906 The Dynamics of Living Matter. Columbia University Press, New York, 1906.

1916 The Organism as a Whole, from a Physicochemical Viewpoint. G. P. Putnam's Sons, The Knickerbocker Press, New York and London, 1916.

Mathews, Albert P.

1916 Physiological Chemistry, A Text-Book and Manual for Students. William Wood & Co., New York, 1916.

INDEX

B

D

E

M

N

O

P

Q

R

T

CPSIA information can be obtained
at www.ICGtesting.com
Printed in the USA
BVHW071030290821
615534BV00006B/412